LAW ENFORCEMENT
HANDGUN DIGEST

Third Edition

By Jack Lewis

DBI BOOKS INC., NORTHFIELD, ILLINOIS

ABOUT THE COVER: The handgun gracing the cover of our *Law Enforcement Handgun Digest, 3rd Edition,* is a Dan Wesson Model 15-2VH in .357 Magnum. It sports a 4-inch, heavy, vent-rib barrel. Also seen is a set of Silencio shooting muffs with special Gun Digest logo.

Art Director
SONYA KAISER

Production Director
BETTY BURRIS

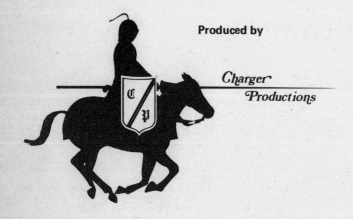

Produced by

Charger Productions

Contributing Editors
MASSAD AYOOB
ROGER COMBS
DEAN A. GRENNELL
CLAUD S. HAMILTON

Associate Publisher
SHELDON L. FACTOR

Publisher
MILTON P. KLEIN

ISBN 0-695-81413-3   Library of Congress Catalog Number: 73-186804

CONTENTS

INTRODUCTION

After two editions of this particular book, one would think an author would be hard-pressed to find enough new material about law enforcement to draw the potential reader.

But with the aid of such experts in the fields of law enforcement and firearms as Massad Ayoob, Roger Combs, Dean A. Grennell and Claud S. Hamilton, it suddenly became obvious that increased throught is being given to the protection of our lawmen. The era of crying humanitarians and do-gooders, who insisted that the felon had rights — even when he was shooting at you — seems to have come to an end. With the ever-climbing crime rate in this country, it is gratifying to find that the politicos have come to realize that the good-guy voters outnumber the bad-guy voters...and it is time that something was done to help the law enforcement types.

Much of that philosophy is reflected in this volume, I believe. My personal thought is that it is about time!

Jack Lewis,
Capistrano Beach, California
December 1979

Chapter 1

GUNSITE

PHILOSOPHY FOR A FIREFIGHT

Cooper's Gunsite Ranch is the home of the American Pistol Institute, an organization that teaches techniques for combat in handgun situations.

Jeff Cooper demonstrates his personal way of reloading the .45 auto pistol, while heading out at a fast run.

JEFF COOPER, IN HIS mid-fifties, is an ex-Marine colonel who keeps himself as trim as he did in his combat days in the Pacific. He lives today at Gunsite, the advanced training facility he built near Prescott, Arizona, in an area so remote he can be reached only by mobile telephone. He is also the founder of IPSC, the International Practical Shooting Confederation, which established a truly representative world championship event for the free-style gunfight simulation that Cooper founded in California, in the late 1950s.

Jeff Cooper entered WWII as a trained marksman, but not a gun expert. For a personal sidearm, he chose a single-action Colt .45 revolver. As his combat experience grew, he quickly realized that such obsolete equipment could get him killed. He replaced his Peacemaker with a Colt .45 automatic, the weapon that was to become his trademark.

Unlike many so-called gun experts who have never been in a firefight, Cooper has killed three men with his pistols, all in military combat. Two of them were armed with fully automatic weapons, the third with a high-powered rifle.

In the past twenty years, a whole new concept of handgun training (which Cooper prefers to call "pistolcraft") has built up around his concepts. The man himself has become something of a cult figure amongst handgun buffs.

He has also become extremely controversial amongst the other experts. Criticism centers on what some consider his obsession with the .45 automatic, to the exclusion of more frequently used combat handguns, and on the feeling that

Drawing On Combat Experiences, Jeff Cooper Aims At Improving The Law Enforcement Officer's Life Expectancy!

many of his subtle techniques are for experts only and do not necessarily translate to the mass training of policemen and soldiers.

Yet many of the experts also feel that he has done more to advance combat shooting than anyone else.

A gun writer, who is frequently at odds with him, says of Cooper: "Were it not for Jeff, American police instructors would still be teaching their people to shoot from the hip and would still be wondering why they missed in point-blank gunfights.

"It was Cooper who taught us that you could bring the gun up in both hands and use the sights every bit as fast as you could shoot from the hip, and with a much greater likelihood that you would shoot your opponent, before he shot you. It was Cooper who taught us that, with proper training methods, even an amateur could control the recoil of a high-powered handgun. And he was one of the first to assemble data to prove that the standard '.38 police special' was an ineffectual thing to trust your life to. More of the

principles seen today in modern police training derive from Cooper's theories that anyone realizes."

"The three factors you look for are speed, power, and accuracy," Cooper explains. "The .45 auto cartridge has ample power, as has been proven since the gun was developed in 1911. It is more than sufficiently accurate for its purpose. And, with proper training, it is easy to control in rapid fire. The design is totally proven."

Cooper has a low opinion of double action 9mm automatics. "The double-action feature is an ingenious solution to a non-existent problem. It is non-selective in these pistols, so you must fire the first shot with a long, hard, trigger-cocking action, and subsequent rounds are fired from a self-cocked pistol.

"This change in trigger pulls, between the first and second shots, makes such a gun difficult to master. People who can fire quick doubles with such a system are as scarce as hen's teeth. The 9mm cartridge is inadequate as a fight-stopper."

Cooper checks the workings of an autoloader pistol for one of his students during a break in the training schedule.

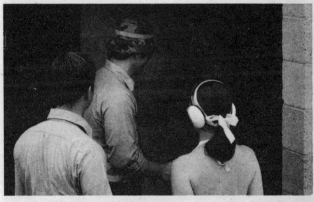

Left: Student uses two-hand hold on an action target in the indoor reaction range. (Below) Students are given a tour of the indoor range, which has become known as the Fun House phase.

His scorn for the 9mm Parabellum cartridge extends to other mid-caliber rounds (which he considers smallbores), most notably the .38 Special revolver round. "I have no confidence in the .38 Special," he said emphatically. "I know of far too many cases in which men were struck well and truly with that cartridge, but still killed the man who shot them. It just doesn't do it. A .38 will kill, sure, but so will a .25 automatic. That isn't the point. The point is, it must hit hard enough to stop the fight, and the odds are marginal that a man struck solidly with a .38 Special will cease and desist what he is doing. I don't like those odds. It's like taking off in an airplane that may or may not get you to the airport."

Cooper's collection of gunfight reports indicates that, with a single solid hit, a 9mm or .38 slug will stop an assailant only about ten times in twenty. By contrast, he says, police and military gunfights have shown that a big-bore slug, notably the .45 automatic, will deliver a reasonably instant stop, in nineteen out of twenty instances. The same, he believes, will be true of .41 and .44 caliber weapons.

The vaunted .357 magnum? Cooper feels it's overrated. Fired from a six-inch barrel and with a full-size 158-grain semi-wadcutter bullet, Cooper feels the .357 will equal the .45. Lighter and faster bullets, fired from shorter barrels, don't do much better than the .38 in his opinion.

"You can't hit your opponent hard enough with anything to be sure one hundred percent of the time, but you can push the odds in your favor by going to a big-bore," he says. "Bore diameter seems to be very important here. Keep in mind that, as you increase the diameter of the bullet, you increase the area of impact by the square of that increase, and you increase the volume of the wound channel by the cube of that increase. This seems to be born out in firing at live targets.

"The original .357 load was a 158-grain bullet that left an 8-3/8-inch barrel at 1510 feet per second. I have some of that old ammunition, and when I fire it next to currently produced loads, I can see that the modern loadings bring it down. Out of the four-inch barrel that is most used by police, you're putting that 158-grain bullet out of the muzzle somewhere between 1150 and 1200 feet per second. That's not bad, but it's not as good as the big-bore.

Police gun experts who favor the .38/9mm class of

The buddy system is used on the Gunsite firing line much as in the Armed Forces, with students correcting students.

Cooper is on the firing line constantly to correct faults, offer advice that may one day save the student's life.

service handgun say that the reputation these guns have for poor stopping power dates back to old-style, non-expanding ammunition. They point to tests that show, by scientific measurement, that light, high-velocity, expanding bullets stop better than heavy, wide, slow-moving slugs, such as those thrown by Cooper's .45.

Cooper says, "I would certainly look at these 'high performance' cartridges, if I was forced by a department to carry a 9mm or .38. I would certainly prefer a hollow-point to hardball in the 9mm, for example. But I don't consider this to be the real answer. I don't think that you can put any bullet into a smallbore that will make it the equal of a large-bore. The reason is that targets vary too much in their impact resistance.

"If you make a bullet that will not expand on light resistance, you may get a bullet that will not expand at all. If you do make a bullet that will expand on light resistance, then you will very likely get a bullet that will expand (or shatter) on anything, including a pane of glass or a thick wallet. You don't know, in advance, what you're going to have to hit, whether your opponent will be wearing swim trunks or a heavy overcoat with magazines stuffed inside of it. You don't know how far away you'll be, what the velocity of the bullet will be when it hits.

"It is simply asking too much to make a bullet which will perform the same way all the time, unless it doesn't do anything, which is true of the large-bore solid projectile. It doesn't have to expand, so it always performs the same way."

The vast majority of American police use the double-action revolver as a service handgun. Second in popularity is the double-action 9mm automatic, such as the Smith & Wesson Model 39 issued by Illinois State Police. Far in the back of the pack are the single-action large-bore automatics, such as Cooper's Colt .45. He doubts that the situation will ever change.

"I don't think police will ever go to the .45 auto in large scale. This is the modern age, and I think it would be simply too terribly unfashionable for public servants to go over to a weapon that was designed before they were born. While a great many small police departments in the Southwestern and Southern United States have been using the .45 automatic with great success for some time now, the notion of the large departments making such a change is unlikely."

Realizing that most police will stay with the revolver, Cooper recommends Smith & Wesson's Model 58, a heavy-duty, large-frame service revolver firing the .41 magnum cartridge. He disagrees with reports from major agencies that have adopted this combination then dropped it because, they said, it was too hard for the average officer to control.

"I couldn't follow that argument. I've always felt that they were using the full magnum hunting load, instead of

Realizing that the majority of police officers today are armed with the .38 Special revolver, Jeff Cooper makes a point of starting them from the basics, when it comes to training with any of the current autoloader handguns.

the lighter police load, but it is difficult to pin people down on that. It would, of course, be natural for a person confronted with that theory to say that both loads had been tried and that the officers couldn't control either of them.

"I find that a little suspect, because anyone who wants to see for himself can simply take a .41 with the police load and shoot it next to a Combat Magnum (Smith & Wesson's medium size .357 service revolver) with full .357 loads, and you simply can't see the difference."

Cooper has some interesting comments on the subject of police holsters.

"Selecting a good holster is a more complicated task than selecting a good handgun. Is the weapon to be concealed or worn in plain sight? Is the officer on a hazardous assignment such that he is likely to have to draw his weapon swiftly and silently, or is he on routine patrol? The uniformed officer on ordinary patrol duty should give much thought to weapon security. I think every police officer knows that, if he is to meet violence in the course of his duties, that violence will mostly be offered hand-to-hand.

"It will be in a situation where the officer is not justified in resorting to the lethal force of his handgun. He may wind up in a wrestling match, falling over chairs and falling down stairs and generally mixing it up, as if he were in an athletic contest. If, during that time, his gun should fall from his

holster and wind up on the street, it is quite likely that someone is going to shoot him with it.

"Security is an important consideration in selecting a uniform holster, and as a corollary of that statement, it is therefore absolutely necessary that the police officer train with that holster with the security device in use. It is extremely dangerous for an officer to carry a holster that locks the gun in place with a safety strap, for instance, then do all his practice shooting with the strap unfastened. That will get you killed.

"I don't feel strongly about backup guns, one way or the other. I think that a man's protective weapons have a great deal to do with his personality. If a man feels good with a backup gun, he should, by all means, carry it. Confidence is the name of the game. On the other hand, I don't know of a single case in which a backup weapon saved an officer's life. I'm not saying that it doesn't happen, it's just that it hasn't come to my attention. I think that I have enough correspondence from police that it would certainly have come to my attention, if it was happening."

On concealable, soft body armor, Cooper notes: "There are several good vests on the market, and the product saves lives. I think I would probably wear such a vest, if I was a line policeman. I'll say this: I, unlike many modern soldiers, am a great believer in the steel helmet. When I was at war, I and everyone under my command wore the helmet. If I have anything I can do which will save my life or increase

Shooting from a moving vehicle is another of the subjects taught at the Gunsite installation by Jeff Cooper and his staff. Camouflage-covered targets tend to blend with the landscape, perhaps harking back to WW II experiences.

my odds of coming back to my family, I am going to do it.

"I know the better armor saves lives, and the decision often depends on how dangerous the officer perceives his duty to be. He will obviously choose to wear it in a high-risk situation. But for most policemen, it is sort of like wearing a seat belt in your automobile. You may have driven twenty years without an accident, but that is not to say you might not be involved in a collision tomorrow."

Jeff Cooper makes most of his living teaching pistolcraft. He is the most highly paid firearms instructor in the world. His intensive courses are limited to small groups of students and are expensive. Some of those classes will contain wealthy gun buffs who want to learn the ultimate in combat shooting for their own reasons. A surprisingly large number of the students will be bodyguards for foreign heads of state, or those who guard executives in parts of the world where kidnapping is becoming epidemic.

Few of those students will be United States police officers, and those who do attend will usually be paying for the advanced training out of their own pocket. Most police departments fund their people only to shooting schools that are sponsored by police (the FBI seminars, for instance) or by the industry (notably the Smith & Wesson Academy).

Still, there are lawmen who dig deep in their savings to learn what Cooper has to teach, because he teaches things that no one else does. There are moving targets in the Cooper courses, and multiple targets, and situations where you have to run through obstacle courses firing all the way. He has literally dozens of formats, and, at Gunsite, he has created ambush courses and assault courses and house-clearing courses that tax judgment and reflex, not to mention marksmanship, to the maximum.

Cooper feels that readiness is a major factor, perhaps *the* major factor, in gunfight survival. He describes that preparedness in four color-coded levels. The first, appropriately, is called "condition white." This is when the person is completely relaxed, without the least thought or expectation of trouble. Attacked while in condition white, he says, even a highly trained man will take some two seconds to assimilate the situation and respond to it.

Next is "condition yellow," the knowledge that an attack could come, but in a situation where there is no particular reason to believe that it will come. A properly trained and experienced police officer, Cooper believes, will almost always be functioning at "condition yellow" while on duty. It is a circumstance in which the individual always is prepared for danger, but not actively anticipating it.

The next increment is "condition orange," the definite presence of danger. There is a lot of latitude in this emotional color band. It can range from an officer getting out of his car to follow through on a suspicious night stop, to the very moment when a man realizes that he is under attack.

Perhaps reflecting SWAT tactics, officers are taught to fire at a series of man-size targets from moving police car, while driving. This, of course, requires being able to fire accurately with the left-hand, which is a must.

In the orange state, says Cooper, a properly trained man will be alert and ready to respond, with the legal and requisite degree of violence, and will usually either have his hand on his gun, or have the weapon out and ready.

"Condition red" is the final step — under attack! In condition red, the individual fully realizes that his life is in deadly jeopardy, and he is prepared to act instantly against those who have placed it there. The officer who has been fired on, or the detective about to kick down an apartment door to effect a felony warrant arrest on a suspect known to be armed, or an officer interrupting an armed holdup in progress, are all operating on "condition red."

That may sound a little bit "cowboy," but ask an officer who has been through any of the above situations, and you will find that Cooper's concept is built on reality. You will also find, as Cooper says, that while response from "condition white" may take well *over* two seconds, a man in "condition red" can react to a danger signal and fire in perhaps a fifth of a second.

Cooper has other, more controversial teachings. For one thing, he makes no great effort to teach his students to take cover, feeling that they'll protect themselves better, if they react instantly from where they are caught at the moment of attack, and drive their opponents to take cover in disorganized retreat.

"There are dozens of little tactical tricks which experienced police officers know, and I'm not for a moment putting them down," he says. "I think that to give a man training in the idea that he should enter a violent situation with a notion of getting behind things and putting things between him and his adversary is not necessarily wrong, but it clutters up his mind when his principal concentration should be with putting his enemy on his back. I know that I am not speaking with a majority on this."

Cooper added, "When an officer is approaching a situation in which he feels there may be trouble or he may have to make an arrest or a confrontation, naturally he should make use of such tactical or atmospheric situations as he can. I recall that boy who got himself killed and precipitated that whole four-man disaster in Newhall, California, some years ago. He apparently did not stay in back of his own lights. You want to be sure that your suspect is covered at ninety degrees between you and your partner, so that you don't find yourself standing on opposite sides of a suspect and shooting at each other. But much of this is more common sense than sophisticated training."

Another precept that has been hotly argued amongst firearms tacticians is Cooper's belief that a man threatened with a gun should not acquiesce, but should go for his own weapon. His explanation is that a swift, precise, and unexpected counterattack may well be the best chance the man has of surviving the encounter, and that there is a certain moral obligation to defend oneself from outlaw transgressors.

The first part of Cooper's argument can be strongly defended with some cases from his files involving his own students. One, a Latin American official whose government was going through troubled times, was at home with his family, when he heard a car pull softly to the curb outside. Peering through a curtain, he saw two men with shotguns

Each of the students undergoes training in rocky arroyo in the Arizona wilds, getting a taste of such combat necessities under the watchful eye of Cooper and staff. Safety record at the school is reportedly unblemished.

All of the techniques taught to law enforcement agents at Cooper's school undergo classroom instruction and discussion before the students are armed and sent out to learn the book lessons from a practical standpoint.

ascending the walk to his front door. He knew that similar situations had involved men murdered in front of their families, and his wife and children were home.

Seizing the .45 automatic with which he had trained at Cooper's Arizona shooting facility, he positioned himself behind the front door, then flung it open as the surprised assassins reached the doorstep, and opened fire.

In another South American nation (Cooper spends a lot of time with VIP security people from that continent and has personally trained the bodyguards of the President of Guatemala), one of his pupils had a different experience. Walking from his driveway to his house, he was set upon by a pair of armed men. He drew his fourteen-shot Browning 9mm automatic and emptied it, reloaded, and emptied the spare clip, firing twenty-seven shots in something like ten seconds. When the slide locked back empty, his assailants were gone. None had been hit, but the sudden and deafening barrage of gunfire had put them into broken retreat.

"In one sense, his experience was a success," Cooper admits a bit grudgingly. "After all, he was unharmed, and did save himself with his pistol. I have had uniform success in that none of my students have been killed in a gunfight, and that is, of course, the object of the exercise. But this one, in particular, conducted himself very poorly. He lost his head completely and just hosed down the neighborhood with such a tremendous volume of gunfire, that his two assailants ran in panic up the street. This is rather a comic

scene, but only in that it worked out that way. It need not have been. I've had six other students involved in gunfights. Five of them did beautifully, and the sixth did, well, so-so. He did all the right things, but didn't concentrate on his front sight, and he missed his target. But the other five shot coolly and carefully and disposed of their adversaries in very neat fashion."

Cooper says there are five basic elements to effective combat pistolcraft. "There are five essentials of the modern pistol technique, one of which is the weapon itself, which is the modern, heavy-duty, self-loading pistol. We feel that the heavy-duty modern automatic of good design is one of the elements of the five. The other four are all equal, but let's take stance first. The Weaver stance is what wins. Next is the flash sight picture, that is, the ability to pick up your sights clearly and sharply in barely a fraction of a second. Third is the compressed surprise break that involves the control of the trigger in very short spaces of time, without jerking on it. The final one is the technique of the draw itself: producing a pistol from the condition of readiness and lining it up, in such a fashion that your eye need do nothing but verify (the alignment of weapon with target). You draw to a hitting stance and your eye verifies your target. All this is put together into one smooth stroke which stops fights."

The "flash sight picture" and the "compressed surprise break" run together into the ability to bring the gun up, instinctively, to eye level, make sight corrections in the

The course of training at the American Pistol Institute also includes extensive night firing, with special techniques for not revealing your own position in the darkness to a felon who may be returning your fire.

fractional part of a second, and "think" the shot off without a convulsive jerk of the trigger finger that could pull the muzzle off target. The draw is perhaps the least unique aspect about the Cooper format.

The Weaver stance, however, is seen by many as the key to Cooper's style of fast and accurate anti-personnel firing and is a remarkably subtle technique. "The position was invented by a sheriff in California named Jack Weaver," he explains. "Back in the 1950s when this type of (fast, pure combat) shooting began, I tried to beat Jack for three solid years, using the old techniques, and he kept banging me into the dirt every time I tried. Finally, being a slow learner, I decided to try his system and adapted his stance to my physique.

"I would say that simply understanding and adopting the Weaver stance would increase the efficiency of police shooting by a large amount, depending upon which person and how good that person was. I see police officers using a two-handed firing position all the time, but they're not doing it right. They use an isosceles triangle positioning of the arms, which is fine for accuracy, but does nothing for speed or recoil control. The proper Weaver stance is one-sided and involves isometric tension."

The essence of the Weaver stance is that one faces the target with the left foot slightly forward, if the shooter is right-handed, and bends the elbow of the left support arm, taking a two-handed hold on the weapon. Right hand pushes forward, while left hand pulls back, locking the gun between opposingly tense limbs with perhaps forty pounds of pressure.

This not only locks the gun pretty tight on target, but, with the bent elbow, the shooter achieves a shock-absorber effect when firing a high-powered handgun. Instead of the muzzle rising, the gun comes straight back a little bit, but the sights stay pretty much on the target. The joints are not locked, so accuracy is not as precise, nor hold quite as steady, as with the two-hands-straight-out position taught to most U. S. police. Cooper feels that the recovery time, in rapid fire, more than makes up for any shortcomings in the X-ring.

Cooper, and Weaver, bend the shooting arm, as well as the support arm. Cooper's star pupil, Ray Chapman, former world champion free style combat shooter, bends his support arm, but locks his right elbow out straight. This position, says Jeff, "forms the whole body into a springy gun mount, which can alter elevation and deflection instantly and very strongly, without regard to recoil or whatever. I am still a little amazed when I talk to modern shooters who are concerned about recoil. In general, recoil is inconsequential. Certainly, you can't shoot anything in a steel frame .45 automatic that'll bother you. Lord, you can shoot the maximum load in a full-size .45 automatic with the thumb and forefinger, without even gripping it, so I think recoil is one of those things that only matters if your technique is wrong to begin with. If you don't know what you're doing, recoil will bother you, but if you know how to shoot, recoil is insignificant."

Cooper also teaches firing in two-shot bursts, as opposed to single rounds *or* extended sequences of shooting. "Ordinarily," he says, "I feel the double shot, the double hammer, is the decisive thing to do. First of all, your first shot may not be right where you want it, and secondly, your first bullet may not do what you intend. If you have to shoot to save your life, clearly, the overwhelming need is to stop the fight and turn your adversary off.

"Firing more than two shots at a time is dangerous, I think, because you're running out, running dry. If you have a revolver, you have only six shots or perhaps even five. You certainly don't want to shoot your gun dry and be caught standing there with your teeth in your mouth. I know that the New York City Police Department, more often than not, teaches you to fire all six into your target, but then where are you when your six shots are gone?"

His students ask, "When do you know that you've mastered combat pistolcraft?" Cooper usually answers, "When a man who tries to kill you, by surprise, is in more danger from you than you are from him."

Long hours of repetitious practice in the various types of accepted positions, and some less standard, make up much of the training at Cooper's combat shooting installation. Cooper tends to favor first-shot accuracy over speed.

Chapter 2

CHOOSING THE LAW

This Semi-Scientific Approach — Seasoned With

MANY POLICE DEPARTMENTS these days allow an officer a much broader choice in sidearms than used to be the case.

Dissatisfaction with the time-honored American police service revolver seems to have begun in the early 1960s. The gun, then, was a Smith & Wesson or Colt, with four-inch barrel, and in caliber .38 Special. The .38 Special cartridge was a 158-grain lead round nose of fine

accuracy fired at about 850 feet per second. There were some variations, such as the 200-grain Super Police but they were rarely seen or used.

What is a good gun for the average law officer? We cannot agree with those who assign certain characteristics or qualities to certain guns, such as one-shot stopping power. We need to pay more attention to the needs and abilities of the average officer, male and female.

The old leg-of-mutton Luger holster, with its full flap, offers maximum protection for the gun, but at the cost of an unacceptably slow draw. The AMT .45 ACP Hardballer, having all its metal parts of stainless steel sidesteps the need for such protection. Opposite, adjustable rear sights are nice, but the fixed service type are more durable.

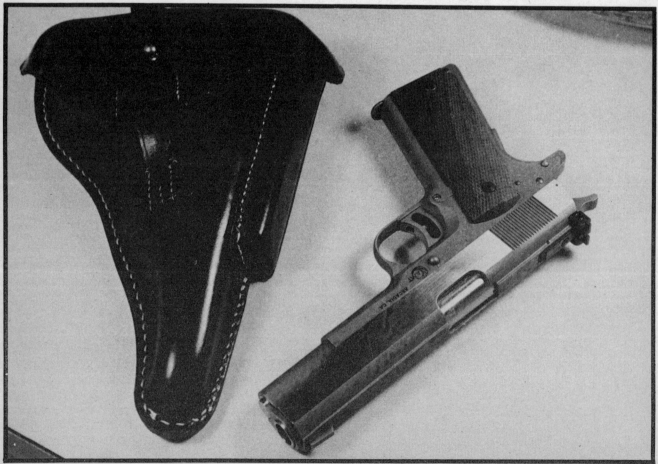

ENFORCEMENT HANDGUN

Common Sense — Offers Some Unlikely Recommendations!

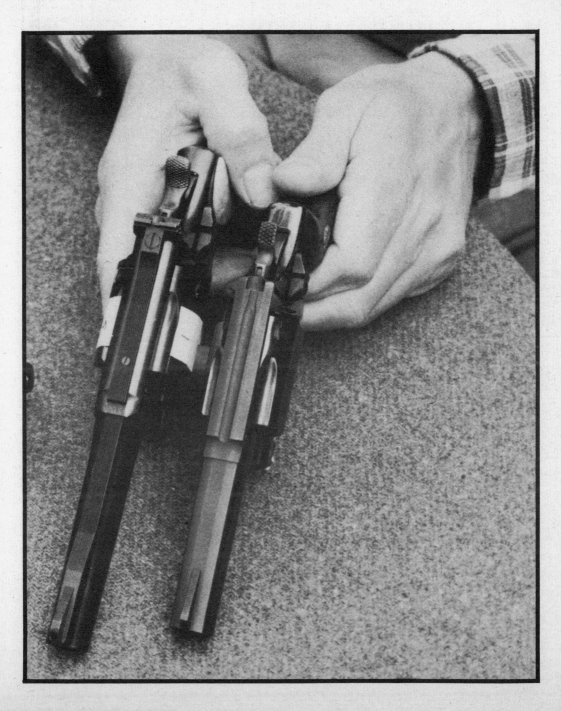

Relative Importance Factor (1 to 10 scale)	Factor	S&W M-36; 158-gr. JSP	Colt Detective Spl.; same cartridge in .38 Sp.	S&W M-59; Rem 115-gr. JHP	Browning Hi-Power; same 9mm P cartridge	S&W M-15; same cartridge as M-36	S&W M-64; same cartridge	S&W M-28 6-inch; Rem 158-gr. JHP	S&W M-66 4-inch; same .357 cartridge	S&W M-58 4-inch; Rem 210-gr. LSWC	S&W M-57 4-inch; same .41 cartridge	Colt Government; Rem 230-gr. FMJ	AMT Hardballer; Same .45 ACP cartridge
2	**WEIGHT:** Fully loaded plus two reloads	26.8 oz.	30.6 oz.	51 oz.	55½ oz.	39.6 oz.	39.1 oz.	54.1 oz.	45.1 oz.	55.2 oz.	55.2 oz.	60.5 oz.	60.5 oz.
	Subjective value	(9)	(8)	(4)	(3)	(6)	(6)	(2)	(5)	(2)	(2)	(1)	(1)
	Total value (multiple of importance factor times subjective value)	18	16	8	6	12	12	4	10	4	4	2	2
5	**COMPACTNESS:**												
	Subjective value	(10)	(10)	(9)	(8)	(8)	(8)	(5)	(7)	(6)	(6)	(6)	(6)
	Total value	50	50	45	40	40	40	25	35	30	30	30	30
8	**READINESS CONDITION:** Fully loaded, locked or hammer down (See note 1).												
	Subjective value	(8)	(8)	(10)	(5)	(8)	(8)	(8)	(8)	(8)	(8)	(5)	(5)
	Total value	64	64	80	40	64	64	64	64	64	64	40	40
4	**FUNCTIONAL RELIABILITY:**												
	Subjective value	(10)	(10)	(3)	(3)	(10)	(10)	(10)	(10)	(10)	(10)	(6)	(6)
	Total value	40	40	12	12	40	40	40	40	40	40	24	24
1	**LOAD ADAPTABILITY:** (See note 2)												
	Adjustable sights	(5)	(5)	(10)	(5)	(10)	(5)	(10)	(10)	(5)	(10)	(5)	(10)
	Load variety	(3)	(3)	(5)	(5)	(3)	(3)	(8)	(8)	(7)	(7)	(4)	(4)
	Subjective value average	(4)	(4)	(7)	(5)	(6)	(4)	(9)	(9)	(6)	(8)	(5)	(7)
	Total value	4	4	7	5	6	4	9	9	6	8	5	7
10	**FIREPOWER:**												
	Shots before reload	(5)	(6)	(15)	(14)	(6)	(6)	(6)	(6)	(6)	(6)	(8)	(8)
	Total rounds carried	(15)	(18)	(45)	(43)	(18)	(18)	(18)	(18)	(18)	(18)	(22)	(22)
	Subjective value	(2)	(3)	(10)	(9)	(3)	(3)	(3)	(3)	(3)	(3)	(5)	(5)
	Total value	20	30	100	90	30	30	30	30	30	30	50	50
1	**SAFETY:** Firing pin must lock out of contact with cartridge when safety engaged.												
	Subjective value	(7)	(7)	(10)	(5)	(7)	(7)	(7)	(7)	(7)	(7)	(5)	(5)
	Total value	7	7	10	5	7	7	7	7	7	7	5	5
2	**ANTI-VEHICLE EFFECTIVENESS:**												
	Subjective value	(2)	(2)	(6)	(6)	(2)	(2)	(9)	(9)	(8)	(8)	(4)	(4)
	Total value	4	4	12	12	4	4	18	18	16	16	8	8
2	**WEATHER RESISTANCE:**												
	Subjective value	(5)	(5)	(5)	(5)	(5)	(10)	(5)	(10)	(5)	(5)	(5)	(10)
	Total value	10	10	10	10	10	20	10	20	10	10	10	20
10	**GUN HANDLING QUALITIES:** (See note 3)												
	Subjective value	(6)	(6)	(10)	(9)	(6)	(6)	(5)	(5)	(3)	(3)	(8)	(8)
	Total value	60	60	100	90	60	60	50	50	30	30	80	80
5	**ROUGH HANDLING DURABILITY:** (See note 4)												
	Subjective value	(4)	(4)	(6)	(8)	(4)	(4)	(4)	(4)	(4)	(4)	(10)	(6)
	Total value	20	20	30	40	20	20	20	20	30	20	50	30
	Total Scores	297	305	414	404	293	301	277	303	257	259	304	296

1. Hard double-action initial pull of the revolver reduces the rating.
2. The reader may disagree with cartridge ranking: .357, .41, 9mmP, .45, .38 Special. With modern bullets the 9mmP has become a much better performer than when it was limited to FMJ.
3. These ratings reflect author's own difficulties with all large frame revolvers.
4. Although adjustable sights have value, they are more fragile than service types.

The average law officer is likely to be of average size and physical ability. All too often he may be a little overweight and not nearly as competent as he would like to be. He's very conscious of these things and tries hard to hold the line and get the exercise he needs but is not always successful.

Perhaps the one thing about him that is hardest for some of the old line big city street cops or Southwestern sheriffs to take is his attitude toward guns and shooting. He may not be too interested in guns and is unwilling to devote long hours of off-duty time to shooting practice and working with guns. His gun training varies greatly from department to department, depending on the level of violent crime in his jurisdiction and upon the quality of leadership in the department. Unless he is an active competition shooter, he's a fair shot and not a competent gun handler. At worst, he may not have handled his gun in the last ten years except to clean it.

As you look over the list of eleven factors on the next couple of pages, many will feel that we have omitted at least two. The first of these is cost and was left out intentionally because the choice of a gun is too important for cost to be a consideration. If the department won't fund the gun of your choice, then it is worth saving for, if the department will allow a "non-standard" gun to be carried on duty. The second factor probably will be stopping power. The one-shot stopping power simply cannot be important to the average young officer who is not a superlative shot under stress. He must go for a gun that sacrifices some of the elephant-felling power for controllability and sustained firepower, both of which better support him at his level of ability.

The best measure of stopping power we have today is still Hatcher's formula, with revisions. Since the advent of modern, expanding bullets for handguns the performance of some much maligned calibers such as the 9mm Parabellum and the .38 Special has improved vastly.

Hatcher, as now written, doesn't recognize that. Hatcher must be updated and the revised formula must use the average frontal area of the bullet and the average coefficient of shape as devised from the information discovered in the recent study done for the Law Enforcement Assistance Agency. Only with such a formula will we get meaningful stopping power data for modern bullets.

We came up with eleven factors we believe to be the most important to the average young officer. In most cases, what is good and what is bad become pretty much self-evident. In some cases figuring up the credit for each gun under each factor is simply toting up points. An

Good gun handling characteristics refer to the ability to assume proper, steady shooting position when time and situation permit. The exact importance of this particular quality will vary to some degree with conditions.

element of subjectivity enters in, however, and we have tried to explain personal views that lead to the assignment of a credit score.

Twelve rather typical law officer guns have been chosen. They are undoubtedly not the same twelve that you would have picked, and we've not included some really good choices. For instance, neither Dan Wesson nor Charter Arms were available for consideration. You're free to make up your own chart and insert the guns, factors, weights and credits you feel would better suit your personal situation.

Weight: The average officer these days is picking up more weight on his equipment belt all the time and the latest addition is likely to be a radio. The last thing that he needs is more weight from gun and ammunition.

Compactness: In similar manner, a good gun is small and compact. It also implies relative freedom from sharp points and corners and things that catch on clothing, bushes, automobile upholstery, etc.

Readiness Condition: The best gun is the one which can be carried and drawn and fired with least effort without having to fumble with slides and safeties or go through other manual gyrations.

Functional Reliability: Here we become subjective, following an old formula which, experience shows, has a certain validity. Mechanical reliability of a handgun decreases as the linear distance ammunition must move through the action increases and as the axis angle of the cartridges must change. In other words, autoloaders, which move their rounds more — particularly those which make the cartridges change direction in going up a loading ramp into the chamber — are usually the least reliable performers. With good, modern guns and quality ammunition, that doesn't mean that the danger of malfunction is great but it is possible.

Load Adaptability: The object is to try to evaluate the gun and available cartridges as to their suitability for differing roles and police situations and the ability of the gun to be adapted to different cartridges. A premium goes to the gun with adjustable sights.

Firepower: How many shots can the officer count on before he must reload? The more the better, for the average officer. Some older lawmen feel, because of their own skill, that stopping power for the first shot is most important. They are not average, however.

Safety: The safer the gun when it is carried and in use, the better.

Anti-Vehicle Effectiveness: Once, we tended to think only highway patrolmen had use for this quality in a gun. The car has become so much a part of our lives that the need to disable one with a sidearm may fall the lot of any officer. Some officers carry a few rounds of metal-piercing ammunition at all times to meet this problem.

Weather Resistance: There was a time when the effects of weather and long hours of outdoor patrol were

Weight of the gun is another factor that will vary according to individual circumstances. To the average officer in uniform, burdened with equipment, every ounce counts. To another in plainclothes, weight is not as important.

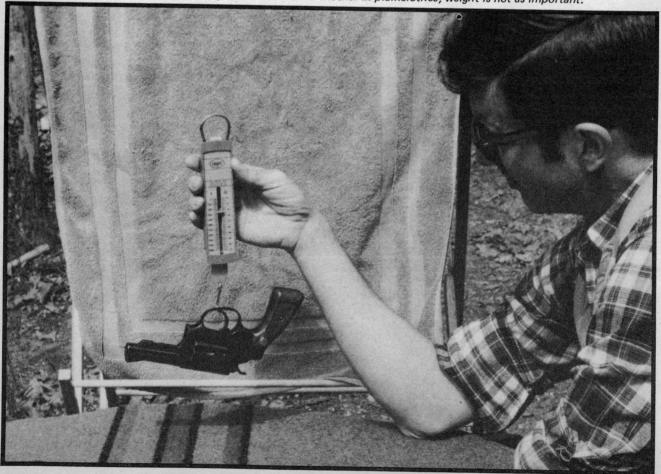

In situations where ammunition capacity and speed in reloading are vital factor, autoloaders have an advantage.

We have drawn up a sample of the table and assigned weights and individual gun credits of our choice. Here is the order for selection that resulted:

Smith & Wesson Model 59

Browning Hi-Power

Colt Detective Special

Colt Government Model

Smith & Wesson Model 66

Smith & Wesson Model 64

Smith & Wesson Model 36

AMT Hardballer

Smith & Wesson Model 15

Smith & Wesson Model 28

Smith & Wesson Model 57

Smith & Wesson Model 58

Admittedly, we are a little surprised by some of the results. Some guns finished higher and some lower than expected. Some experienced lawmen would roast us over an open fire for ranking their favorite .41 Smiths dead last and then do it again for having the audacity to put two 9mms at the top!

If you're about to embark on a career in law enforcement, or even if you're just a homeowner or businessman thinking of getting a handgun to provide protection for your property and family, give the table a try. You may find it helpful if used with the changes that best fit your situation and personal convictions about guns.

With practice, many of the speedloaders on the market can reduce the reloading time for revolvers drastically.

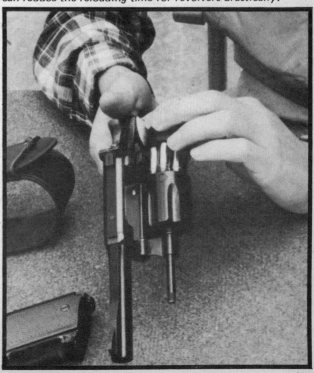

something one had to accept and live with. The new stainless steel guns offer a degree of protection which is welcome, indeed.

Gun Handling Qualities: By gun handling, we refer to all those physical things the officer must do to get the gun into action and keep it there. It includes the draw, the quick assumption of a good, two-hand hold, smooth assumption of shooting position if time permits, the ability to recover instantly from recoil and get back on target and the ability to reload smoothly and fast. Reloading merits special discussion. Revolvers are not easy to reload. There are a number of modern speedloaders for revolvers on the market today. Most hold five or six rounds in a circular position to be dropped or pushed into the empty chambers of the revolver. To use these loaders requires skill and practice. The alternative, loading from dump pouch or belt loops, is even slower and more difficult. For the average officer, the autoloader with greater magazine capacity and easier reloading offers an advantage.

Rough Handling Durability: This final factor has to do with the ruggedness of the gun and its ability to take the hard knocks of street duty. Here, the adjustable sight exacts a penalty.

Sgt. William Lee checks to determine if a pair of bullets match, using the ballistic comparison microscope. As noted, although the instrument has an accessory for making photographs, the usual preference is to go to court with expert testimony rather than macrophotographs of evidence bullets.

Chapter 3

TEST TUBE COPS

This Los Angeles Police Team Specializes In Firearms Investigations With Surprising Results!

IT WAS WELL before the advent of the Twentieth Century that Arthur Conan Doyle's fictional super-sleuth began employing the esoteric techniques of the laboratory to ensnare the wily criminals of Victorian London. Sherlock Holmes' contemporary, the dour Lestrade, of Scotland Yard, tended to belittle the value of such foolishness and this attitude on the part of police officialdom seems to have endured for a number of years.

It was on Wednesday, the first of July, 1925, that the Los Angeles Police Department officially opened their Chemistry Laboratory, staffed by one Rex E. Welsh, badge number 691. So far as it can be determined readily, this was the first example of a full time police laboratory in this country. The FBI labs still were a few years in the future, as were those of other municipal departments. It is doubtful if even the fertile imagination of Holmes' creator could have foreseen the manifold and intricate paths which scientific criminal investigation would pursue in the decades to come.

Volume I of the permanent records of the LAPD chemistry lab has been retained down through the years and it affords some fascinating insights into the day to day

A child's toy gun served as the starting point for making this swastika-decorated zip gun from the lab's extensive collection of confiscated weapons.

affairs of that vanished era. Silent Cal Coolidge was in the White House and would remain there until the elections of 1928, for which he "did not choose to run." That noble experiment, prohibition, was in full bloom and bootleg liquor, often suspected of containing poison, accounted for a quantity of the chemistry lab's investigations. "Pint of Bum booze to be tested for percentage & contents," notes the entry for February 13, 1929, "(Wood Alcohol, Acetone Aldehydes etc. all in it)." Similar entries occur frequently: "Poison liquor with terrible odor...Poison liquor for analysis, 2 people dead. Wood alcohol & creosote...Poison whisky — plenty of Acetone & Fusil Oil..."

Lieutenant Donald Mann, the assistant commander of the Scientific Investigations Division — the present designation of the activities which have grown out of Welsh's chemistry lab — skimmed through the yellowing pages of the old ledger and shook his head, ruefully.

"I wish that was all we had to take care of today," he commented.

Volume I of the chemistry lab records commences with the fourth year of operations, from July 1, 1928, through the same date in 1929, with a sort of preamble giving the box score for the first three years. There were 389 cases for the lab to handle during its first year, with Welsh appearing in court as a witness in sixty-two cases. The second year saw a modest drop to 307 total cases — court appearances not specified — but business came back up during the third year, with 408 cases and eighty-two court appearances.

There seems to have been a degree of lively curiosity aroused by the chemistry lab in other jurisdictions, as there are frequent entries concerning visitors from other departments to inspect the operation. In addition, it seems to have been the practice to assist other departments which lacked comparable facilities. There are cases listed in which

Welsh worked with the police of Riverside in a gruesome multiple murder and another one upon which he worked with the Ventura police concerning a gangland slaying with all of the classic touches: "Frank Rocco and companion, from N.Y. had a Stolen Packard Rdstr. with Maine license number 25055 also stolen. They took Jim Brady (alias) Slim Alias Johnny for a ride up near Camarillo and left him there with three bullet holes in his head. The clothing of Rocco and his companion were found in the Louise Hotel Appt. 311, and brot to the Research Lab for Analysis."

Apparently, by early March 1929, Welsh's bailiwick was being referred to as the Research Lab, since he uses that term in the foregoing quote. The Brady killing is one of the comparatively small number of Welsh's cases in which firearms played a major role. A small ax had been used in the Riverside case, for which a marginal note indicates that a man named Northcott was sentenced to hang. Careful study of the journal yields no clue as to the fate of the unfriendly pair from New York, who were presumed to have treated the late Mr. Brady in so fatal a fashion. There is, however, a cryptic entry for May 1: "Made out reports on findings for Ventura Co. and got bawled out by Capt. Cross, for not sending all reports thru his office." Another note, for February 18: "Capt. Cross informed me to keep my door locked at all times." Next to this entry, in the margin: "Pension papers made out!"

The renown of Los Angeles' test-tube cop must have been spreading afield by this time, for there are entries such as (Feb. 12): "Mrs. Connaly of Arizona, came to see if I would identify and compare some hair which she had taken off her husbands clothes with some of the suspected woman's hair." And (May 29): "Samples of Poison from Georgia." Again, no clue — or clew, as Welsh preferred to spell it — on the disposition of either case. There are an

Here's another zip gun, downright throat-catching as to esthetic appeal and workmanship — what, you don't agree?

uncountable number of such loose ends left dangling to frustrate the mystery story addict, but that and the freestyle spelling are among the many distinctive charms of this singular daybook.

Everything comes to an abrupt end on July 2, 1929, with well over four hundred blank pages left in the book to tantalize the reader. Presumably, Volume II was launched at that time and it is not available for examination.

By modern standards of ballistic investigation, Welsh was none too sophisticated, seeming to have been content with weighing bullets and measuring their diameter and noting that they "seemed pretty much the same." No mention of comparing rifling marks or striae is made, although there are various entries which indicate that he felt the need for improved expertise on the subject: accounts of shopping for bullet checking equipment, ordering it and receiving it. Near the end of the account (June 18), he seems to have been given some assistance: "Moxley on hand to help on bullets." But the sole remaining reference to the new man is (June 19): "Made three blood slides of Moxleys blood."

If the present-day head of the SID feels wistful envy for the simple existence of Police Chemist Welsh, who averaged around one case per day in the closing months prior to the great depression, you can imagine the sense of wonder which Welsh would feel if he could but view the manifold activities with which the SID occupies itself today.

The main headquarters of the Los Angeles PD is a large, modern building known as Chief Parker Center. The various subdivisions of SID occupy all of one floor and part of

another in the seven-story structure. Latent prints is on the second floor, while the fourth floor is taken up with the photographic lab, the polygraph section, electronics, blood alcohol analysis, narcotics analysis, worthless documents, comparative analysis, survey section and the firearms lab. Personnel of the firearms unit double in brass as the experts on bombs and explosives, in addition to their main specialty.

The photo section has responsibility for all photographic supplies and equipment used by the entire department, prepares photographs for evidence and processes photographs taken in connection with routine investigations.

Latent prints is concerned with the detection of fingerprints at the scene of a crime, developing and lifting them, preserving them for future courtroom work, classifying, filing and identification.

The LAPD makes extensive employment of the polygraph — often termed the lie-detector — as a tool for eliminating false leads or establishing the probable innocence of a given suspect, so that time and manpower will not be wasted in fruitless efforts.

The electronics lab is concerned, primarily, with making tape recordings of such things as suspect interviews, polygraph sessions and similar matters.

The comparative analysis section endeavors to identify tool marks, tire prints, hair, bloodstains and similar physical evidence connected with investigations, apart from fingerprints.

Another specimen from the lab's display of seized street weaponry has been rather redundantly emblazoned with a name respectfully regarded in firearms circles. The craftsmen at Oberndorf might wince and call it a "Mickey Mauser!"

The survey section covers activities such as preparing composite drawings of suspects of whom no photographs are available — as made up, for example, from descriptions by witnesses — and operates teams which make thorough surveys of the scenes of major crimes for reference as the investigations proceed. Later, should it be necessary, the survey section prepares mock-ups or exhibits for presentation in court.

The blood alcohol section processes samples taken from drunk driving suspects while its companion facility, narcotics analysis, makes identifications of contraband seized in the course of arrests. Blood analysis also is used to detect the influence of drugs or narcotics by means of samples.

The worthless document section is concerned with forgeries, handwriting identification, worthless checks and comparison of typewriting, printing, paper samples, inks and related matters.

Traffic through the firearms laboratory fluctuates somewhere between two to six hundred cases per month in firearms-related incidents or investigations. One of the chores of the gun lab is to establish that a given firearm is functional, when such evidence is required in court. Often, this is something less than an enjoyable experience. The typical firearm seized in connection with criminal investigations is a cheap piece of junk, poorly made and carelessly maintained. If it's a revolver, the chambers are apt to be in poor alignment with the barrel, causing lead to be shaved from the bullet and sent spattering to the sides.

Some of the cheap, imported autoloaders show nasty habits such as going full-auto or firing when the safety is put on, when the cartridge is chambered or at almost any unexpected moment. The personnel who have to run the function tests learn to be prepared for anything.

One case still is recalled with shudders in the gun lab: During the investigation of the shooting of Senator Robert Kennedy, a team was sent to the Fish Canyon range of the San Gabriel Valley Rifle & Pistol Club, where the suspect, Sirhan K. Sirhan, was alleged to have brushed up his marksmanship in preparation for the crime. All of the spent .22 rimfire cases were gathered up and examined individually in an effort to find one or more with firing-pin marks which matched the Iver Johnson Cadet Model .22 revolver belonging to Sirhan.

As .22 rimfire cases are non-reloadable, most shooters drop them to the ground and they accumulate to form a brassy carpet underfoot. An idea of the quantity and the size of the awesome task is gained by the tabulation of the spent case comparisons of the Kennedy case: 37,815 shell casings!

While precise statistics are not available readily, personnel of the gun lab estimate that the incoming traffic involves approximately seventy-five percent handguns, fifteen percent rifles and ten percent shotguns. Breaking the handguns down by calibers, the .22 rimfire is far and away the one encountered most frequently, followed by the .38/9mm categories, the .45, the .32 and .25 sizes, in that order. The .44 and .41 calibers are brought in quite rarely —

again, for the obvious reason that they're available only in expensive, high-quality arms and the person bent on crime prefers the cheapest junk obtainable and would prefer to steal it, if possible. When asked, none of the personnel could recall ever having dealt with such handguns as the Thompson/Center Contender, the Remington XP-100 or the Ruger Hawkeye.

During the years of the unit's operation, a collection of sample arms has been accumulated; some 600 handguns, representing practically every make and model, with all variations of certain common designs such as the .45 auto. There even is a sample of the scarce Luger stamped with the American eagle. But it's a working collection, not merely maintained for show. Specimens can be pulled from the racks to check for illegal modifications: for example, an incoming auto pistol may have been converted for full-auto fire, which can be determined through comparison to a straight sample. Robbery victims can be shown several

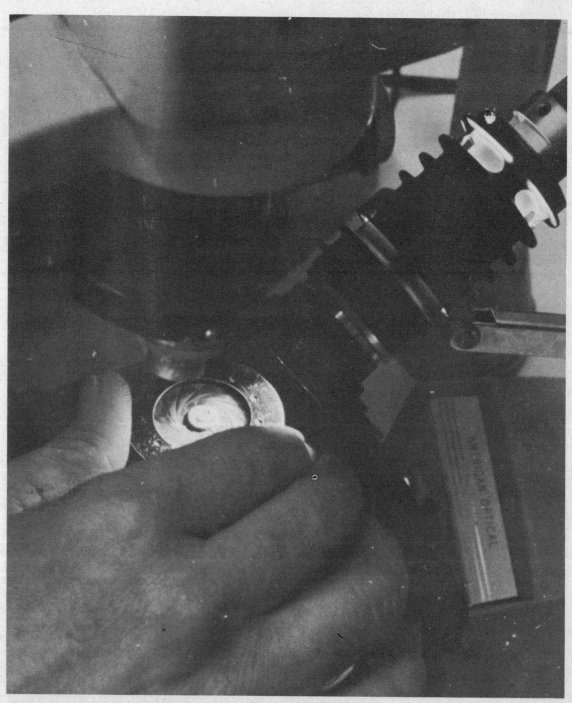

Examination of the head of a fired cartridge case can yield useful data on the gun from which it was fired. Here the evidence case is held in an adjustable iris stage in preparation for microscopic examination.

Design of this zip gun is about as simple and primitive as such things can get. Operating principles are considerably mysterious!

different guns in an effort to help them identify the arms used by criminals and this can be of definite assistance in getting a line on suspects.

One of the more interesting sections of the exhibit is the collection of homemade zip-guns which have been confiscated from suspects over the years. Uniformly, the workmanship is atrocious: cobbled together from hunks of pipe, held together with tape, wire or rubber bands — but they have one thing in common. Each of the unsightly specimens, upon being function tested, proved capable of setting off ammunition and, more or less, guiding the projectile in a forward direction at velocities which would be hazardous to anyone in its path. You look at these scraps of deadly junk, products of warped minds, misapplied ingenuity (and precious little of that), asking yourself what price gun-control laws, when a moron with a hacksaw can create one from scrap iron!

Not all of the home-made jobs are pistols, either. There's a really peachy shotgun, handcrafted from galvanized plumber's pipe, with a stock made of bent bar-stock, tack-welded in place and a striker of round rod which is held back against spring tension and released to fire the shell. To reload, you have to unscrew the pipe which comprises the barrel, worry the empty shell loose, stuff in a fresh one and screw the barrel back into place: hardly the proper fowling piece to handle a covey of quail. It was,

however, used in a homicide and, yes, the victim was the one in front of it.

Frequently, in the course of an investigation, it is necessary to establish whether or not an individual has fired a gun. One of the older tests to determine this is the paraffin/nitrate test, in which melted paraffin is applied to the hand and adjacent areas on the suspect or subject. After it solidifies, it is peeled off and the inner surfaces are treated with reagents which react in a distinctive manner if residues are present which contain nitrates. Such deposits, typically, are left on the skin by particles of unburned powder, leaking powder gases or similar by-products of firing a gun.

The LAPD employs the paraffin/nitrate testing technique to some extent, but they have had encouraging results with new methods which are not dependent upon the actual firing of the gun.

The normal perspiration of the living hand has a mild solvent effect upon many materials, varying to a considerable degree between individuals. As many a firearms enthusiast has learned — often the hard way — there are some people whose perspiration is so potent that they can leave a fingerprint, clearly etched in rust, upon the blued surface of a gun, merely by touching it. This is an extreme example, but the effect is present to some varying level in all hands.

Sgt. Lee removes a sample cartridge from drawer of lab's extensive file of different calibers and bullet types.

When any gun is held in the hand for a period of time, the materials of which it is made will dissolve and deposit themselves upon the skin in contact with them, in exceedingly minute quantities. Such vestigial traces are difficult to remove completely, even by vigorous washing.

All that remained was to find a technique for detecting and identifying the presence of deposits left upon the skin through contact with a firearm. As sometimes happens, the solution was simple, once discovered. An organic compound, listed in the catalogs of chemical supply houses for many years, when applied as a spray to the test areas, will fluoresce under ultra-violet illumination. Even better, it reacts in distinctive manner to the presence of deposits left by contact with different materials. Steel, aluminum, brass, hard rubber, pearl, the various plastics – all leave their distinctive and identifiable traces.

If desired, the hand or test area can be photographed under the ultra-violet light to record the size and appearance of the reacting areas. The corresponding portions of the firearm can be photographed in similar manner and the two can be superimposed to demonstrate the extent of matching with each other.

In effect, the firearm can be put back into the hand which held it and the technique has proved to be of great

value in several cases. Among them, there was a suicide case in which the fatal gun was found lying some feet away from the body of the deceased. There were reasonable grounds for suspecting the involvement of a second party but, when the new test was given, it established that the gun had been held in the hand of the deceased, prior to death and that it had not been held in the hand of the surviving suspect.

In other typical cases, a holdup suspect, surprised during the crime, fled the scene and threw away the gun while running. Apprehended, the suspect was subjected to the new test and comparison of the positive reaction was made to the gun, which had been retrieved by the pursuing officers. Identification by witnesses at the scene of the crime was backed up solidly by clear and positive reactions to the new test – details being clearly apparent, such as the position of the slot in the head of a stock screw, a crack in the pearl grip – and the conviction of the suspect was secured.

The obvious advantage of the new technique is that, with fair frequency, crimes involve the display of a firearm without the actual firing of it. The paraffin test is ineffective in such cases, as it detects only those deposits of nitrate compounds left by firing of one or more rounds. The new testing technique serves not only to establish that a firearm was held in the hand but also as a means of establishing that other objects were held: a knife, for example, or certain categories of what are euphemistically termed blunt instruments, or those troublesome devices known as alleged firearms — toy guns, cap pistols and the like.

Firearm serial numbers are another major area of activity for the gun lab. It is an automatic felony to be in possession of a firearm whose serial number has been ground off, covered over or changed. In spite of this, tampering with the serial number is a common occurrence and detection techniques to restore the original serial number have been refined to a high degree by the LAPD gun lab.

There is one method which works magnificently if the missing number has been stamped in steel or any ferrous alloy. Stamping modifies the response of the iron molecules to magnetic fields, to a point well below the bottom of the indentation left by the stamped numbers. Sergeant William Lee, in charge of the firearms laboratory, brought out the receiver of a GI .45 automatic and let me examine the portion on the right side, above the trigger, where the serial number is stamped on most .45 autos. The area on this one was perfectly smooth and had been nickel plated for good measure. Even under a strong magnifying glass, no slightest markings could be detected.

Continuing with the demonstration, he turned to a stout wooden box on a stand. Inside the box, with its two poles positioned beneath the upper platform, there was a large permanent magnet, weighing perhaps eighty pounds or more. The powerful field seized the receiver, plucking it from Lee's fingers as he moved it toward the platform and anchored it to the wood with a sharp "clunk!"

Experimentally, I tried to lift the receiver from the wood and estimated its apparent weight to be upward of fifteen pounds, when in the grip of the magnetic field.

Lee produced an aerosol spray can containing a solution used in Magna-flux testing: finely divided particles of red ferrous oxide, similar to the coating of the tape used for recording, suspended in what appeared to be an oil-base vehicle. Holding the nozzle about a foot above the receiver, he directed an even and gentle spray of vapor down onto the area where the serial number should have been and, as if by magic, suddenly the serial number was there: crisply detailed as the day it left the factory and perfectly legible to the unassisted eye. The particles of iron oxide, clustering in the spray vehicle, positioned themselves to pick out the hidden changes in molecular structure which had been left by the original stamping. It would have been no problem at all to photograph the restored number for purposes of evidence.

While the demonstration was going on, Patrolman Lawrence Baggett was engaged in restoring the blotted-out number on a single-action .22 revolver of recent manufacture. The admirable magnetic technique was of no help in this case, since the frame in which the number had been stamped was of an aluminum alloy and thus quite unresponsive to magnetic flux. He was using a soft camel's hair brush, dipped in a special reagent developed by the department laboratories and a really impressive amount of patience. All of the digits had been developed to a readable degree except one which could not be identified clearly as a nine or a zero.

The LAPD, by the way, is one of the few facilities authorized to restamp new serial numbers and has their

Plumber's pipe, Plexiglas, tin and scrap wood went into this hand-crafted little monster, but it shoots, after a fashion!

A massive permanent magnet beneath steel receiver produces a field that causes microfine ferrous particles in the Magna-flux spray to cluster over filed-away serial number, restoring it.

distinctive code-group which is included in the new number to denote the origin of the re-stamp.

The general public thinks of police ballistics — if at all — in terms of matching the lands, grooves and scratches (striae) of a murder bullet to a sample bullet fired from a gun known to have been owned by a suspect. While it's true that this is an important part of the operation, there are several other areas in which a "make" can be secured which will forge the chain of evidence leading from a crime back to the criminal. Under stress of firing pressures, the cartridge case takes on distinctive markings from the gun in several areas: the tip of the firing pin, the area around the recoil plate through which the firing pin protrudes, the walls of the chamber, minute scratches on the feed ramp or magazine lips of autoloading pistols, extractor marks, ejector marks — to name but a few.

In fact, there have been cases in which a canny criminal went over the scene, wiping away prints from everything he touched, but neglected to remember that he had left a nice, identifiable portion of a print on the spent cartridge case, in the process of loading it into the magazine and the latent print has been lifted from the brass to convict him.

The gun lab is a fascinating place in which to rubberneck about and, if one is prudent, to look but not to touch. As has been noted, the crew of the unit answer calls for bombs, explosives and similar infernal devices — working in close cooperation with other agencies such as the sheriff's

A portion of the lab's collection of more than 600 sample guns can be seen as Dave Butler fields an incoming call.

bomb and arson squad, the FBI, Secret Service and Treasury Department — and the premises have all sorts of relics and mementoes left from what must have been stirring incidents in their time. It is not an appropriate place to play the busy-fingers.

There's an elaborate comparison microscope, built by American Optical to department specs and priced about on the scale of one of the less pretentious Cadillacs. Sergeant Lee rummaged about the work area and selected a couple of spent .32 ACP cases, mounted them on the twin iris stages of the instrument, turned on the lights and spent a bit of time twiddling and fiddling with the controls. He invited me to have a peek to see if I thought both were fired from the same gun. It did not appear likely and I said so, but cautiously, scenting a trap. He moved back to the eyepieces, gave one case head half a turn and suggested a second look. This time, there was no slightest doubt: both the same, with a perfect match of striae and a mark left by a tiny, burred flat on the tip of the firing pin. They still were the same cases, but the difference was in how you looked at them.

Although the big comparison microscope has sophisticated facilities for photographing exhibits through the lenses, Lee said that they rarely prepare photos of ballistic evidence for courtroom purposes. They have found that it is more effective to qualify the testifying officer as an accredited expert and offer his testimony as to whether or not the given item of evidence is or is not connected to the firearm in question. The trained eye can detect similarities or differences which are difficult or impossible to capture on film.

Some of the specimen bullets that the lab has worked on are retained and filed for future reference. There have been a few instances wherein some particular gun came back to their attention a second, perhaps a third time. At the outset, a typical case will present the lab with a recovered bullet, possibly a fired cartridge case, as well. The first step is to determine the general description of the gun out of which it was fired: a revolver or autoloader, the caliber, the make and similar details. Trained personnel can winnow the possibilities down to a comparatively small number. At this time, if the nature of the case warrants the effort and time, the incoming bullet can be compared to bullets on file which fall into the same category.

Although no system has been worked out for the classification of fired bullets, comparable to that used for fingerprints, it is possible to assign a category to it, based upon number and dimensions of lands and grooves, right or left-hand rifling and related factors, so as to reduce the number of comparisons which must be made.

Scientific investigation is only one phase of police operations, but it is an important one and Rex Welsh surely would take pride in the complex and efficient system which has grown from his pioneer activities.

EVERYTHING FOR THE .357 MAGNUM

Chapter 4

Properly Loaded, This Cartridge Should Meet All Police And Home Defense Needs!

A LOAD for all seasons and reasons? Something for everyone and everything. Got a special problem? Need a tailored load? Perhaps the answer is to be found in the reloading thoughts compiled by James K. Geddes.

The .357 magnum lends itself admirably to the solution of most problems and requirements. Caliber of bullet, size of case, strength of appropriate firearms and thus increased working pressures, handgun velocities available — with the

Below, .357 magnum cartridges with the 125-grain jacketed hollow points (JHP) by Sierra and the 150-grain cast bullets from Lyman No. 358477 mould. Bottom, bullets in foreground, from left: 90-grain Sierra 9mm; 90-grain metal-piercing; 110-grain Sierra JHP, 125-grain Sierra JHP; 150-grain Sierra JHP; 115-grain Lyman 358345; 148-grain Speer hollow base wadcutter; and Lyman 358477 at 150 grains. Six of the eight are shown seated in .357 cases.

fact that recoil and muzzle blast can be handled by most serious handgunners — all add up to one of the most popular cartridges of today. And rightfully so, for in the right hands with the right loads, it will handle most situations effectively, including law enforcement need.

NOVICE LOADS

"I had carefully thought these out," Geddes reports. These loads were to be used when introducing newcomers to handgunning. In doing so, an intelligent instructor realizes that the use of full power loads in the beginning would indeed be counterproductive to all his best efforts. By gradually increasing the power of the loads, one allows the trainee to become accustomed to a predetermined amount of recoil and noise before advancing to the next stage. In this way, the problem of flinching can be kept to a minimum. In addition, more hits will be registered on the target, increasing the shooter's confidence.

Live-center supports end of steel rod in turning it down to correct diameter for the homemade metal-piercing bullets discussed here.

Vernier caliper is used to check inside diameter of the now-discontinued .38 half-jackets from Speer.

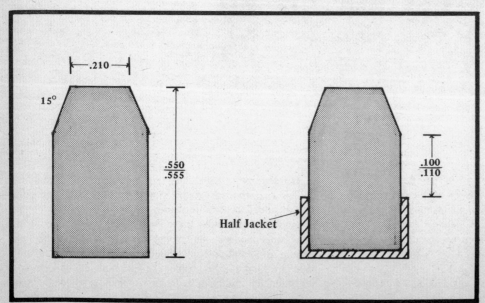

15°

.210

.550
.555

.100
.110

Half Jacket

Dimensions for the metal-piercing bullet, as discussed.

Speer's 148-grain HBWC, seated with cavity foremost, showing expansion at progressively increasing velocities. From left, with 5.0 grains of Hercules Unique in a 2" barrel; remainder from 6" Ruger at 5.0, 6.0, 7.0 and 8.0 gr. Unique.

First Level: Using the Lyman No. 358345 cast bullet of 115 grains, Geddes backed this up with just 2.8 grains of Bullseye. A CCI 500 primer ignites this load to exit the muzzle at 788 feet per second from his six-inch Ruger Security Six of stainless steel. This, by all definitions, is nothing but a pipsqueak load, with little noise and almost no recoil. It is the perfect load with which to introduce the novice to the world of handguns. With the majority of people, it doesn't require much time before they have overcome their initial apprehension of "shooting a revolver," using such a light load.

Second Level: Using the same bullet, "I now propel it with 5.0 grains of Unique and a CCI 500 primer. This is a moderate-power .38 Special load, and at this level a degree of realism finally comes into the picture. The muzzle velocity of this load is 970 fps. If the purpose of this training is to prepare an individual for the .38 Special, this could be the level at which to stay. Intimidation with the following and more powerful loads would be detrimental and fruitless," Geddes feels.

Third Level: Using a 150-grain cast bullet — Lyman's No. 358477 — and CCI 500 primers, Geddes used a charge of 6.5 grains of Unique. "This is a good working load and a good working level to stay with. It is the one I use for most of my target practice. This is a good three-quarter-power load. Velocity of 1037 fps and sufficient energy are created to give an individual a feeling of .357 magnum realism. Not being a max load, it is easier on the gun itself, as well as the shooter's hand and pocket. With this 6.5-grain load, more than twice the amount of rounds can be loaded using Unique than could be with the more potent 2400 in 15.0-grain charges. A shooter can put through fifty to one

From left, 90-grain metal-piercing; 90-grain Sierra 9mm JHP; 125-grain Sierra JHP; 150-grain Sierra JHP and the Speer shot capsule containing three round lead balls of approximately .300" diameter, as discussed.

Photo at left gives a closer view of the homemade metal-piercing bullet, shown at right after penetrating 3/16" steel plate.

hundred rounds of this stuff without developing a sore web-of-hand or wrist, thereby benefiting from longer and more thorough practice sessions.

Fourth Level: The same 150-grain Lyman cast bullet is used, switching to a CCI 550 primer and a max load of 15.0 grains of 2400. "This load moves along at a respectable 1410 fps from my revolver. It's loud, the recoil is right up there if you're in the mood for that sort of thing, and the bullet smacks its target with real authority." All maximum .357 magnum loads should be used with discretion, especially when being consumed by an inexperienced person. Women, since their wrists are not likely to be very strong, should use this load very infrequently — only often enough to maintain an awareness of the .357's potential.

Entry of the three-ball load at three yards in ¾" plywood shows cluster effect at this distance.

METAL-PIERCING LOADS

For those who may need a metal-piercing load, we have only two approaches. Over-the-counter rounds are available to police only, generally speaking, at the price of about a buck a round. Or if one has access to a metal lathe and swaging press, he can make his own.

Step One: Turn a three-eighths-inch piece of cold rolled steel to an outside diameter of .3205 to .3210-inch.

Step Two: Cut off lengths of 19/32-inch. This is a bit long, allowing for truing up the ends.

Step Three: Face off both ends to a final overall length of .550 to .555-inch. Chamfer both ends with a file — one end lightly to facilitate insertion into half-jackets and the other heavily to fit into the nose portion of the swaging press. Without sufficient tapering, the nose punch could become damaged.

Step Four: Move to the swaging press (Herter's, in this case) and insert the piece of steel into a Herter's half-jacket of .38 caliber. Final length overall should be at or very near .575-inch.

Step Five: It's back to the lathe to put on the following taper: fifteen degrees to a nose diameter of .210-inch.

"Using a 550 Magnum primer, I almost fill the case with 21.0 grains of 2400. This compressed load comes out of my Ruger barrel at 1850 fps and pierces three-sixteenths-inch mild steel at twenty-five yards or a piece of one-eighth-inch steel at fifty yards. It does this at both ranges, with power to spare. Using the 90-grain slug, minus the half-jacket that gets stripped off when bullet meets metal, it fully penetrates a 1100-page Sears catalog located behind the steel plate," Geddes reports.

SELF-DEFENSE LOADS

The old stand-by is putting Speer's 148-grain, hollow-base wadcutter in backwards so the immense cavity of this soft lead bullet faces forward. Even at reasonable .38 Special velocities, this round has the reputation of expanding quite well. Driven at .357 Magnum velocities, this bullet literally becomes a small explosive.

1. 5.0 grains of Unique delivers 850 fps and expands to a full .560-inch at seven yards in dry sand.

2. 6.0 grains of Unique gives 950 fps. This really begins to show the potential of this round by expanding to .625-inch.

3. 7.0 grains of Unique creates a muzzle velocity of 1030 fps from my six-inch Ruger. In dry sand, at seven yards, this bullet almost flattens out by expanding to .700-inch.

Exit hole of same test firing on opposite page shows massive splintering and complete penetration of all three .300" balls.

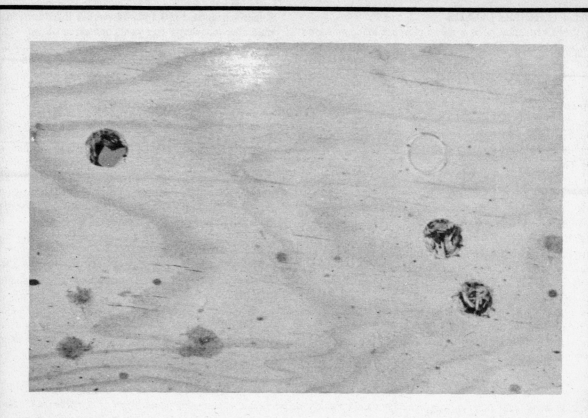

Entry and exit holes in ¾" plywood at seven yards. Firing the three-ball load shows comparative dispersion.

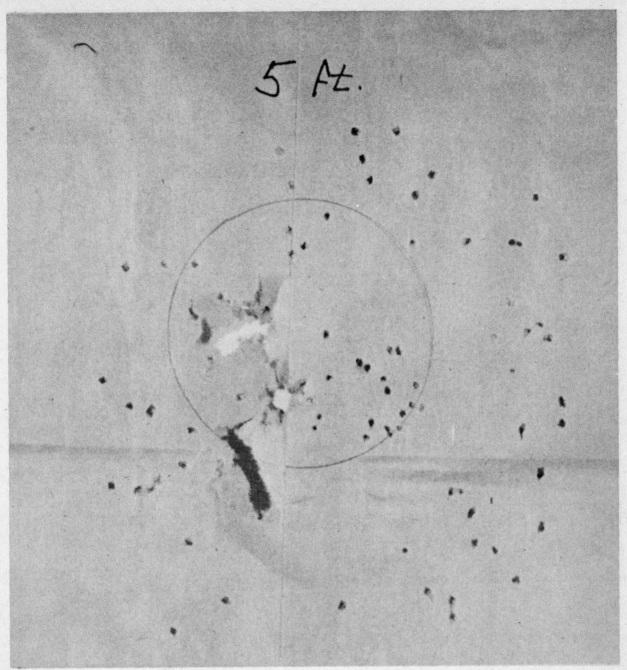

Here, the Speer .38/.357 shot capsule was loaded with conventional shot and fired from five-foot distance.

4. 8.0 grains of Unique causes the bullet to exit at 1125 fps and expands to a full inch. This is the upper limit for this round. Beyond this velocity the lead bullet actually blows up.

MULTIPLE-PROJECTILE LOADS

For self-defense loads, especially for use indoors or wherever excessive penetration can prove to be a danger to others, the multiple projectile load is just the ticket. Using Speer's .38 caliber shot capsules, load up with three round balls of .300-inch (No. 1 Buck). This 1102 fps load (CCI 500 and 6.0/Unique) serves any homeowner with the

ultimate in stopping power, along with the distinct advantage of not worrying about a missed shot penetrating walls and endangering other members of the household. The three balls will just penetrate a piece of plywood three-quarters-inch thick at seven yards. This is generally considered the equivalent of "adequate penetration" when referring to the human body. It also will tear a jagged hole through a six-hundred-page catalog, leaving an impressive "wound." This load personifies the ballistics axiom that "the sum of its parts is greater than its total." Three round lead balls entering into the human form are going to spread out and tend to go their own separate ways. Thus, three

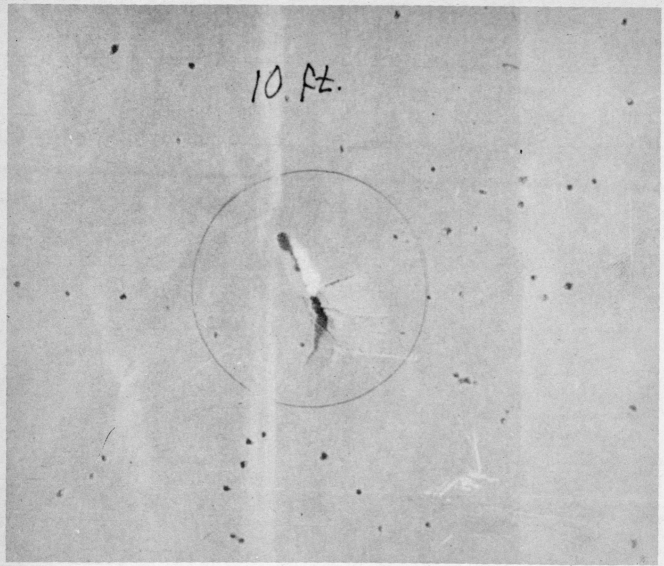

At ten-foot distance, the shot load has spread too much to be effective against snakes.

40-grain .300-inch diameter bullets are going to create their own individual wound channels.

Using the same plastic capsules from Speer, fill them up with No. 9 shot (approximately 130 pellets). Pushed along by 5.0 grains of Unique (no advantage in going to heavier charges, as poor patterns result) and a CCI 500 primer, this load is ideal for those who are likely to be prowling around in snake country. At just over 1000 fps, it will dispatch any rattler out to five feet or so from the muzzle of the gun. (Add another two feet for an outstretched arm and you have an effective range of over seven feet.)

FULL POWER LOADS

Where target practice and/or deep penetration is of more importance than expansion, the use of a heavy, cast bullet (1:15 or harder) is preferred. For most applications that fall into the "business" category, the knowledgeable reloader switches to jacketed slugs. Weights range from 90 grains for 9mm bullets to the heavy 150 to 160-grain bullets.

1. Sierra 9mm (.355-inch) 90-grain JHPs; CCI 500 primers and 21.0 grains of 2400; muzzle velocity of 1821 fps. At fifty yards, the accuracy of such a short slug leaves something to be desired; five-inch groups are the rule. However, at close range, this fast-stepping bullet would prove quite explosive, with the emphasis on violent expansion to create a devastating wound channel.

2. Sierra 110-grain JHP; CCI 550 primers and 20.0 grains of 2400; MV of 1724 fps. Same type of accuracy as the 9mm projectile. Again, owing to its inefficiency in retaining downrange velocity, this would be better suited to short ranges (under twenty-five yards). Again, expansion would be terrific.

3. Sierra 125-grain JHP; CCI 550 primers and 19.0 grains of 2400; MV of 1676 fps. At the fifty-yard marker, this weight bullet begins to realize fully the potential of the .357 magnum. Its accuracy is about three inches at the distance. Downrange knockdown power and penetration are peaking with this bullet, for this caliber.

"Velocities at ranges out to seventy-five yards or

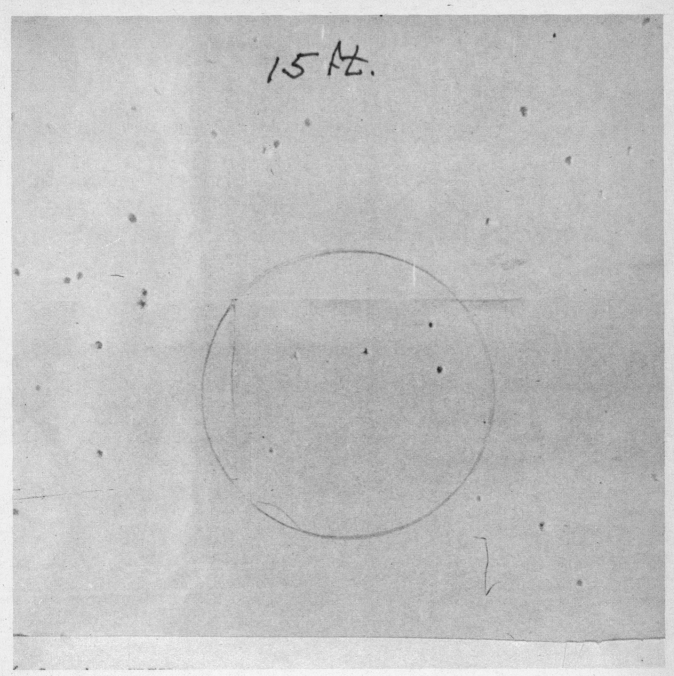

At fifteen feet, the shot load is such a to-whom-it-may-concern proposition it's far better forgotten.

thereabouts assure the best compromise between good expansion and deep penetration. This is my personal choice for a self-defense load. With it, I feel prepared for any emergency," Geddes reports.

4. Sierra 150-grain JHP; CCI 550 primer and 15.0 grains of 2400; MV of 1425 fps. This is the most accurate of the lot, producing groups of around 2¾ inches at fifty long paces. For those who subscribe to the heavier-bullet type theory, or who want to trade off some expansion for more penetration...this is the correct weight range. The unique cavity design of all Sierra hollow points assures that even this heavier, slower moving slug, still will give a respectable amount of expansion all the way out to those longer ranges.

From the Super Vel aficionados to those who line up behind Elmer Keith, the argument continues to rage on as to the relative merits of lighter bullets and higher velocities versus slower moving but heavier slugs.

Take your pick. Test them for accuracy, penetration and expansion. Shoot the bullets into pine boards, catalogs, putty, steel, sand or whatever. Talk to police officers who have been involved in or have first-hand knowledge of gunfights, or any other person who has *practical*, not *theoretical*, knowledge of various bullet weights and types.

Make your own determinations, so that you will be fully satisfied as to the final weight choice. After all, *you* must have confidence in the bullet of your choice.

Chapter 5

There Has Been Much Discussion - Past And Present - Regarding This Cartridge's Potential

Gunsmith Haywood Nelms prepares to test a lot of 9mm ammunition over the screens of his portable chronograph.

THE 9MM & LAW ENFORCEMENT

Past and present, there has been a good deal of discussion as to the relative merits of the 9mm Parabellum cartridge as the future handgun cartridge for American law enforcement work.

It is one of those discussions that often seems to have great merit, yet never really gets off the ground when it comes to implementation of the cause.

So we asked Claud S. Hamilton, a knowledgeable gent, to take a long hard look at what's happening and the current thinking on this bit of controversy. Here's what he reports:

"The plain fact is that the pistol, not the revolver, is the arm of the future. While I, personally, would really prefer a pistol cartridge of about .400 caliber, the 9mm is the best that we have — so that's what it has to be. And it's not a bad choice, either.

"I have a young, but experienced, law officer friend in the Southwest who has a real thing about what he calls liberal, pro-criminal do-gooders. One of the things he views with jaundiced eye is a tendency he sees these days for these elements to bring pressure upon police department policymakers to arm more and more departments with the 9mm Parabellum. To him, this is an insidious expression of the liberal do-gooder philosophy: 'If you *must* shoot them, shoot them just a *little* bit.' I know that I shall never separate him from his personal belief in the .41 Remington magnum. 'I've made up my mind...don't bother me with the facts, boy.'

"And he is not alone. The majority of lawmen I have spoken to or who have put their thoughts in writing seem overwhelmingly to agree that the 9mm Parabellum cartridge is just not satisfactory for American law enforcement use. The reason is not hard to discover; most of these gentlemen formed their opinions in the days when the only 9mmP ammunition available was the full-metal-jacketed military load, and much of that was of the older, German high-pressure kind.

"No question about it; that ammunition penetrates much too much for safe use on city streets, and is poor at transmitting its energy to a human target — no stopping power. A felon shot two or three times in non-vital places with it might very well keep on shooting at you, kill you, and make good his escape! Then, too, there is the strange anti-pistol prejudice I find so deeply ingrained in many lawmen in this country. Somehow, they just don't feel a pistol is safe in the hands of the ordinary officer.

What I believe and these gentlemen all fail to take into account is the full capabilities of modern 9mm pistols; improved effectiveness the new bullets of high quality give the 9mm; and the great advantage of light recoil and low blast. Police training officers long have known that recruits

Though hardly logical for law enforcement, this highly engraved Browning Hi Power 9mm is an example of one of the many pistols chambered today for the 9mm Parabellum.

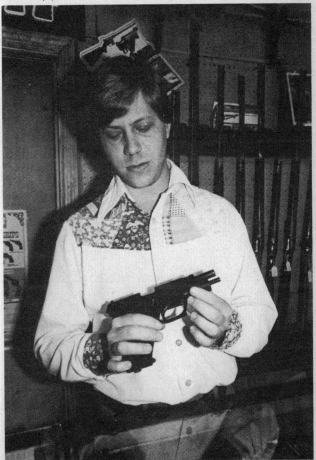

Steve Richards of Hunters Haven in Alexandria, Virginia, examines one of the new Browning 9mmP double actions.

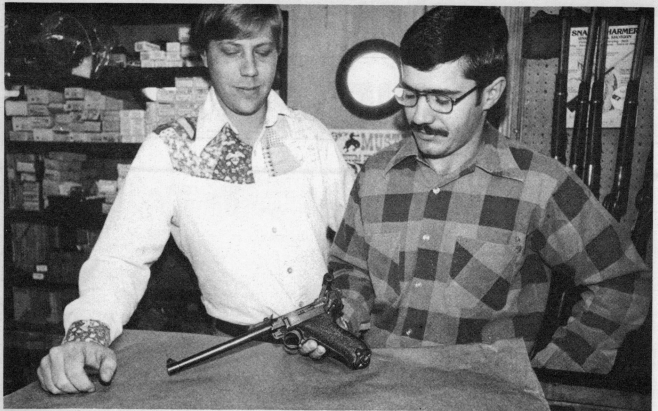

The long-barreled artillery Luger, hardly designed for police work, is one of those designed for the 9mmP. (Below) Steve Martin and Richard Johnson examine two typical police revolvers: the .357 Colt Python and the Smith and Wesson Model 64, chambered for the .38 Special.

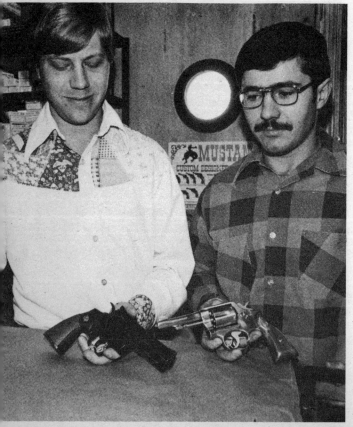

are more easily trained and achieve generally higher levels of proficiency with arms of moderate recoil and blast levels."

No serious discussion of the 9mm Parabellum — or 9mm Luger cartridge, as some insist upon calling it — is complete without considering at least briefly the background of this ballistic achievement. In a sense it was one of the very first magnum handgun loads, operating regularly at pressures over 30,000 copper units of pressure (cup) a full thirty years before Major Wesson brought out the first revolver to do that: the .357 magnum.

It was not until the decade of the 1880s that the state of the art in manufacturing reached the point where all the requirements for a successful pistol could be met. They came in a rush. The ability to make strong, center-fire metallic cartridge cases which could be crimped tightly to bullets; hard, full-metal-jacketed bullets to take the beating of operating through semiauto actions; and the smokeless powder needed to power the systems uniformly and consistently.

An American, Hugo Borchardt, brought out the first commercially successful pistol in 1893 at the German plant of Ludwig Loewe. The years that followed did not lack for brilliant inventors. John Browning, working at Fabrique Nationale (FN) in Liege soon had produced several pocket pistols in what came to be known as the .32 Auto Colt Pistol caliber in this country.

Georg Luger's pistol which he called the "Luger" first appeared about 1902 chambered for the same 7.63mm cartridge used by Borchardt. The Luger pistol was not

Above: The typical revolver cartridges used in tests are: (from left) Remington-Peters .41 magnum police load; the Remington-Peters 158-grain .357 and Winchester-Western 158-grain .38 Special. Note that the .41 did not expand at all. (Below) The six 9mm test cartridges are shown with recovered bullets after meat/bone test. From left are: S&W, Remington-Peters, Speer, Norma, Super Vel. The Exploder is not shown, although a bit of the base and a recovered case fragment is shown in front of the other bullets, which were involved in series of tests.

Among the handguns used in these tests were (from left): the Colt Lawman, the Smith and Wesson Model 15, S&W's Model 59 in 9mm, and the S&W Model 57. Claud Hamilton feels the results of tests are revealing for police.

designed to meet a stated military requirement and, as it turned out, Luger and the Mauser people were initially more successful at selling it abroad than in Germany. When the German Army did finally adopt the Luger in 1908, the pistol adopted was somewhat different from earlier models and was chambered for a new 9mm cartridge destined to be far more important than the gun itself.

The 9mm Parabellum cartridge as originally loaded had a bullet of truncated cone shape with a flat nose. It was, of course, a full-metal-jacketed bullet of about 123 grains weight. It was loaded to about 1200 feet per second (fps) muzzle velocity in four-inch guns which is quite a stiff load. In later versions it was found that a smooth, parabolic ogive gave better feeding performance, and this is the form of the FMJ bullet we usually see today.

The Luger never was intended to be a significant weapon of war as was the Colt-Browning Model 1911 pistol. The M1911, after all, was designed to meet a specific military requirement of the U.S. Cavalry for a weapon for mounted close combat. Rather, the pistol, in German and general European service, was more a symbol of rank and position than anything else. It was only a few years later that the Luger's potential as an arm for artillery and naval landing parties led to the development of special, long-barreled models to take better advantage of this superb cartridge.

The outstanding qualities of the cartridge were not long in being recognized. Arms designers, primarily in Europe, were quick to see its efficiency of design, its light weight

for the power delivered, and its small size. Also, there is a certain rightness about the dimensions of the 9mm when it comes to functioning through self-loading actions. A number of new arms were built to take the cartridge, perhaps the best known being the Browning Hi-Power, John Browning's last design which he completed in 1927.

"N.F. Strebe, the dean of District of Columbia area gunsmiths, tells me that soon after World War I American ammunition makers realized that a number of cheap foreign arms were entering this country, mostly from Italy and Spain, that could chamber and fire the 9mm Parabellum cartridge," Hamilton reports. "In order to lessen the danger of blow-ups, it was decided to 'load down' the 9mmP cartridge to safer levels, and this practice has been continued here right up to the present. This is why, if you happen to be the proud owner of a Luger, you will find that it will not opeate reliably with American ammunition. The Luger pistol is notoriously sensitive to recoil forces. It demands loads appreciably hotter than current U.S. standards if it is to work well.

When General John T. Thompson offered his so-called Tommy Gun right after World War I, it was to have been available in nine different calibers including 9mmP. Except for prototypes, however, only guns in .45 ACP were manufactured. The gun sold slowly at first and did not really come to public attention until the gangland battles of the Prohibition Era. As the Allied Forces later learned to their sorrow, it was the German army which first saw the

Hamilton experienced some difficulties in his tests with the Smith & Wesson Model 59, shown with the 125-grain Speer JSP handload. He reports that the cartridge caused repeated jams by prematurely latching the slide open.

potential of the machine pistol when used en masse in close combat, and it was their guns chambered for the 9mmP cartridge which showed the world the way in World War II.

"What makes the 9mmP so outstandingly effective in submachine guns are the same qualities described earlier — plus greater effective range. Its excellent ballistic design makes the 9mmP effective in SMGs out to nearly a hundred yards while others, like the .45 ACP, lose their velocity and drop rapidly.

"There have been rumors that the Germans, during WWII, loaded certain lots of 9mmP ammunition specifically for use only in SMGs. These usually have black-nosed bullets and are reputed to generate pressures too high for safe use in pistols. Ordnance research done after the war has pretty well confirmed that this was not the case. Certain lots were loaded with light bullets and to quite high velocities, but these bullets were made with sintered iron cores to save valuable lead. The pressures were no higher than in ordinary pistol ammunition.

"All things considered, my message for American lawmen is to take a good look at modern American 9mm Parabellum ammunition loaded with the new bullets. You may be in for some pleasant surprises," Hamilton says.

"Does it still penetrate too much? Has the stopping power been appreciably improved?" Hamilton believes the answer to both questions is an unqualified Yes! and set out to prove it. To accomplish this, he enlisted the help of a gunsmith friend, Haywood Nelms.

"We decided to test three of the best police cartridges we know of today in the opinion of American lawmen against a representative sample of available commercial 9mm of recent make. We planned to first chronograph each load, then test actual performance in targets made of meat and bone. The ability to deliver energy in the target would be gauged by measuring the penetration of bullets in a series of tightly packed polyester pillows placed behind the meat and bone target. These pillows have the added desirable characteristic of catching the bullet without further deforming it after it leaves the target."

For the meat and bone target, Hamilton originally built a wood stand so that a layer of lambs' ribs could be placed front and rear to simulate a chest cavity, then the space between could be filled with franks and meat scraps to represent internal organs.

"We soon found that we shot this target to pieces right away and began packing the same ingredients in tightly taped-up old T-shirts to get better effect," he reports.

"The first thing that happened to us was that my chronograph refused to function under the existing light conditions, so the values shown are those found from earlier tests of the same loads and lots of ammunition.

"The police loads selected were the Remington-Peters .41 magnum 210-grain lead semi-wadcutter, the Remington-Peters .357 magnum 158-grain jacketed hollow point, and the Winchester-Western .38 Special 158-grain lead hollow point(+P). These we decided to fire in more or

THE 9mm PARABELLUM

THE 9mm PARABELLUM...

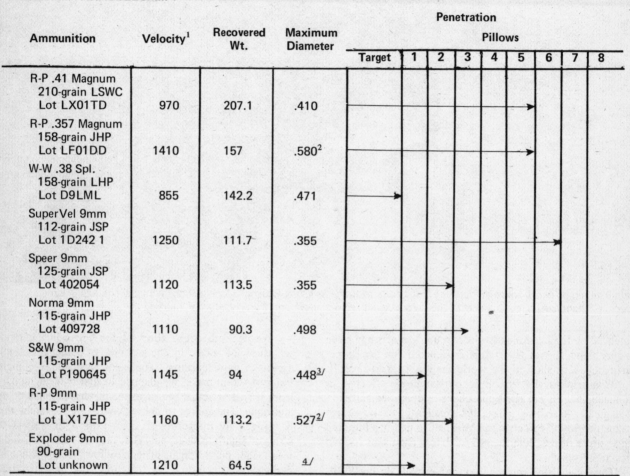

Ammunition	Velocity[1]	Recovered Wt.	Maximum Diameter	Penetration (Target / Pillows 1–8)
R-P .41 Magnum 210-grain LSWC Lot LX01TD	970	207.1	.410	→→→ to 5
R-P .357 Magnum 158-grain JHP Lot LF01DD	1410	157	.580[2]	→→→ to 6
W-W .38 Spl. 158-grain LHP Lot D9LML	855	142.2	.471	→ to Target
SuperVel 9mm 112-grain JSP Lot 1D242 1	1250	111.7	.355	→→→ to 6
Speer 9mm 125-grain JSP Lot 402054	1120	113.5	.355	→→ to 2
Norma 9mm 115-grain JHP Lot 409728	1110	90.3	.498	→→ to 3
S&W 9mm 115-grain JHP Lot P190645	1145	94	.448[3]	→→ to 2
R-P 9mm 115-grain JHP Lot LX17ED	1160	113.2	.527[2]	→→ to 2
Exploder 9mm 90-grain Lot unknown	1210	64.5	[4]	→ to 1

NOTES:
1. *Velocities estimated from previous performance.*
2. *The two loads showed excellent, consistent performance and expansion.*
3. *This load has a tendency to shed the jacket.*
4. *Only the torn case and a small fragment were recovered.*

The new Heckler & Koch pistol is one of many made in Europe which is designed to handle the 9mm Parabellum round.

less typical guns: a Smith & Wesson four-inch Model 57 .41 magnum; a Colt Lawman .357 Mark III; and a Smith & Wesson .38 Special Combat Masterpiece."

The 9mm loads selected all featured bullets on the heavy side; 112 grains and up. Nelms and Hamilton both felt these better use the energy potential of the cartridge and ought to be better manstoppers. Included in the six loads picked was the Exploder, which features an exploding bullet. Hamilton's Smith & Wesson Model 59 did the honors.

"Many fine pistols are available in 9mm, but one must use either the 59 or the Browning Hi-Power if full advantage of the large capacity magazine is to be realized.

The results of the shoot are listed on the accompanying table.

Hamilton says, "I was not favorably impressed by the performance of the .41 magnum. Its lead semi-wadcutters did not upset at all in meat and bone, and penetrated much too deeply to seem safe for street use. I feel sure a soft lead hollow-point bullet, if available in this load, would be a real winner. The hard LSWC certainly is not. The .357 penetrated deeply, which was no surprise, but it also expanded beautifully and uniformly. The W-W +P 158-grain .38 Special gave as near a perfect performance as I think I have ever seen, and was the only load in which bullets were recovered 'under the skin' at the back of the target.

"Among the 9mm loads, the jacketed soft-points did not perform in the same league with the hollow points, and the SuperVel still penetrates way too much. The R-P 115-grain

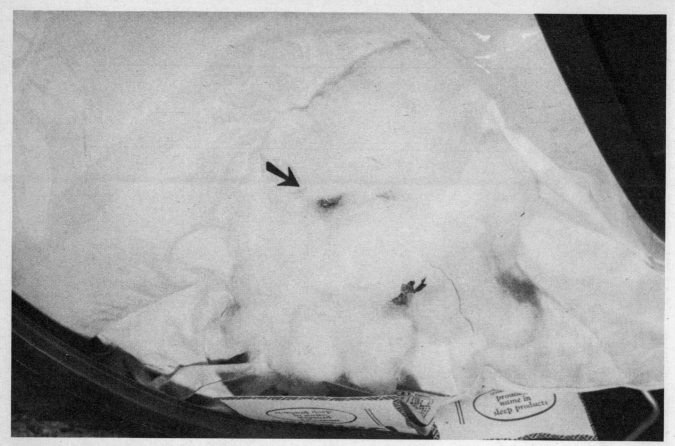

Above: At center of photo is a .41 bullet that Hamilton recovered in pillow stuffing into which round was fired. (Below) Meat and bone target was wrapped tightly in old clothing and placed in front of the eight-pillow polyester backstop that was used in the tests. Note that plastic garbage pails were used to hold this target together.

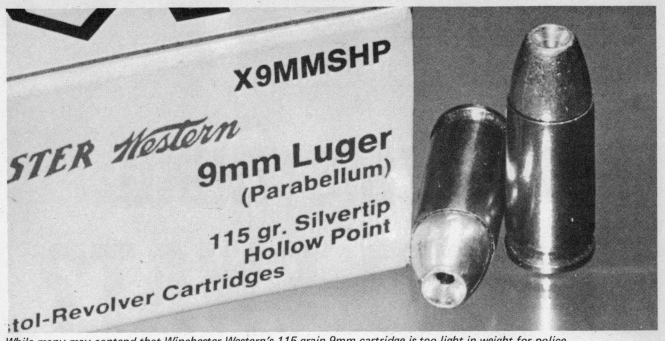

While many may contend that Winchester-Western's 115-grain 9mm cartridge is too light in weight for police work, the hollow point makes the difference wherein expansion is concerned for purposes of felon stopping.

JHP gave the most consistent performance, which came as no surprise. I have used this load before, always with excellent results. The bullet shape is so nearly the same as that of the FMJ as to be almost indistinguishable from the side view, and it functions flawlessly through the Model 59 action.

"I think the Exploder probably did the most damage in the target, though no 'autopsy' was possible. It seems to go off in the front layer of ribs and does most of its damage there. I was surprised that portions of torn jacket and bullet case managed to make it all the way through the target."

Something interesting and unexpected almost always happens on a test like this one, and this was no exception. In late 1977, Smith & Wesson called in their Model 59s for modifications to the slide latch, extractor and magazine followers. These had been found desirable because some of the "new" bullets vary far enough in shape from that of the FMJ to cause the slide latch to function prematurely as they move up in the magazine. Thus, the gun can latch open as though it had fired the last round while there are still several in the magazine.

"That sort of thing will never do in a gun you plan to bet your life on, so I sent mine in and had it fixed. Up until that time I had never had a malfunction of that kind. But in our shooting test the Speer 125-grain JSP jammed this supposedly repaired gun twice in one string of five shots!" Hamilton reports. This brings home once again the vital importance of shooting a pistol extensively with the ammunition you plan to use in it to make absolutely sure you have a reliable combination before you bet your life on it.

"How did the 9mm make out? Well, I think. Except for the two JSP loads, penetration was not excessive and expansion was good," Hamilton comments.

There are other factors to keep in mind. Weight for weight, for the eighteen typical revolver rounds an officer might carry — six in his gun, twelve on the belt — here's how many he could carry in 9mm 115-grain JHPs: .41 magnum, thirty-three; .357 magnum, twenty-six; .38 Special, twenty-four. And how do the unloaded guns stack up for weight? Model 57 .41 magnum four-inch, forty-one ounces; Lawman Mk III .357 four-inch, thirty-three ounces; Model 15 Combat Masterpiece four-inch, thirty-one ounces; Model 59 9mm, twenty-seven ounces.

"And, there is something else that the Browning and the Model 59 offer: 2½ shots for each shot in your revolver before you have to reload. This magazine capacity, plus the light recoil of the 9mm, makes it possible for you to train yourself to fire two quick shots instead of one. Thus you increase your hit probability and your stopping power, a point not to be overlooked for those who are not the best of shots and don't get in too much practice.

"These two pistols and others available offer yet another special capability not to be overlooked in a pinch. If, as I do, one always carries two spare magazines when armed with a pistol, one of the spares can be loaded with a special purpose round which might be needed in special circumstances. An example is the KTW round for use against cars. In a matter of seconds you can pull your magazine full of JHPs and insert the one with KTWs for stopping a car. The operation is safe and easy, and much faster than can be done with the revolver in similar circumstances.

"To me the evidence seems pretty clear. Modern U.S. commercial 9mm Parabellum ammunition has pretty well overcome the main complaints against the cartridge: too much penetration and too little energy transfer to the target. I think today's American lawman is giving up a valuable advantage if he overlooks what the 9mm has to offer in combination with the Browning Hi-Power and the S&W Model 59!"

The case rests!

Chapter 6

WHAT'S THIS THING CALLED SWAT?

Orange County deputies often practice their tactics in the dry Santa Ana River bed flood-control tunnel, near pistol range.

This Southern California County Sheriff's Department Uses Time, Talk And Tear Gas — Firearms Only When Necessary

"OUR CONSTANT objective is to take the suspect into custody without injury to our own Orange County Sheriff's Special Weapons And Tactics team members." With those oft-spoken words, Sergeant Larry Richey outlines the philosophy of the elite Southern California organization to which he belongs.

"We hope that every situation to which we're called will result in no shots being fired," says Richey. If the use of firearms does become necessary, however, the deputies are well trained and ready to take whatever action is required to save lives and apprehend the suspect. The Orange County SWAT organization is made up of volunteer members of the sheriff's department, headed by one lieutenant and includes two seven-man tactical teams. Each group consists of a team sergeant, two rifleman-spotters, and two two-man entry teams.

While SWAT teams differ in makeup and armament from one community to another with minor variations, the purposes and techniques appear to be universal. Each city or town with such a team, of course, trains and designs the team to fit its own specific needs.

For example, several major cities have charted the sewer

Part of realistic training includes use of concealing smoke which also offers control problems to overcome.

Standard equipment for the SWAT members includes the Armalite AR-180 with scope sight. Armalite enjoys favor among team's deputies.

When the need arises, team members may be armed with Remington Model 870 12-gauge slide-action shotgun.

Approximately eight hours per month are devoted to combat practice and movement by the Orange County SWAT team.

systems beneath their streets and SWAT teams have become as familiar with these unlikely routes as with the thoroughfares above. Such training might not be conducive to social acceptance until you've hit the showers, but being able to approach a dangerous suspect from below can be protective of one's health and personal welfare.

The principle of the three Ts — time, talk and tear gas — is employed when dealing with an armed suspect, who may be barricaded within a building and who may be holding one or more hostages. Time is a primary advantage on the side of the law enforcement officers in a dangerous barricaded-suspect situation.

"We've found through our own experience and that of other departments that the single best thing we can do

when arriving on the scene is merely to wait, wait and wait," says the SWAT team leader. Sergeant Richey contends that most suspects in a typical case are on an emotional high, may be angry, frustrated, on drugs and irrational at first. "We must consider the possible danger to hostages, bystanders and the police, of course, but for the most part, many suspects will begin to calm down with time. That's why the most important factor is simply the passage of time," says Richey. Time gives the suspect an opportunity to calm down, become more rational and contemplate his situation.

The second major factor is talk; communication. "If we can establish communication with the suspect, we feel we have an excellent chance of avoiding gunplay," notes

Armalite 2.75-power scope sight mounted atop AR-180. Sporter version of AR-180 has 18¾-inch barrel, is 38 inches overall, weighs about 6½ pounds unloaded. Scope and mount are quickly detachable, scope positively returns to zero upon replacement; retail price, $119.95.

SWAT team member assigned as sniper/rifleman, must spend extra training time perfecting his techniques with 40-XB.

Richey. "The team leader will do everything possible to establish some sort of communications link with the suspect. Sometimes that means talking through a door or window, sometimes through a telephone or loudspeaker. We may be able to use a third party to relay messages. The important thing is to talk."

Communicating with the suspect may accomplish several things: The suspect may realize that his situation is hopeless and the best thing for him to do is simply to surrender to the authorities. The mere act of talking about his problem is often enough to bring him down from the emotional high, bringing about more rational thinking and cooperation. A clergyman, a lawyer or a relative can sometimes convince the suspect to give some thought to the consequences of his actions. If a hostage is involved, the aim is to talk the suspect into releasing the hostage.

Many situations can and have been quietly resolved through the use of time and talk. The SWAT team quietly takes the suspect into custody with nobody hurt. It doesn't always work out just that way, of course. There are times when the last T, tear gas, must be employed.

"If the suspect is shooting at us or if there is a danger

Uniform for deputies on team includes military utility trousers and shirt, boots, black knit cap and gas mask strapped to thigh. Each team member must be familiar with armament and assignments for all other members.

Deputies are equipped with a standard handgun as well as additional SWAT arms. Training is conducted under conditions approximating possible actual situations.

that the hostage is about to be harmed, we have the obligation to throw in some tear gas," states Sergeant Richey. "Tear gas can save lives. True, the hostage, if there is one, may be uncomfortable for a while but the gas gives us a chance to flush out the suspect without any real injury to anyone."

If none of the above works, the deputies are trained, prepared and equipped to employ their firearms. In a typical situation, a rifleman-sniper and his spotter will be stationed at a vantage point with the Remington Model 40-XB, caliber .308. The rifle mounts a Redfield 3X-9X scope sight, resulting in a highly-accurate combination. Other SWAT members may surround the location armed with Colt AR-15s, scoped Armalite AR-180s, Remington Model 870 12-gauge shotguns and/or standard sidearms.

Probably the most intense members of the team are the two rifleman/snipers. The glass-bedded Remington 40-XBs are carefully maintained and cared for only by the designated deputies. Each spends many extra hours at the rifle range, on his own, improving his marksmanship. Ammunition is Winchester factory-loaded 125-grain soft point. A sling and bipod are part of the rifleman's equipment.

Each member of the Orange County SWAT team is highly-trained and motivated. Members are recruited from

After each training or real call-out, the tasks of debriefing and weapons cleaning are mandatory.

SWAT sharpshooters have chosen the caliber .308 Remington Model 40-XB with Redfield 3X-9X scope. Zeroing is carefully maintained by assigned rifleman who spends many additional hours sharpening his shooting skills on the rifle range.

Glass-bedded Remington 40-XB may be bipod mounted and fired from prone position for maximum effectiveness.

Applicants for duty with SWAT must demonstrate abilities with Colt AR-15 before tentative acceptance on team.

Special weapons for special uses include the Armalite AR-180, Colt AR-15, Remington 40-XB and Model 870 shotgun, sidearm.

among the regular sheriff's department deputies, although "recruited" may not be the correct term. There is a constant waiting list of members who have volunteered for the team. Prospective members are rigidly tested mentally, emotionally and physically before they are placed on the waiting list. Openings are few and infrequent. There seems to be little turnover within the team.

Recently, no less than eighteen deputies vied for four openings on the team. Some could not pass the psychological screening; no grandstanders or glory-hounds need apply. Each applicant must demonstrate his proficiency with the AR-15, AR-180, shotgun and handgun. The ability to function as a member of a team is essential.

Once accepted, the SWAT team members sharpen their skills with eight hours special training per month, on their own time. Each SWAT member has other normal duty assignments required of him, such as patrol, jail guard and so forth. When a SWAT situation develops anywhere in the county, the team members are notified by radio, they assemble at the department headquarters and proceed to the scene. One week out of the year, the fifteen members and two alternates train together using special facilities such

as the Marines' Camp Pendleton combat town to perfect their building entry and search techniques.

The average deputy in the special organization is thirty years old, the oldest being 44. Team members have from three to fifteen years of law enforcement experience behind them. They furnish their own military-type utility uniforms and boots. Each has a "ready kit" stored at headquarters. When the whistle blows, the team leader nearest to headquarters that day will see that the special weapons are drawn from the armory, ammunition is issued and the members briefed as they change uniforms.

"We don't consider a SWAT call complete until we've held an intensive debriefing session back at headquarters," says team leader Richey. Whatever the outcome, each member goes over the events as he saw them. "We ask each other what we did wrong, what we did right and how we might improve our performance. Each member is cross-trained to the other man's assignment so that if someone is out sick or on vacation, one of us can fill in," Richey adds.

In this day of budget restrictions, tax cuts and inflation, it would seem that the citizens of Orange County, California, are well-served by their sheriff and his Special Weapons And Tactics team.

Chapter 7

A MATTER OF RELIABILITY

From The Troopers Themselves, Here Are Some Views On What Makes The Best Law Enforcement Handgun!

IT IS NO SECRET that a lot of Illinois State Troopers would like to turn their automatics in for the revolvers that were carried until 1967. Their main complaint, of many, is probably: "The damn things are too likely to jam." There are reports of other departments whose officers feel the same. Those in Illinois who favored the automatic replied, "There is no case on record of an ISP automatic actually jamming in a firefight." That argument disappeared two days before Thanksgiving, 1976.

Briefly, it was a point-blank shooting situation on the highway in which the trooper was caught by surprise. He was hit in the right arm before he could reach for his gun. It was the first bullet that struck him; the next three or four went wide of their mark, and the gunman's revolver misfired on one chamber. At this time, the officer drew and fired two shots. His weapon failed to eject the second spent case, freezing the pistol.

The trooper in question was not shot because his gun jammed, though he may be thankful his assailant(s) fled instead of continuing the firefight, since he was now helpless to clear the weapon. The bullet had hit him in the right arm causing a sympathetic convulsion of the muscles that shriveled the arm. He was able to draw left-handed from his crossdraw holster, fumble the safety off by brushing it against the curled-up fingers of his numb right hand, and open fire.

When he called in to report the incident, he left his pistol on the squad car seat; the sergeant who arrived and took over wisely left the pistol intact and shipped it to state police ordnance, where the gun was analyzed to determine what had caused the malfunction.

When it arrived in Springfield, the pistol contained a spent 9mm casing jammed in the breech, with the open mouth of the shell against the edge of the chamber and the base of the case wedged against the breech face of the slide.

The jam could have been caused by any of three things. One would have been a bad cartridge, which didn't fire with enough force to fully eject the casing with recoil impetus. Another could have been inadequate lubrication of the pistol, which would have created friction drag as the slide moved back and prevented the weapon from completing the eject-and-rechamber cycle.

The S&W Chiefs Special, here in the Airweight version with aluminum alloy frame, is one of the lighest, most compact guns chambered for the .38 Special cartridge with the two-inch barrel.

The S&W Model 15 Combat Masterpiece, here with two-inch barrel, has a loaded weight of thirty ounces, nearly twice that of the alloy Chiefs Special, but it has six chambers to the Chiefs Special's five, plus it has a two-way adjustable rear sight. A similar version, the Model 12 Military & Police Airweight has a fixed rear sight and round butt instead of square, as here. Empty weight of the Model 12 is eighteen ounces.

S&W Model 39 fires the 9mm Parabellum (Luger) cartridge, with eight-round magazine capacity and option of carrying a ninth load in the chamber. It can be fired double-action on the first shot, after which the hammer is cocked by cycling of the slide for following shots unless the hammer is lowered manually. Available in a choice of blue or nickel finishes, it weighs 26½ ounces without the magazine. Its rear sight adjusts for windage only.

The third possibility is that the gun might have been fired from a "broken wrist" position; that is, being held loosely. Most automatic pistols require that the grip be solidly held as the slide slams back; otherwise, the frame moves back with the slide, and recoil impetus is lost, preventing the slide from traveling completely back and ejecting the spent case.

All three possibilities are consistent with the type of malfunction that occurred in this particular pistol. There is no way to diagnose positively which of the three, or which combination of the three, caused the jam that could, under other circumstances, have been fatal.

Since the cartridge had been fired, there is no way of knowing whether or not it was underpowered. The possibility certainly exists, but it is statistically unlikely. Of course, gunfights *are* statistically unlikely. The trooper involved believes that a bad round was the reason for the jam.

Lubrication? Ordnance says that when they got the trooper's gun, it was virtually dry. Several malfunctions occurred in initial testing, according to Homer Clark, who supervised the weapon test. After the gun was disassembled and oiled, it again was put through an exhaustive firing test, with no further malfunctions.

The trooper involved in the shooting is not an amateur. He is a Master pistol shot who competes in shooting matches, and who was the top marksman in his academy class. He lubricates his pistol with WD-40 aerosol, wiping off the excess so dust will not cling to the weapon. He states that his pistol had malfunctioned in a similar way perhaps four times over the years, and that range officers inspecting it found nothing wrong with the gun.

A great many police officers clean and lube their guns with WD-40. An excellent product in many ways, most gun experts are coming to think of WD-40 as a detergent more than a long-term lubricant. ISP Ordnance does not recommend it for lubricating the Model 39.

It is possible that, at the time of the last cleaning, sufficient lubrication was present to satisfy the trooper and that, in the time elapsed between then and the shooting incident, that film disappeared by evaporation.

The third possibility is also strong: that the gun malfunctioned because it was being held loosely or awkwardly. This is certainly consistent with the situation: the officer was wounded, had drawn the gun left-handed (something that is not taught to Illinois troopers or to almost any other police department in the country), and he was not trained to fire left-handed, except on the barricades using both hands. It is possible that the angle at which the gun was held kept the slide from traveling in the proper manner in relation to the frame, preventing the fired casing from clearing the ejection port.

S&W Model 59 is much the same as the Model 39 on the facing page except that it features a staggered column magazine with a capacity of fourteen rounds of 9mmP and stocks of black plastic.

Some semiautomatic pistols are unusually susceptible to this phenomenon: an accurized .45 automatic, with its tight tolerances and mid-range ammunition, will do it every time. Bob Cappelli of ISP Ordnance notes that some S&W automatics will jam when lightly held, and some won't; in the Model 39 it's an idiosyncrasy of the given specimen of the product.

It could have been any of the three, or a combination. Perhaps a shortage of lubrication produced an amount of friction that would not normally bother the weapon, but which, coupled by an awkward hold, was enough to cause the jam.

The officer in question does not blame the gun; he feels confident with it still.

According to Trooper William Orlowski of District 15, the latest ISP range officer to go through Smith & Wesson's Armorer's School, the manufacturer recommends that *no* lubrication be used in the firing mechanism area, i.e., the trigger and sear and hammer assemblies.

Bob Cappelli states that a light film of gun oil (not aerosol gun spray) should be applied to the major moving parts; the slide and the barrel and frame rails over which the slide travels. He recommends a drop or two of oil on each slide rail, a little on the inside of the barrel bushing, a touch on the outside front of the barrel, and a little on the outside of the barrel above the chamber area. The slide should then be worked repeatedly to get a well-distributed film of lubricant.

The brand of oil is another question. When the Model 39 was first introduced, Smith & Wesson recommended Anderol as a lubricant. In 1976, however, Eddie Mitchell, the man who heads the semiautomatic pistol manufacturing section at Smith & Wesson, stated that Anderol was too thin in its consistency, and that over a period of time when the gun was carried in the holster, the Anderol would drain out into the bottom of the scabbard, leaving the gun too dry.

Cappelli personally favors Hoppe's Gun Oil. Of late, Central Ordnance has been using military gun oil with excellent results. Many district range officers have this product in stock, and the rest can get it from Springfield Ordnance upon request of the troopers assigned to them.

For the trooper who insists on continued use of an aerosol gun spray as sole lubricant, pistolsmiths have told the author that G-96, of all aerosol brands currently available, has the most effective lubricant properties. Some other brands, designed primarily as detergents to be removed after cleaning the gun, will actually leave a gritty film on the moving parts and can hamper normal functioning.

The Smith & Wesson Model 39 is not a terribly complex instrument, but *any* mechanical instrument is subject to

Colt's Lawman MKIII is chambered for the .357 magnum, also handles .38 Special, with choice of two- or four-inch barrels, round or square butt, blue or nickel finish.

Dan Wesson Arms Model 14-2 is unusual in its ability to use barrels of various lengths, plus a variety of interchangeable stocks.

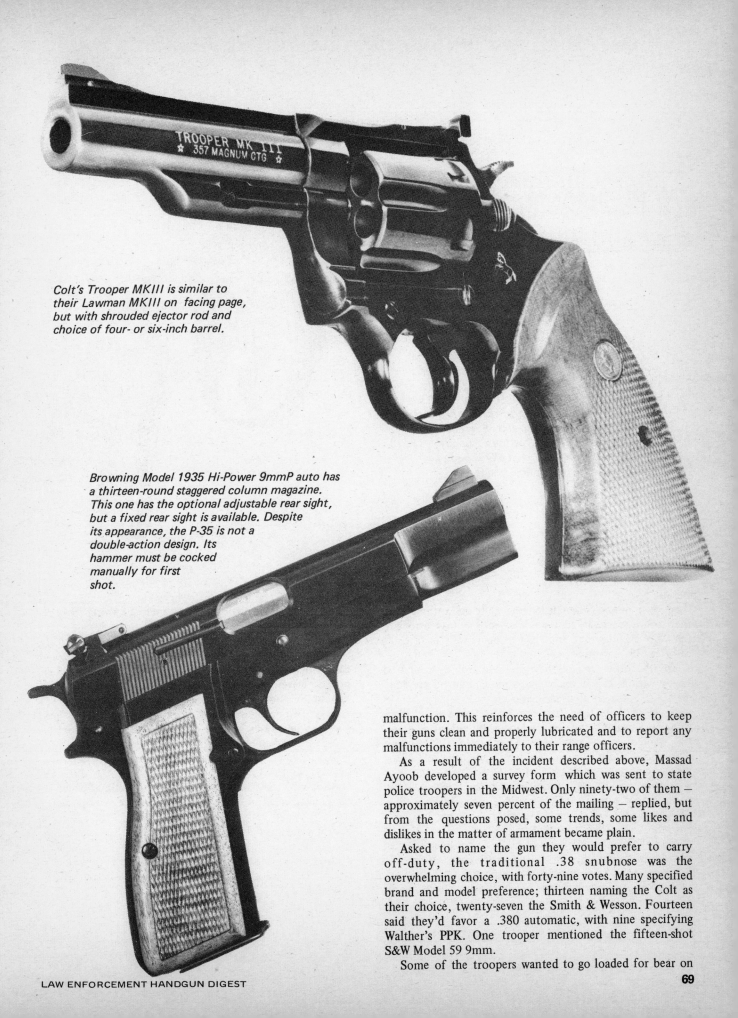

Colt's Trooper MKIII is similar to their Lawman MKIII on facing page, but with shrouded ejector rod and choice of four- or six-inch barrel.

Browning Model 1935 Hi-Power 9mmP auto has a thirteen-round staggered column magazine. This one has the optional adjustable rear sight, but a fixed rear sight is available. Despite its appearance, the P-35 is not a double-action design. Its hammer must be cocked manually for first shot.

malfunction. This reinforces the need of officers to keep their guns clean and properly lubricated and to report any malfunctions immediately to their range officers.

As a result of the incident described above, Massad Ayoob developed a survey form which was sent to state police troopers in the Midwest. Only ninety-two of them — approximately seven percent of the mailing — replied, but from the questions posed, some trends, some likes and dislikes in the matter of armament became plain.

Asked to name the gun they would prefer to carry off-duty, the traditional .38 snubnose was the overwhelming choice, with forty-nine votes. Many specified brand and model preference; thirteen naming the Colt as their choice, twenty-seven the Smith & Wesson. Fourteen said they'd favor a .380 automatic, with nine specifying Walther's PPK. One trooper mentioned the fifteen-shot S&W Model 59 9mm.

Some of the troopers wanted to go loaded for bear on

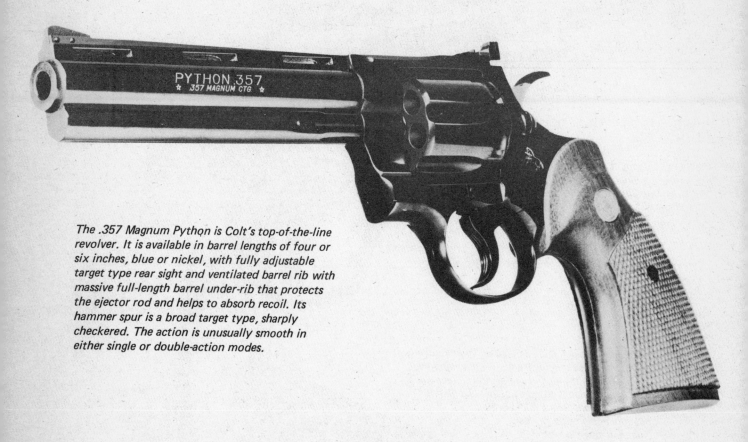

The .357 Magnum Python is Colt's top-of-the-line revolver. It is available in barrel lengths of four or six inches, blue or nickel, with fully adjustable target type rear sight and ventilated barrel rib with massive full-length barrel under-rib that protects the ejector rod and helps to absorb recoil. Its hammer spur is a broad target type, sharply checkered. The action is unusually smooth in either single or double-action modes.

their own hours. Seven listed the Colt .45 automatic as their off-duty choice if it was allowed, one leaned toward the S&W .41 magnum, and eight troopers were in favor of carrying .357 magnums.

On the other end of the scale, one trooper would be happy with a .25 automatic, and three said they'd probably carry a .32 off-duty if given their choice.

Seven of the officers had been in firefights, six of them firing in anger. Of those seven Model 39 combat veterans, six wanted to change guns. Only one rated himself "supremely confident" and wanted to keep the 39. Of the rest, four were "sort of confident" with it, one "very confident," and one "definitely not confident." Three would rather carry Colt Python .357s, one a custom S&W .357, one an S&W Combat Masterpiece .38 revolver, and one a Browning 9mm automatic.

One of those troopers remarked, "I do not like the 9mm round, but I think there's little doubt that our (Model 39s) firepower that night caused the suspect to flee and the ability to reload quickly added to our own protection and safety. "However, that trooper wanted to switch to a revolver with speedloaders.

At the time of the survey, when holsters were still in transition, fifty-one were carrying their spare magazines in their crossdraw flap holster. Nine carried their clips in their pocket, eleven in the glove compartment, four in briefcases, two in the trunk, two (presumably non-smokers) in the ashtray, two on the sun-visor, three in their equipment box, one each on the dashboard, in the radio console, on a clipboard, on the belt, and nowhere.

Asked where they would prefer to carry it, a landslide twenty (of the forty-one who didn't have the old style holster) said they'd like to have the spare clip attached to the holster as before, with all but four of the rest opting for some type of belt carrier. Of the latter, two preferred pocket carry, and two were comfortable with their spare rounds in the glove compartment. Here is the clearest mandate to emerge from the survey: the troopers obviously wanted to be allowed to carry their reload where it will be accessible if they ever need it.

In duty holsters, the obvious favorite was the straight-draw style with thumb-release safety strap. A distant but still strong second was the old crossdraw flap, with nineteen votes. Fifteen troopers wanted a straight draw, but open-topped and with conventional safety snap. Four thought a crossdraw thumb release would be the ticket. Open-topped crossdraws, straight-draw flaps, and clamshell holsters got three votes apiece. Two officers thought the breakfront ideal, and one suggested a swivel holster.

Asked what caliber they'd be happiest with in a service gun, a whopping thirty-three of the ninety-two said .357 magnum. Second, surprisingly, was the .45 automatic with thirteen votes, followed closely by the 9mm with twelve. The .38 Special and .41/.44 magnum got eight votes each.

Asked what model revolver they'd select if given their choice, the deluxe, expensive Colt Python .357 was the favorite with twenty-seven votes, while seventeen would opt for the heavy frame S&W Highway Patrolman in the same caliber. The compact S&W .357 Combat Magnum got sixteen votes, the Colt MK.III Trooper or Lawman .357, nine votes. Six wanted Smith & Wesson .38s, three wanted .41 magnum S&Ws, and one vote each went to Ruger and Dan Wesson .357s, Colt Officer's Model .38, S&W .44 magnum, and S&W Model 27 deluxe .357.

Fifty-one thought blue steel suitable, while twenty-six would prefer stainless, and six would favor nickel.

Given the choice of a service automatic, our troopers went to the Colt .45 (twenty-eight votes), followed by the S&W Model 59 (twenty-one votes), and then the Model 39

For those who prefer heavy autoloaders, Colt offers their MK IV Series '70 Gold Cup National Match, the top entry in their autoloader line. Superbly accurate, it performs well in matches but can be used with full-power "hardball" loads to equally good effect. The regular MK IV Series '70 is also available in .45 ACP, .38 Colt Super and 9mm Luger.

Beretta's Model 92 is a double-action autoloader for the
first shot, shifting to single-action until the hammer is
lowered manually. Chambered for the 9mmP cartridge,
its magazine holds fifteen rounds with a sixteenth in chamber.

(nineteen votes), with many respondents adding, "It's the only automatic I'm familiar with." Twelve troopers liked the Browning 9mm, three the Beretta in the same caliber, while one vote each went to the Colt Super .38 and the German Walther P-38.

Asked if they'd rather carry a revolver than an automatic, sixty-six of the ninety-two said yes. Of those troopers who preferred to carry an automatic, six indicated that they'd prefer the Model 39, and for three of those, it was a multiple choice. A dozen wanted the Colt .45 automatic, eight named the S&W Model 59 (a fifteen-shot Model 39), and six would rather carry the Browning 9mm.

Sixty-eight of the troopers keep their guns loaded at home, and virtually all who mentioned it said they felt the automatic was at least as safe as a revolver in this situation,

and generally safer because of the safety catch and the magazine disconnector.

In ammunition configuration, an overwhelming fifty-four wanted hollow points, twenty-four were happy with the present semi-jacketed soft point, five wanted armor piercing, five like the old full jacket load for its feeding reliability, three were partial to the Glaser Deadeye Safety Slug, and one trooper specified a handload with 112 to 115-grain soft nose, flat point, semi-jacketed bullet at a velocity of 1300-plus feet per second. Coupled with IPS Ordnance's findings of the hollow point's superiority in tests, the brass has a clear mandate for change in this area.

As to training, a number of the survey respondents felt that practice shooting could be made more realistic. Specifically mentioned were night shooting courses, firing with the weak hand only, more quick draw, pop-up targets, more two-hand shooting at close ranges, and generally orienting the course to combat and dispensing with bull's-eye targets and positions. Many of these changes have already been under study by Homer Clark and his Ordnance staff.

There are three kinds of liars, cops like to say: liars, damn liars, and statisticians. It's easy to manipulate a survey and make it come out saying whatever you want it to.

It would behoove the department to take its own survey, a complete one, with feedback from every sworn trooper who carries a gun. It should be anonymous; it should be mandatory.

When fifty-two percent of the officers feel somewhere between "less than confident" and "totally insecure and unsafe" with their guns, things are in bad shape. If you count the ones who feel "sort of confident," that becomes eighty-four percent. And eighty-six percent of those who've had to defend their lives want to change guns.

Should ISP choose to switch to revolvers, there are a number of excellent models that could be chosen. They would not be one hundred percent malfunction free, by any means, because revolvers today are not produced the way they were ten or twenty or thirty years ago. But then, neither are automatics.

Finally, it is apparent that the men want the superior stopping power and reduced ricochet and overpenetration danger that comes with well-designed hollow-point ammunition.

Superintendent Lynn Baird of the Illinois State Police, Director Ty Fahner, and even the governor do not object to hollow-point ammo for state troopers if (a) it is recommended by Ordnance and (b) it will not cause unfavorable publicity. Ordnance has already recommended the hollow-points.

S&W's Model 28, also known as the Highway Patrolman, is a .357 Magnum available in a choice of four- or six-inch barrel.

Chapter 8

A MATTER OF LEARNING

There Are No Hit And Miss Techniques
Taught At The Smith & Wesson Police Instructors Academy!

SMITH & WESSON supports — at a financial loss — the S&W Academy, which teaches firearms handling to police who may or may not carry S&W hardware. The academy is run by Charlie Smith, noted ex-FBI instructor and pistol champion. Classes are taught by Smith, his highly qualified aides, and big-name guest lecturers from the worlds of firearms, law and psychology.

The courses, open to police and security personnel only, encompass crowd control, chemical agents and night vision devices, but the primary thrust is on weaponry, and nowhere does one see the soul of what they're doing more than in the Police Weapons Instructors' School. This article is not a reflection of the curriculum — because a lot of what the lawmen learn is privileged information that could be lethal in the wrong hands — instead, it's a vignette approach to give a glimpse of true professionals in action in a highly responsible task.

"Seven yards, hip-level shooting," says Smith. "You will draw on the long whistle, fire one shot and holster on the short whistle. Start with your hand away from the gun. Your time is three seconds per shot." Three seconds is a lot, but this beginning exercise is just that, an exercise. There are four men on the indoor firing line, and three seconds draw-and-fire gives the instructor plenty of opportunity to observe their form in minute detail.

Tweet, bang bang bang bang, tweet. Again and again. On the far right, one of the officers exhibits a strange stance. At the whistle he draws with his right hand, takes a step forward with his left foot and bends forward stiffly at the waist. He holds his left arm straight down, punches his Military & Police .38 about five inches in front of his belt and, with his gun arm elbow still around his kidney

somewhere, jerks off a shot. Even at seven yards, he is missing the bulky silhouette to the right.

Two instructors behind the lines exchange glances. After the first six rounds, no command to reload is given. Instead, Charlie Smith gives a short lecture on form. "I notice that some of you are taking a step forward with your left foot when you draw," he says. "Let's talk about that for a minute. The FBI developed that little step to the left because their men all carried their guns on their right hip, under their suitcoats. The step to the left moved the body away from the jacket, so the man could get his hand in on his gun without snagging the fabric. But a step forward, or to the right, doesn't do anything for you. In fact, a forward step with your left foot throws your body off-angle, and in instinct shooting your rounds will go to the right of your target. Now, let's keep that in mind and try it again."

Nowhere during all this has Smith mentioned the single individual who had committed the transgression of style. One of the first things he teaches his instructors is not to single out an individual student for criticism.

"The man knows already that he's doing badly," he tells you, "and if you stand him up in front of the others for criticism, you'll finish the job of ruining him as a shooter. Believe me, he'll know that you've done him a favor by not picking him out, and that creates in him a desire to do everything right and please you in return. You give him confidence instead of more nervousness.

"There's something else to consider, too," he says. "Whether the man you're training is a rookie or a superior officer back on the range for a refresher course, you've always got to remember that some day he might be the chief or the senior administrative officer, the man you have

Charlie Smith, former chief weapons instructor for the Federal Bureau of Investigation, now is director of the Smith & Wesson Instructors Academy.

to come to for your firearms training budget. If he remembers five or ten years ago when you made a fool of him on the range in front of all his friends, he's going to have a bad taste in his mouth when he even thinks of firearms training. He's apt to tell you, 'I'm not only not going to double your shooting budget, I'm cutting it in half. Now get the hell out of my office!"

"You see what I'm getting at?" Smith continues. "Ten, twenty years from now, some young officer may die because he wasn't trained properly with his weapon, and that situation may come about because you once humiliated the future chief on the firing range, turning him against the whole concept of weapons training. If that happens, you'll be as much responsible for the death of that young officer as he is!"

The seven-yard exercise begins anew. The wayward officer tries it Smith's way for the first shot. It's good; on a living target, it would go belly-through-spine, probably an instant stop. But over the next five habit takes over, and he gradually comes out of position, stringing his shots higher

and farther right, and by the last shot he's back in his awkward stance and back off the target.

Unobtrusively, an instructor takes him aside. "I'm curious about that position of yours," he begins easily. "Why do you shoot like that?" The student shrugs, "That's the way I shoot."

At this point, most instructors would snarl in frustration. "The reason you're here is to learn to do it right, not do it wrong like you've been doing!" But this isn't your average instructor.

"I'll tell you, though," he suggests, "One of the reasons for coming here is to learn different styles. Now, some of your students, when you get back home, may be shooting really bad, but they'll tell you, 'Gee, Sarge, this way is more comfortable for me.' Then it'll be up to you to show them how to try a couple of other positions."

Patiently, the instructor goes back through the basic combat crouch technique. What he has done is to deftly maneuver the awkward student into the position of having to learn something new for his own students' sake, instead

Below: Students at the S&W Academy change firing line yardages during live-fire segment. Since some of the students are not familiar with the academy-furnished Model 39 automatics, the handguns are carried, not holstered. (Right) Students at the academy are lectured on the proper use of the shotgun in today's law enforcement techniques.

of rudely telling him that his own style is all screwed up. Through the rest of the week this man's scores go upward, and his positioning becomes smoother and more conventional.

On Friday, he will win second place in one class of the shoot-off.

"One of the most satisfying things in your job," Smith tells his instructors' class one morning, "is that someday what you do may save the lives of the men who study under you."

He remembers his first time as if it were yesterday. He was a young FBI instructor then, handling firearms classes for municipal departments in his area as well as for the bureau. One young patrolman had been having problems. He was just one of those people who are to firearms courses as natural sinkers are to swimming classes. Smith spent extra evenings working with him, and when he was done the kid could shoot as well as anyone else in his class.

A few months later, something happened on the street and Smith's young student came out unscathed — although his two ambushers didn't — and when the young cop was selected for the Policeman of the Month Award, he asked that Smith sit next to him at the testimonial table. Before Smith could seat himself, an older woman ran up to him and grabbed him in her arms. "God bless you," she sobbed, "you saved my son's life! God bless you!"

Much, much later, when Charlie was chief instructor for the FBI, two young agents made a tragic mistake. They had been checking out an apartment where a bank robbery suspect was supposed to spend a lot of his time. They had been there three times and when they dropped by for a fourth visit, they didn't expect him to be at home. But the door swung violently open and a gun exploded at point-blank range. The two young agents lay dying in the hallway, their hands clutching hopelessly at their hemmorhaging chest wounds instead of their holstered guns.

Smith went to both funerals. The second was a quiet family affair in a suburban mortuary, and when Smith walked into the chapel he could hear the buzzing among the mourners: "That's the FBI firearms teacher, that's the Big Gun himself, Charlie Smith."

He kept his eyes forward and walked to the bier. "My God," he thought, looking down at the dead agent. "He's only 28. He's only 28."

Smith was kneeling by the casket when he suddenly heard a strangled cry and felt small hands tearing at his jacket, trying to throw his heavy frame to the floor. It was the agent's mother.

"God damn you!" She screamed. "You're the gun teacher! Why didn't you teach my boy to protect himself? He's dead! And it's your fault! God damn you!"

Smith finishes his story and looks around at the student/instructors gathered around the big table in the academy classroom. "I had never seen her son before," he explains softly. "He wasn't one of my own students. I known damn well that whoever did train her son told him not to stand in front of the door with his revolver buttoned beneath his jacket when he was going in on an armed robbery suspect. But how do you tell that to his mother? Whose fault do you tell her it was? Has anybody here got an answer?"

Charlie Smith's eyes slowly scan around the table, but his thirteen student/instructors are silent. There is no answer for the question he has posed them.

When the instructor-trainees file out of the classroom and back downstairs that morning, there is none of the usual chitchat, and on the range everyone seems to be listening a little more closely.

One of the singular moments in the instructors' course is the two-hour lecture by Dr. Arthur Bertrand, professor of psychology at American International College in Springfield. His topic is training and emotional preconditioning, and how they all come together for police officers in moments of extreme stress.

When things happen in seconds, or fractions thereof, there is extremely little time to think. What time there is should be devoted to matters of judgment: Is my life in danger? Should I fire? Are there bystanders too close to my target?

There is no time to think "Reach for safety strap, grab gun butt, draw, insert finger into trigger guard, take a short step to the left..." Instinct will have to do this for you. Instinct, in this case, is synonymous with training. If you have to clutter your mind with thinking about how to get your gun out, there is no time left for judgment decisions, and the likelihood of a tragedy on either side has increased enormously.

Bertrand places a lot of emphasis on the emotional biases and preconceptions of the individual. If a police officer, subconsciously or otherwise equates a certain race or a certain appearance with the word criminal, then it is all too easy for that bigotry to become so ingrained that in a sudden decision some night in the dark shadows, the brain will bypass the judgment factor and send that electrical impulse directly into the trigger finger. In tense situations like this, some hellishly ugly things have happened because the man behind the gun was a little too prejudiced. A lot of black men have been shot who wouldn't have, had they been white, which is why black police officers are extremely careful about drawing their guns off duty. No one knows this better than the police officers themselves, and no one wants to stop it more. Part of the reason is that the prejudice works both ways.

A red-neck cop who hates blacks or Latinos or long-haired kids lets his prejudice take over and something tragic happens. This officer represents but a tiny minority of the whole force. Yet every black or Latino or long-haired kid who reads the media report of the shooting gets his own prejudice reinforced: "The pigs have really got it in for people like me!" And some night when a uniformed officer approaches that person — and the programmed fear sets in — the reaction might be a panicky swing at the cop or a grab for a weapon, then that person and that cop are caught up in a maelstrom of needless violence.

It's a vicious circle and conscientious cops want to do their part to break out of it. That's why Charlie Smith includes these hours in his instructors' course.

As the lecture ends and the students file out to lunch at the AIC faculty cafeteria, one would-be police weapons instructor lags behind to speak privately with Dr. Bertrand. He has recognized some of what Bertrand was talking about in himself, and he wants to cope with it. He makes arrangements with the doctor for a battery of personality inventory tests, which include review and counseling with a psychologist. This is an exceptionally different kind of police firearms course.

Steve Van Meter is on the Westfield range explaining the subtleties of shotgun safety: "These are the two types of safeties used on police shotguns," he says, demonstrating with a pair of 12-gauge short-barrel pumps. "This Remington Model 870 has a cross-bolt safety; theoretically, it's more mechanically fail-safe than the thumb safety on this Smith & Wesson Model 916. But in terms of operating ease and speed, the thumb safety is more natural and more fumbleproof.

"Sometimes," he goes on, "the safest thing you can do with the safety is to flick it off. Policemen have died because they went in on a known danger situation with their 12-gauge on safe or with the chamber empty, and some punk with a .22 pistol shot them in the head before they could get their shotgun into firing mode. When you're going into a possible shooting situation, put a round in the chamber, and move the safety off. The most effective safety is a trained operator."

Safety with the police shotgun, Van Meter explains, goes far beyond crossbolt buttons and thumb slides. "In riot situations, a lot of you have been taught to use the shotgun butt for upward blows, as in military bayonet training. I'm not saying you won't ever have to do that, but remember to have your finger off the trigger and the safety on." He cites the accidental death of a Chicago police officer during the 1968 Democratic Convention riots: a demonstrator lunged at a shotgun-wielding patrolman with a two-by-four, and the cop swung his shotgun butt up and mashed him. But the barrel of the shotgun was pointed directly over his shoulder, and when the gun butt smashed into the assailant's body the shotgun discharged, sending a full load of No. 4 buckshot into the face of a brother patrolman standing directly behind the first officer.

Van Meter teaches the student instructors to carry their cruiser shotguns with a full magazine, action not locked, chamber empty, and safety off. This has always been a subject of great debate among police weapon teachers, and immediately a student responds, "Steve, my department carries them locked on an empty chamber. That way we can keep the safety on, and to fire, the slide release on the trigger guard has to be flicked. An unauthorized person who grabs the gun will probably have to fumble for a few

Officer undergoing training at the S&W-sponsored academy familiarizes himself with Startron night vision scope.

A separate course at the academy is devoted to full-auto weaponry, but in the instructor course the individual law enforcement student receives a short familiarization course in such firearms as Smith & Wesson's currently made Model 79.

seconds to get the gun into firing condition, which gives the officer more time to take him."

"Excellent point," Van Meter concedes readily. "To be honest, that's the way I'd rather carry the shotgun in my own cruiser. And for you thirteen guys here, it's good, too. But we're all instructors, we're all into guns, and we've all done a lot of work with the shotgun. Hitting that slide release is instinctive for all of us. But can we train that instinct into ten or a hundred or ten thousand patrolmen we have to instruct? Will the department let you train them that heavily on shotguns? Oftentimes not, and that creates the danger of an officer grabbing that shotgun out with the action locked and forgetting where that little lever or button is that lets him pump a round into his gun. That can get him killed, too. He's already trained to keep suspicious people out of his squad car and away from his shotgun, and the general feeling is that he's more likely to get killed by not being able to get the shotgun into action quickly enough, than by having someone else shoot him with it."

This is one aspect of safety that you see emphasized again and again during the Smith & Wesson Academy course; a safety habit that works fine for civilians on a range can get you killed in the street, and therefore is worse than no safety at all.

Handling of weapons after fired strings is the classic

example. In an NRA Police Combat shoot, for example, when the officer finishes his string he will empty his last cylinder into the palm of his nonshooting hand, then hold the open and empty revolver downrange until a rangemaster has checked both his weapon and his brass and given him the command to holster. This is not actually done for reasons of maximum safety: Its real purpose is to let the instructor know that he got all his rounds off and isn't fudging on his target score. But, somewhere along the line, this system of checking weapons has been adopted by most police training officers.

The people at the Smith & Wesson Academy don't see it that way. "The last thing you want to teach your men," they'll tell you, "is to empty their gun and stand there holding the empties. Under stress, a man does what he's been trained to do, and when he reloads his service revolver in a gunfight he may drop his brass into his hand and hold it there for a second until he snaps to and realizes what he's been doing. By then it may be too late." At the academy, officers are trained to dump their empties instantly to the ground and either reload or holster empty, as ordered.

This carries over into areas of equipment as well. Reloading from the pockets is thoroughly discouraged. "A man under great stress will go through the sequence of movement he's been trained with," Van Meter repeats.

"Dead police officers have been found after gunfights with their pockets full of empty shell casings because they were trained to save their brass on the range. They've also been found with a handful of coins all over their empty guns, because they were trained to scoop ammo out of their pockets and shove it into their guns. When instinct took over, they tried to load their pocket change or car keys and forgot their ammo was on their belts."

Nonservice guns are likewise discouraged. At every school there's at least one guy who shows up with a six-inch, bull-barrel combat competition revolver. Van Meter, as instructor, likes to take the approach of examining the issue as a question for the officers to take up with their own classroom people. "A lot of the officers you train will be administrative or investigative people who carry a two-inch gun on the job. But they'll show up for qualification with a four-inch or six-inch gun with target sights, so they'll get a nice big score on their record. Well, the handling characteristics of the two guns are completely different. If you qualify a detective with his six-inch K-38, have you trained him to defend his life, or maybe some night your life, with the Airweight Chiefs Special he carries on duty?"

This is a sobering thought. One instructor recalled that during the Advanced Combat course the week before, three students approached him, eyed the six-inch heavy-frame S&W and the Dade speedloaders on his belt, and asked, pointedly, "Is that the gun you carry on duty?"

"No," he had answered truthfully, "I carry a Colt automatic, but that would have created some problems here with everyone else shooting revolvers. Besides, I couldn't expect Smith to furnish me free .45 ACP ammo."

But this didn't cut much ice, and for the instructors' school this individual made a point of firing nothing but a four-inch fixed-sight .38. Lesson learned.

For an instructor, this can have even more subtle complications. "Sure, you may be a competitive combat shooter," Van Meter tells the class. "That may be one reason you were assigned as a firearms instructor. You want to impress your students, so you maybe get out on the range on qualification day and show them how well you can do with your six-inch bull-barrel target gun. But what does that really put in their heads? They'll think one of two things: 'My instructor is so insecure he doesn't dare shoot with a regular police gun,' or 'what's the use of my practicing with this lousy fixed-sight four-incher? I'll never be able to shoot like that.'

"It's counterproductive," Van Meter goes on. "If you're going to demonstrate or even qualify in front of your students, shoot a gun like they shoot. Even if you're on the SWAT team or something and the chief lets you carry a Model 59 or a .45 auto, you'd better show up on the range with a Model 10 if that's what the rest of the officers carry. Otherwise, you're creating a feeling of inadequacy in the men you're supposed to be teaching to feel confident."

But then Van Meter poses an even more involved question: "Should you shoot in front of your students at all? Suppose you've got a hangover that morning or you're just due for a bad day, and you shoot the lousiest target you've shot in five years, right in front of your men. Suppose maybe twenty-five percent of your students who subsequently shoot the same course beat you? A lot of

patrolmen then will start thinking, 'Hell, our teacher's no good, he's just run-of-the-mill. How can I learn anything from somebody who isn't a whole hell of a lot better than I am?' That sets his mind. No matter how much he can learn from you he's stopped listening, because he's already lost respect for your expertise and authority.

"The fact that you are the appointed instructor, and have the credentials from places like the S&W Academy, will be enough to establish you as an authority. Don't jeopardize that by competing against the best shots in the department. It could be that they're great with target pistols, but they know nothing of tactics — and the subtleties of deadly force — and are, therefore, far inferior to you as an instructor. Yet, if they outpoint you on the range, a lot of your students are going to think the sharpshooters should be teaching them instead of you. Unless you are extremely good and quite cool, it's a foolish risk to shoot against your sharpshooter students."

In the lexicon of police gun instructors, Van Meter explains that a sharpshooter isn't just a student who's good with a gun; he's a student who thinks he's better than you because maybe he's got more police science textbooks piled up in his basement than you have, and he'll keep asking you questions he knows the answers to just to see if you know the answers. "Read everything in the field," Smith advises. "Gun magazines, police journals, IACP Weapons Center reports, everything. Hit the combat matches so you can see what's new before it gets on the market. Knowing what's new is part of being up-to-date."

Everyone leaves that lecture with two things in mind: when they get home they're going to order some subscriptions to gun magazines, and they've already decided never to accept challenges from their students on the range.

But some people are a little dense that morning. After Van Meter's lecture, Model 39 automatics are handed around: the students are to take turns running a familiarization course with the semiautomatic, taking alternate roles of instructors and students. One of the people enrolled in the course, who knows Van Meter from the combat matches, talks with him for a few minutes. After things are set up on the firing line, Tompkins selects a student to handle the first relay and then says, "Van Meter, why don't you fill out the firing line." The student Van Meter is talking to, who also is scheduled to shoot this time around, suggests without thinking, "Hey, Steve, let's go for the head on the bobber target and shoot for a buck."

Van Meter's only hesitation is from surprise, and it lasts but half a second. "Sure," he answers, picking up a Model 39 at random, a box of ammo and striding toward the firing line.

The person he was talking to, an instructor who has been in the game for a while, realizes instantly the glaring breach of professional conduct and courtesy that he has made. He feels a sudden urge to grab one of the Swinglines from next to the target frames and staple his own tongue to the roof of his mouth. He had forgotten where he was, and what would have been casual fun at a match has suddenly become an unintended challenge to the course instructor.

To call Van Meter back, he realizes, would look as if he thought he were better than the man teaching the course, or as if he had suddenly realized he was in over his head and was trying to beg off. Pride mixes with the recognition that

An instructor demonstrates the proper method for holding a police flashlight to avoid drawing opponent's bullets.

he has just, without meaning to, done something that is terribly unprofessional. People have overheard the byplay, and there is nothing he can do about it at this point.

On the line, a student from North Carolina who had never fired a Model 39 before coming to the Smith & Wesson Academy, is running the familiarization relay perfectly. In the previous week and a half, this was what Smith, Tompkins and Van Meter had taught him to do. Students watch as Van Meter and the unintentional smart-aleck sharpshooter conspicuously group their rounds in the head of the bobber.

The observers know that this is opposed to the body-aim Van Meter has taught them, and they sense that he is delivering another object lesson. Van Meter, who has a great deal to lose at this moment, holds coolly and calmly for center head. So does the unintentional sharpshooter, who realizes that any attempt to throw it at this point would be an even greater insult to the man in charge of the course.

When the last shot has been fired at twenty-five yards, the targets are scored: Van Meter has all fifty hits in the blank face of the silhouette, only two even near the neck; his hapless challenger has forty-five center head, four in the throat, and one in the right shoulder from a double-action jerk at fifteen yards. The passing of the dollar is observed by all, and a wordless counterpoint to the earlier lecture is accented and underscored: Don't make or accept challenges when you teach firearms class, unless you're as good as Steve Van Meter.

Friday afternoon at a motor inn in Chicopee, a few miles from the S&W Academy, it is graduation time for the instructors. The morning was spent in a tension exercise. Three targets were erected: a B-21 silhouette in the center flanked by white bobbers on either side. The student holds the left target at gunpoint, then turns on the whistle and shoots the silhouette that has suddenly intervened in the hypothetical armed arrest situation.

The officer fires from standing and moving positions. He doesn't learn until afterwards that this isn't the course for which the prizes were awarded. Wally Tompkins, who ran the course, didn't exactly trick to induce stress in a training exercise. A double-action combat course on the B-21 is shot for the prizes. A 98 out of 100 wins.

Later, at the banquet, Charlie Smith talks quietly about why the course is run the way it is.

"Shooting at a target is a mechanical skill," he explains, "and there are a thousand places you can go to learn it. But the crucial thing to learn, and to teach to your own students, is not how to shoot, it's when to shoot. This is why so much stress has been placed on court judgments and moral aspects of applying lethal physical force. We teach combat shooting here — I feel we teach it better than anyplace else — but we also teach attitudes, and that, in the last analysis, is the big thing."

Attitudes — in the moral and political climate of America today, in a time when the public is re-examining the actions of the police establishment and the cops are re-examining their own approaches, attitude becomes even more important than technique.

Proper use of less lethal weapons also is taught, including the Pepper Fogger, which the makers say can fill a football field with incapacitating tear gas in a matter of only seconds. It is also a Smith & Wesson product.

Chapter 9

THE COMBAT COMPETITION REVOLVER

You Can Win With Your Duty Handgun — Maybe — But There Are Better Ways Of Scoring!

McLennan used the Ransom Rest to check out the accuracy of his Model 19 Smith & Wesson with 4-inch barrel.

*This K-frame Smith & Wesson Model 10 features Bob Day's
1500 conversion. It also has grips made by Fuzzy Farrant.*

"WHEN I first got into Police Combat Competition I didn't know what I was getting into. Today we speak of bull barrels, rib sights and double-action trigger pulls of only four pounds. When you talk of PPC custom revolvers cost can get prohibitive," says Bill McLennan, a detective with the police department in San Antonio, Texas.

During the middle 1960s, McLennan spent some time in the three-gun game while serving in the U.S. Marine Corps Reserve. His battalion didn't have any experienced pistol shooters so the team had to start from scratch. "In retrospect I developed some bad habits that could have been avoided, but the equipment I was issued was as good as any in its day. Nor did I enter into police combat shooting with any guidance, but after a decade of the sport, I have formed some very definite ideas," the detective says.

"After my discharge, practice came to a slow pace, as I could not afford the large quantity of ammo that Uncle Sam had furnished. There were no active combat pistol clubs in the San Antonio area, and my profession demanded the more rational aspect of practical shooting.

"The revolver is my duty weapon, so I began to use it exclusively. I soon learned that I could hit better double-action than single-action and have all but forgotten my Smith & Wesson revolver has the two-fold capability. Several other officers and I attempted to start a pistol club but interest was nil. Then one night, when I reported for duty, I learned that the department was going to sponsor a police pistol team; interested officers should contact the training bureau to make arrangements for entering the qualifications."

McLennen immediately signed up. Several weeks passed while the rangemaster ran the prospects through the course, a modified Practical Pistol Course, as the basement range is limited to twenty-five yards. On record day, McLennen showed up with a four-inch S&W Model 19 and a set of Safariland Fire-Power speedloaders; certainly not PPC equipment of the late 1970s, but practical for duty and practical enough to let him edge out several hundred competitors for a spot on the pistol team. He found the Model 19 a definite advantage over the department-issued, fixed-sight Model 10 and the speedloaders a better choice than belt loops or the pants pocket.

Not having an experienced PPC shooter in the group, the team set out to its first match in Los Fresnos, Texas. With less than a month to prepare for the nationals in Jackson, Mississippi, foremost in mind was practice and match experience. "In Los Fresnos, we got our first taste of match pressure at the U.S. Border Patrol Academy. Here I was introduced to the Douglas Premium bull barrel and the combat rib sight. Such equipment was unheard of in our area of Texas, but plentiful among the Border Patrol agents at the match. They knew how to use these instruments and were eager to assist us."

After several matches at the Border Patrol Academy the San Antonio team began to show marked improvement; the

The Day 1500 conversion with custom grip removed shows some of the work accomplished by San Antonio gunsmith.

U.S. Border Patrol Team was extremely helpful in advising on match procedure and equipment. After this initiation, team members realized standard issue revolvers were inadequate for this game. As Greg Whipple put it, "Your four-inch duty gun may give you a more realistic feel, but if you are going to compete and win, you need a full-house custom revolver." Whipple was a member of the winning four-man team in the 1976 Nationals.

"I don't like to lose, so I set out to build the best pistol I could afford. I ended up with a sixty-ounce monster. I settled on the six-inch Douglas bull barrel with a twist of one-in-fourteen inches. Douglas makes several different twists, but through tests, I found the one-in-fourteen to be the best choice. Its advantage over the stock S&W one-in-18.75 is that there is no bullet tippage at the fifty-yard mark. I use the term 'tippage' instead of keyholing, because the standard S&W tube will not stabilize the 148-grain wadcutter bullet at fifty yards and it has a tendency to tip just slightly as it punches through the target; a true keyhole tumbles through in profile. The custom tube also comes in one-in-ten, one-in-twelve and one-in-sixteen twist ratios.

"The factory tube was designed around the 158-grain round-nose service ammunition and handles it magnificently. The bull barrel increases the balance and hang of the pistol. The additional weight allows for a steady hold and dampens recoil, so that disturbance of sight alignment is almost nonexistent, it dissipates heat, thus increasing accuracy. It is common knowledge that when a barrel heats up it begins to sling bullets in an ever-widening group and the thinner the barrel, the quicker it opens up."

The bull barrel comes in several shapes and sizes. The two

With sideplate of Model 10 S&W removed, one is able to see extended stirrup, frame modifications.

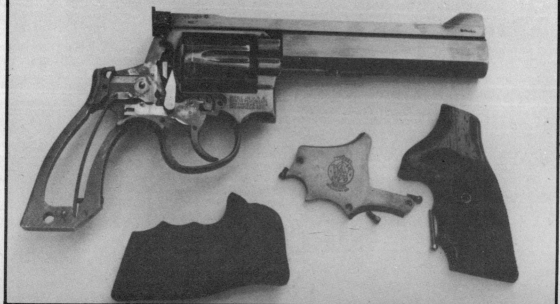

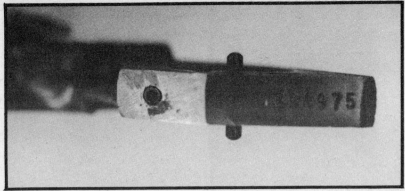 

Upper left: Grip frame has been modified, angled to take lock screw that holds the strain screw at the desired degree of tension. (Upper right) Photographed from the top, the palm swell of Farrant grips is seen.

most common are the round one-inch diameter and the one-inch slab-side. McLennan chose the slab-side, but this is a matter of individual preference. The barrel blanks are cut out in the rough, cut to length, threaded and polished. A recess is milled for the front locking lug, which may be cut into the barrel or machined separately and attached by weld or screws.

"It was assured by one pistolsmith that the front lug was not necessary if the cylinder is lined up right and the revolver locked tightly into alignment. I reluctantly took his advice and more than 20,000 rounds support his theory.

"I know this is a controversial statement, but if the cylinder locks into proper alignment, the ejector rod should not bear on the front locking lug except for slight spring pressure on the center pin, which has nothing to do with holding the cylinder in place. I do not slam the cylinder shut, nor throw it open and I have not had problems. I

would not remove the front lug on my duty gun, however."

In conjunction with the bull barrel comes the combat rib sight. There are several makes on the market and McLennan feels one is about as good as another; some have various gadgets which allegedly reduce the chance of human error, e.g., forgetting to make the proper adjustments. "The problem I found with the preset types which are changed at each range, but must be set during practice, is that they cannot be changed readily during a stage of fire without considerable loss of time. With the standard type sight if one needs to make any adjustment, he can do so quickly with an ordinary screwdriver, be it a few clicks or several turns.

"In theory, one can hold off if his shots are a bit low, but I have found Kentucky windage requires thought and this means loss of concentration on the sights. If you are one who does not need to concentrate on the sights, more

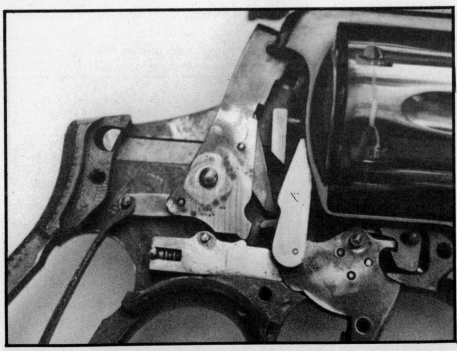

This view reveals extended stirrup, the lightened hammer, trigger stop, stippling on the backstrap and the surfaces that have been polished.

Note rings on end of crane where cylinder sits. Tool was made from pipe cutter and is used by Day to stretch gun's crane evenly.

power to you. I find that, as my concentration becomes intense upon the sights, I forget to hold off and go back to my normal hold, therefore pouring my entire string into the off-centered group."

With the combat rib comes added weight, distinctly shaped sights, more precise adjustment of windage and elevation than with factory-installed sights, and wings to protect the front sight from holster wear, not to mention the bits and pieces of leather that often catch on the front sight when it is drawn from a holster. The wings also eliminate uneven distribution of light and reduce shadows from side light.

If you are of the school who paints his sights or uses sight black, you will find the wings prevent said applications from being rubbed off during an entire aggregate, which may last all day, if entries are of large number.

The combat rib, in a variety of makes and models, can be had for the tiny snubnose or the eight-inch jobs. We suggest the preset types for those who can't remember which way to turn the screws and don't own a screwdriver with directions on the handle.

The bull barrel and combat rib are the initial steps in building the custom competition revolver. There are various custom pistolsmiths who specialize in the PPC revolver; the most advertised are Behlert, Clark, Davis, Powers, Roberts and Day. McLennan chose the last, "because the price was right for the quality and the Day Arms Corporation is located in my hometown and I would not have to contend with the possibility of mail theft or the Gun Control Act of 1968."

Bob Day is a retired Air Force gunsmith/machinist and has probably rebuilt, customized, blown up and cut up more sidearms than any ten civilian gunsmiths. In the Air Force, he was assigned to research and development and has conducted some unique experiments on today's pistols which only the taxpayers' dollars could provide. He now puts this knowledge to good use and is far ahead of many competitors.

"After the barrel and rib were installed on my pistol I fired several thousand rounds through it and dry-fired it many more. Once I was assured of not having any malfunctions I set out to see just how accurate the Day 1500 really is," the detective reports. "I set up my Ransom

Rest at fifty yards and put the 1500 through the paces. At fifty yards, I found that ammunition which groups superbly at twenty-five yards may not stay on the silhouette. Don't test your gun and ammunition at any range but fifty yards or farther. If it will shoot well at fifty, it will shoot as well or better at closer ranges. Without the aid of a rest, don't be quick to blame your gun if you have problems; it may be ammunition, but more than likely it's you."

At fifty yards with W-W Supermatch, 3-D (remanufactured) wadcutters and his own handloads, McLennan's Douglas tube will consistently hold 2¾-inch groups. The 1500 will produce six-shot groups that will fit under a silver quarter, and stay there if the barrel is allowed to cool between each cylinder full. "Groups fired from one chamber were not any tighter than those fired from all six, obviously when properly timed the outdated wheelgun will shoot with the best of the self-loaders," he insists.

The chamber openings on this revolver have been chamfered for rapid reloading, an advantage in combat competition.

The Day 1500 Conversion features a full rib for an improved sighting plane, as well as winged front sight.

"The heavy barrel will dissipate heat very well and evenly; it apparently reaches its tolerances between eighteen and twenty-four rounds of sustained fire."

Many custom revolver builders advertise X-ring accuracy, but this is for six or ten rounds; for a true evaluation of your handgun, you must duplicate the most demanding stage of fire, so a string of twenty-four rounds at fifty yards in 2¾ minutes or less is a good test. McLennan's 1500 stays

well within the ten-ring and lives up to its name.

"I did not have Day tune the action other than to check the timing. My Smith & Wesson was produced in the early 1950s and I was satisfied with the workmanship. I stayed with the factory action for several months, until I came across a Colt Python that had been modified and tuned by Reeves Jungkind. The Jungkind double-action Python is one of the finest Colt modifications I have ever seen. This Jungkind composite sent me on a trek for a Smith & Wesson of similar excellence. I talked with several local gunsmiths, who told me my action was good enough; to leave it alone. I was convinced that, if the Python could be improved, an S&W could be better since the lock time is shorter. After all, the short lock time makes it the most popular revolver in today's competition. If you don't believe it, take a walk down the line at the nationals next year and see what fills most of the holsters."

McLennan's quest led him to Steve Velchoff, considered a most conscientious craftsman. Like Day, Velchoff is a retired Air Force gunsmith, and probably has had more opportunity to alter and experiment with the double-action revolver mechanism than any gunsmith in the country. Velchoff prefers to work strictly on the action and does not install custom barrels. He has been working on these modifications for many years, but had only contracted a few jobs for civilian customers. It seems there was little

The front locking lug has been removed by Bob Day, but the strut is left in place for what he terms protection.

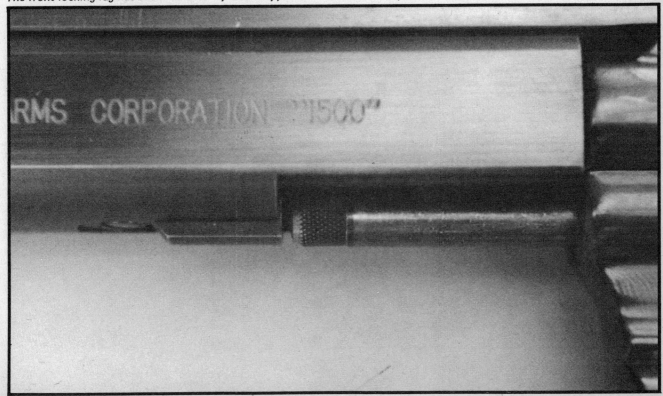

On the Model 10, Bob Day polishes off the edge of cylinder release, which is meant to make reloading more rapid.

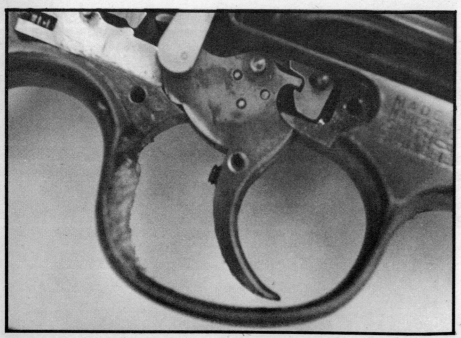

Day installs a screw-type trigger stop, also a synthetic stop made of silicone adhesive, which he says is showing increasing popularity.

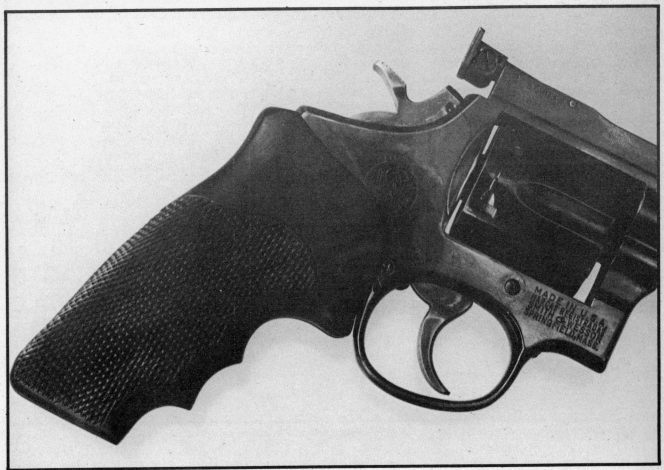

The careful workmanship and checkering of ebony grips made by Farrant are reflected in these installed on K-38.

demand for such precision until the PPC fad swept the nation.

"Steve confided in me that he had a few ideas that needed testing before he took on the commercial market. I agreed to test whatever ideas he wanted to try and help perfect them. Over a period of weeks, Steve made several minute changes and after each I would put in a session on the range to check them out. It has been my experience that a couple of cylinders full may not reveal minute problems. Each time I tested a speicific change, I would fire at least one 1500 aggregate; sometimes several. Trial and error produced the Velchoff short double-action S&W revolver."

Steve Velchoff was methodical about each little change and he is no stranger to the demands of the competition shooter, having built match pistols for the Air Force team for many years.

It is common knowledge that the cylinder release must be cut down to facilitate speedloaders and the steel checkering may as well be polished off and the edges turned so it will be easier on the thumb. The grips must be cut down to simplify the entry of speedloaders, if the manufacturer neglected to include this in his design. To

round off the rapid reload department the chamber mouths need to be chamfered in order that wadcutter ammunition will not hang; cylinders that are recessed such as those of the Model 19 S&W do not need alteration.

It has become standard to install a mainspring locking screw, especially if you are one of the advocates of lightening the trigger pull by backing off on mainspring pressure. Otherwise you may find the strain screw will loosen from continued recoil and misfires will result. The locking screw is installed by drilling and tapping the butt for a 5x40 set screw.

McLennan says, "I prefer to polish the grooves off the face of the trigger and install a 5x40 set screw which protrudes through the backside of the trigger acting as a triggerstop. I also install a 4x40 set screw through the side of the trigger so that it will lock the triggerstop in place once it is set. The same results can be obtained by applying fingernail polish or Loc-Tite.

"The trigger is case hardened and it must be softened in order to drill it with normal bits. Chuck it in a vise and heat it until it becomes cherry red then lay it on your work bench to cool. The bearing surface and notched area should be chucked in the vise; the vise will draw heat away from

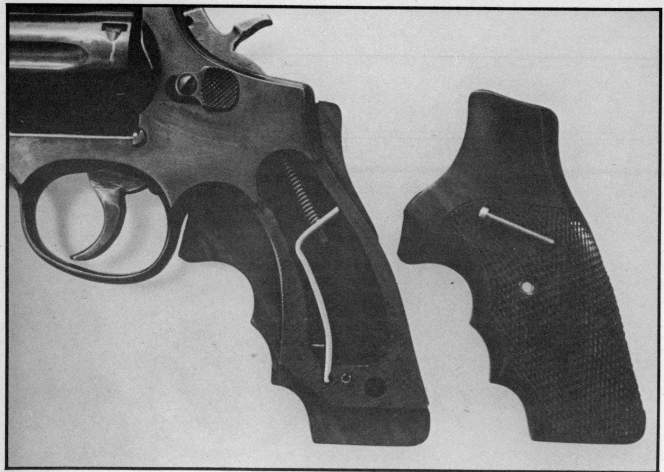

The design of the Farrant grips requires that the forward edge of the grip frame be ground in bevel for grips to fit.

these areas and they will retain the original hardness. I wrap a small piece of wire through one of the pin holes before I heat it so that it can be removed with ease and safety and allowed to cool. Once it is drilled and tapped, it is reheated and then by means of the wire it is dipped in light oil to retemper it; Marvel Mystery Oil works fine. The trigger may also be ground down to a satisfactory width if it is not compatible to the shooter.

"I personally prefer the standard narrow trigger that comes on the duty pistol, then I grind the grooves off and polish it. I also have seen the wide target trigger smoothed down or one can purchase the smooth Ranger trigger over-the-counter, which is a compromise between the standard and target width. I find the wider surface sometimes causes a slight flip, which is even more amplified than the same mistake made with the narrow piece."

There are two schools of thought on the competition hammer. One is a heavy hammer fall which crushes the primer. Ignition is consistent, however the heavy fall also causes a slight movement of the weapon when it strikes and has a psychological effect on the shooter. This interference is only noticeable in precision shooting and does not present a problem in practical training or actual defense situations; it is preferred in the service pistol.

"For competition, I prefer the school of thought on the speed-hammer. The hammer spur and back hump of the hammer is completely ground off to produce as light a hammer fall as possible, yet provide reliable ignition which is pertinent to accuracy. Instead of the heavy crushing blow we get a high-speed slap, which produces little disturbance in sight alignment, an obvious advantage."

After the spur and hump are removed the hammer should be polished out and blued to prevent any glare or reflection, which might distract from conscious effort on the sights. All sides and surfaces of the hammer should be polished, especially any areas which show signs of rubbing. The hammer nose should be spring-loaded and the proper firing-pin protrusion set. If firing-pin protrusion is insufficient, reliable ignition cannot be obtained. To increase the protrusion, the face of the hammer must be milled down a few thousandths. If the protrusion is set properly and misfires still occur, then the cylinder must be set back by stretching the crane. This will increase the flash gap and the barrel then may have to be turned in and possibly milled off to obtain proper clearance at the flash gap. Once clearance is gauged properly, the forcing cone can be relieved and polished.

When the cylinder is moved fore or aft the headspace will have to be set and some competition shooters prefer a minimum, which may require milling off the back of the ratchet in order to move the cylinder backward for proper clearance. "When minimum headspace is set, I prefer to polish the face of the recoil shield," McLennan adds. "It is not unusual to encounter variations in case head thickness and an excessively thick rim may ride against the back of the recoil plate. A high polish permits the cases to slide freely."

The hand must be polished, especially on the front surface where it rides through the notch in the frame. The amateur pistolsmith might be interested to learn that the hands come in different thicknesses and sometimes it is necessary to swap one in order to time the cylinder properly.

While modifying the hammer, the coil spring behind the sear can be cut 2½ or three coils, as well as the rebound slide spring and the cylinder lock spring. It is important to keep the tension of these three springs in balance and this step may require a bit of trial and error due to variation in spring tensions. The front surface of the sear should be polished and any burrs on the edges of the trigger notches which come to bear should be removed.

Velchoff removed the double-action notch from the hammer so that the trigger directly engages the sear instead of picking up on the hammer notch, then transferring to the sear, but we do not recommend this procedure to the neophyte. This procedure eliminates the single-action capability and changes all of the angles of the hammer and trigger notches and produces the short, fast action for which Velchoff is renowned.

To finish off the hammer modification a longer stirrup is installed and the mainspring is shortened to lessen the tension on the trigger and obtain a faster whip-like motion of the hammer throw. These modifications, when properly applied and balanced, will produce a double-action pull near the four-pound mark.

"I have had my trigger pull down below the four-pound level but misfires occasionally occur if the chambers are not cleaned after every match; this is not worth the hassle.

Groups remain tight with these modifications and I believe, in the not-too-distant future, reliable ignition will be obtained under the four-pound mark without the constant problem of having to swab out the cylinder.

"Once these steps have been accomplished I assemble the gun and dry-fire it several thousand times and put in a few sessions on the range. Then tear it down and polish out any rub marks so that all parts mesh perfectly and slide without friction."

Also conducive to light trigger pull is properly setting up the cylinder release latch. The latch must not hold tension on the cylinder pin. The back of the latch may have to be ground off so it moves far enough to the rear without exerting pressure on the center pin. Undue tension on the pin will cause drag on the cylinder which will be transmitted down through the hand and be felt in the trigger. The cylinder should lock into battery, then open freely when the cylinder stop is disengaged. It is only necessary for the pin to snap into the locking hole in the rear of the frame; pressure from the cylinder release and the front lug will not let it spin freely. As mentioned earlier, McLennan removed the front locking lug and has not had any ill effects, but again this is a matter of personal choice.

Every handgunner knows that accuracy depends on how the revolver is held; the hold must remain consistent from shot to shot. It is obvious the grip that fits one person will not be suitable for another. Hands come in all shapes and sizes, short or long, skinny or fat fingers, meaty or leathery palms. The conventional factory grip is made for the average person, but may not accommodate your hands. It is small at the top and swells into a thick base where it meets the meaty part of the hand. The factory grip looks good — it looks like revolver grips have looked for more than a century — but it does not necessarily allow one to shoot well. So why be traditional? You're in a specialized game, with a customized revolver, so why spare the grip?

This close-up illustrates manner in which the strain spring stirrup has been extended, the double-action notch removed for smoother operation.

Chapter 10

OFF-DUTY HANDGUNS AND HOW TO USE THEM

Proper Choice And Use Can Be A Life Or Death Proposition

FEW AMERICAN police agencies require their officers to be armed off-duty. It would be too expensive to issue each cop an extra, concealment-size pistol, and it would be unfair to require them to pay $100 or more out of their own pocket for a compact plainclothes sidearm. This is the rationale of most police departments in America.

Indiana State Police Troopers, for example, are in this situation. They are not required to be armed off-duty, but the nature of their work presses them to carry off-duty guns of their own accord. It's easy for the typical Indiana trooper to picture a situation where he may be either called in to assist, or happen to pass by and stop to help at the scene of a firefight, and be unable to assist a stricken brother trooper because he has left his firepower at home in the closet.

The only nightmare more terrible than killing a man is watching a partner wantonly murdered while you stand by, helpless to protect him. It's a nightmare that law enforcement officers can understand. That's why most of them carry guns on their own time, despite the fact that they usually pay for those weapons out of their own pockets, and the fact that the department does not pay for their training in the use of any firearm other than those carried on duty.

The majority of off-duty officers carry snub-nose .38

revolvers. A few carry tiny .25 automatics, and there is a growing trend toward double-action .380 automatics.

The off-duty gun question must consider training, comfort, discreet carry, and other factors that pertain to our officers' use of sidearms off-duty.

There are five basic types of handguns that the Indiana trooper is likely to carry off-duty: the .25 automatic, the .380 automatic, the snub-nose .38 revolver, the .357 magnum service revolver, and the high-powered sidearms that the department allows for off-duty use, but doesn't permit its men to carry while wearing the uniforms. Let's look at each type of handgun, and see how it stands up to the criterion of a true off-duty combat weapon for the ISP Trooper.

The .25 Automatic: They call the .25 auto a ladies' gun, because its extremely small size adapts it to an evening bag. Generally speaking, the .25's stopping power is somewhat less than that of the .22 caliber pistol outdoorsmen use for shooting rats and squirrels.

Analysis of gunfight situations involving these pistols indicates that an opponent can be stopped by a .25 slug only if the bullet penetrates the brain or spine. A heart-shot will allow a felon to fire back enough times to kill the off-duty officer. While the heart wound kills, there is little shock effect transmitted, and the assailant can keep firing for several seconds, until he has lost so much blood

This 1972 model Colt Detective Special has been customized and hard-chromed by John Williams. The combat stocks are by Fuzzy Farrant. Norma's Index No. 19119 load with 110-grain JHP bullets is one of the most potent snubnose performers.

The lower gun here is a Model 29 S&W .44 magnum, customized by Austin Behlert, with Pachmayr's Signature rubber stocks. Shown for size comparison is S&W's .38 Special Combat Masterpiece 4".

that his blood pressure drops sharply and he passes out. Gunmen hit in non-vital areas with .25 slugs have reported that they only feel a sensation of moderate pain, and sometimes not even that, if they are under the influence of drugs and/or natural adrenalin during the excitement of a gunfight.

The .25 automatic, some will say, has killed an inordinate number of people. But those situations were mostly murders involving unsuspecting and unarmed victims.

Police officers pack .25s only because if there wasn't something that small to carry, they might not carry anything at all. Certainly, a .25 is better than nothing when the off-duty cop walks into a combat situation. But the officer who wants a discreetly concealable sidearm can still carry a bigger gun that will give him a better chance of surviving a combat confrontation, without burdening himself with cumbersome hardware.

.32 and .380 Automatics: Such pistols as these are larger than .25 autos, but substantially smaller than .38 snub-nose police revolvers. Their comfortable size accounts for their popularity. The .32 is a notoriously poor stopper, while the .380 delivers roughly the same effectiveness out of a small automatic pistol as the .38 Special cartridge does from a Detective Special when the gun is loaded with standard round-nose bullets.

The officer who carries a small automatic should stick to the .380 caliber. In years past, ballistics authorities equated the .32 with the .380, but more recent experiments show that the .380 actually equals the .38 Special standard police

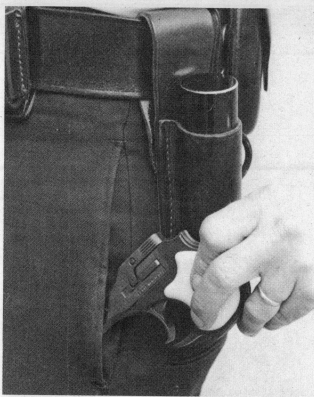

High Standard's two-barreled over/under derringer, in .22 WRFM, is compact enough to be unobtrusive in pocket, but it can prove effective as backup in emergency situations.

Dan Wesson .357 magnum revolver is uncommonly flexible, due to the variety of ammunition available for it, plus the ability to interchange barrels of several different lengths as well as stocks proportioned to be suited for many special uses.

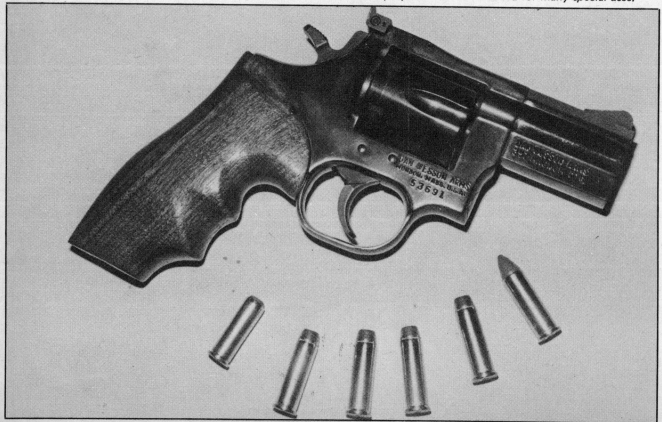

The Thomas .45 — no longer made — was designed to provide ample power for any reasonable need, combined with highly concealable dimensions. It employed a unique breech locking system and each round of .45 ACP was fired double-action.

Walther Model PP is a double-action pocket auto available in several popular small cartridges, including .22 long rifle, .32 and .380 auto.

Walther Model PPK is a shorter version of the Model PP, sharing its general features except for barrel length; both are currently made in West Germany, although there are plans to make them in the U.S.

This Colt Detective Special has its grip area wrapped with friction tape to provide a more secure grip.

Made by Beretta in Italy and distributed in the U.S.A. by Browning, the Model BDA-380 features a staggered-column magazine with 13-round capacity plus a fourteenth cartridge in the chamber.

load in a two-inch revolver, in terms of penetration, shock, and wound size. The flat automatic is much more comfortable inside the waistband, and more pocketable due to its compact shape. Another element to consider, though, is the fact that some departments forbid officers to carry hollow-nose bullets on duty, but they may use any ammo they choose in the gun they carry on their own time. A .380 auto loaded with Super-Vel hollow points, or Deadeye expanding bullets, or KTW armor-piercing loads, is a particularly formidable weapon. We would caution, however, that such high-powered ammo be used only in top-quality guns such as the Walther.

Snub-Nose .38 Revolvers: The small-frame, snub-nose .38 is the second most popular firearm in the entire police arsenal: the choice of virtually all plainclothes officers, it is

also the most popular off-duty gun for uniformed patrolmen.

One advantage of this weapon for private-time carry, supposedly, is that the officer has been trained already in the double-action revolver system and therefore his training with the duty sidearm carries over into the little one he packs off duty. This is not necessarily so. The small five-shot S&W, for example, doesn't have as smooth an action as its larger-framed counterpart, the Combat Magnum. Sights and grips are both too small on the five-shot Smith; such a gun requires a different hold and more precise sight picture. Recoil in these small revolvers is fierce, especially in the aluminum frame models. Also, the small frame puts the trigger closer to the handle, resulting in a hand position where the second joint of the finger is

The Charter Arms .44 Bulldog has a three-inch barrel and it's chambered for the capable .44 Special cartridge making it another compact powerhouse.

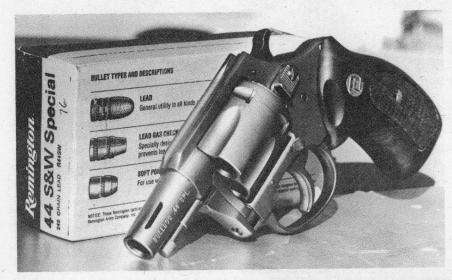

An especially customized version of the .44 Bulldog was produced by Mag-na-port Arms under the designation "Backpacker," the idea being that you carry it beneath the belt at the small of the back. It has no front sight.

In order to keep dimensions as compact as possible, the Bulldog has but five chambers, not six.

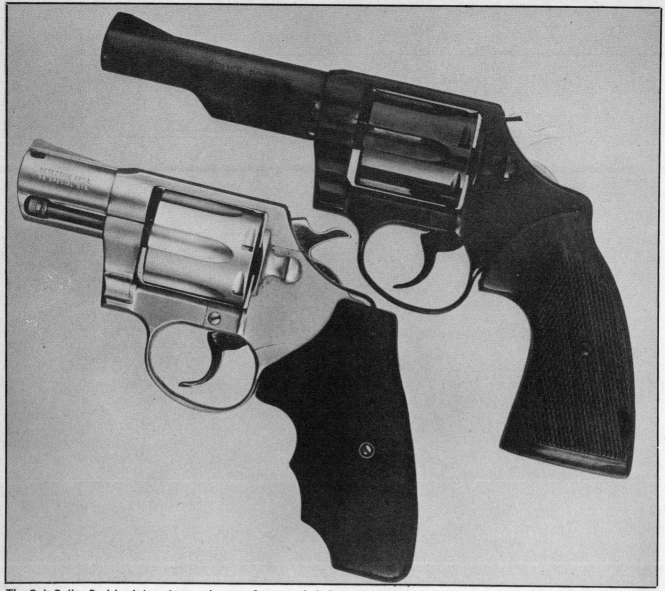

The Colt Police Positive is based upon the same frame as their Detective Special and various versions have been produced in years gone by. The one shown here with a four-inch barrel is the model produced for a short time during the mid-Seventies.

more likely to be on the trigger than the first joint, which controls the trigger action of the full-size revolver with which the officer is trained. The result is a weapon with a totally different set of handling characteristics than the service sidearm the officer spends most of his practice time with.

In favor of the snubby .38 is the fact that it generally functions the same way as the gun the officer is trained with, and that it is small enough to carry inside the waistband, or in an overcoat pocket when the officer is off duty. Moreover, the officer who wants to load his second sidearm with maximum-capability ammo is better off with the revolver, since the .38 can handle high-powered loadings

that would cause jams in many models of small automatics. Generally speaking, the officer in mufti will get more per-shot stopping power out of a snub .38 than from any other compact sidearm.

.357 Magnum Service Revolver: The issue sidearm of the Indiana State Policeman is the Smith & Wesson .357 Combat Magnum. Whether he has the blue steel Model 19 or the stainless Model 66, he still holds a medium-sized revolver with a four-inch barrel and oversize stocks designed to soak up the recoil of the high-powered magnum round.

Many police officers carry their issue Combat Magnum under the seat of their cars. What few of them realize is that this weapon can be carried discreetly and comfortably on

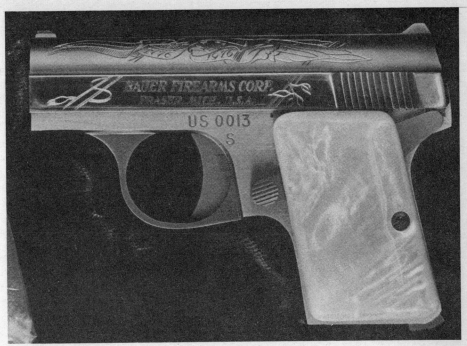

For those who favor the .25 ACP cartridge, Bauer's little autoloader is exceptionally well made, reliable.

the person, providing the lawman is willing to purchase a suitable off-duty holster for it.

The Combat Magnum isn't that bulky a gun. Its cylinder is no thicker than that of the Colt Detective Special or Cobra, popular among plain clothesmen. The bulk of the Combat Magnum is in its stocks and its four-inch barrel. Men who have carried both four-inch and two-inch guns undercover know that barrel length is not significant to the gun's concealability: indeed, when carried on a belt holster, the snub-nose gun may bulge more, because its center of gravity is closer to the grip, which therefore sticks out. A service revolver's four-inch barrel lies alongside the wearer's hip, thus stabilizing it and keeping the butt from hanging outward: the pressure of the barrel on the hip pushes the handle of the gun inward toward the hollow under the ribcage, where the coat drapes over it smoothly with virtually no bulge.

Some officers are not permitted to alter their sidearms with custom grips — when on duty. Since there are no regulations for off-duty guns, the officer may simply purchase a set of round-butt stocks for his Model 19 or 66, and keep them in his locker at the post: it takes only a minute and a screwdriver to switch grips, turning the holster gun into a revolver with a trim enough profile to comfortably carry undercover without bulging.

The service Combat Magnum has three principal advantages as a private-hours sidearm: it doesn't cost anything; the officer has a week of intensive basic training with it, plus bi-monthly refresher courses; and he has a more accurate and high-powered sidearm than any of the so-called off-duty guns.

Many police agencies allow their men to carry any gun they want off duty, but limit them to a particular model when wearing the uniform. We therefore have the strange situation in which an officer may be better armed off duty than on.

The officer who is looking for total gunfight capability rather than off-duty convenience has several options. The

Safariland's leg holster affords secure concealment for several popular undercover guns. It features a Velcro fastening strap to keep the gun in place at all times.

first is ammunition; high-velocity, hollow-point bullets should be his choice whether the gun he carries is a .380 auto, a snub .38, the .357 service gun, or a combat-customized high-power automatic.

The last type sidearm is what professional police gunfighters choose when the department gives them their choice, and when they know they'll be facing bad odds: New York City's stakeout squad, which had more gunfights in any given year than any three metropolitan police departments all told, carried mostly 9mm and .45 automatics before a bureaucratic department edict forced them to revert to .38s.

The big automatic's main advantage is firepower: eight to fifteen shots instead of five or six, and fast magazine-reloading in less than two seconds. The 9mm cartridge, with a high-speed, expanding bullet load, is roughly equivalent to the softnose Super Vel out of a .38 Special. The .45 automatic is renowned for its ability to stop with one hit anywhere on the torso.

The high-powered automatic, by nature of its design, is the same size or smaller than the .38 or .357 service revolver, even though it may deliver more than twice the firepower. Because they work around a spring-loaded slide instead of a fixed cylinder, they're much flatter in profile, and therefore much more convenient to carry concealed. One major reason neighboring Illinois State Police adopted the S&W 9mm automatic was that it was more suitable for the required off-duty carry: it was compact enough that the department could reasonably demand that their men carry it at all times; it was easier to shoot accurately in rapid combat fire than any small-frame revolver; and the men had been trained to handle this particular sidearm, whether they were on duty or off.

The .25s are normally carried without notice, while a snubby .38 revolver, because of its thick cylinder, will cause a conspicuous bulge. Most officers who carry short .38s and .380 automatics on their person put the guns in belt holsters, which are covered by either a coat, or a sportshirt with its tail hanging out.

A lot of officers are taking a sharp look at the paddle holsters mounted on a piece of steel-reinforced leather that fits inside the waistband. It allows gun and holster to be

The S&W Chiefs Special is an ultra-compact, .38 Special revolver with a five-chambered cylinder, available in blue as the Model 36 or in stainless as the Model 60. Exit holes in hardwood block show the power of handloaded cup-point bullets.

quickly put on or taken off, and holds the gun fairly close against the body.

The best undercover holster design is the inside-the-belt model available from Bucheimer, Bianchi, or Safariland. The gun is worn inside the belt, so that bulge is reduced as much as possible. At the same time, the tension of the belt keeps the gun from falling out, eliminating the need for a safety strap: a pistol can be drawn from such an undercovering faster than from a uniform holster, the safety strap of which must be unfastened before the Combat Magnum can be cleared. These holsters are available for any size gun, including the four-inch service revolver.

Shoulder holsters are a joke among real police. Most popular are the Bucheimer-Clark belt holsters for the off-duty guns, the inside belt holsters and thumb-release scabbards such as the Bianchi, Bucheimer, and Safariland.

Off-duty police officers have been slain by their uniformed brethren who mistake them for armed felons. Police unions have brought suit against departments and communities to rescind the requirement that they be armed twenty-four hours.

The reason is that there have been so many shootings involving mistaken identity. It's not hard to see how it can happen.

The off-duty policeman, dressed casually, witnesses a serious crime in progress, such as a robbery. He draws his

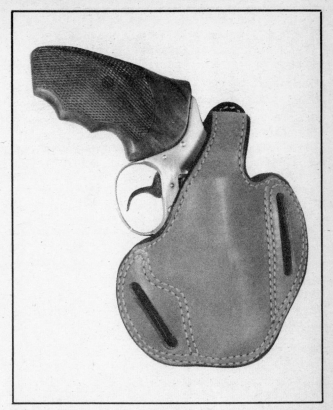

Bianchi "Shadow" holster is designed to ride on the belt beneath a suit coat with minimum bulge or visibility.

Gun at left is an earlier model of the Colt Detective Special. Gun at right is a more recent Colt Diamondback with 2½-inch, ventilated-rib barrel and square stocks. Both are chambered for the popular .38 Special.

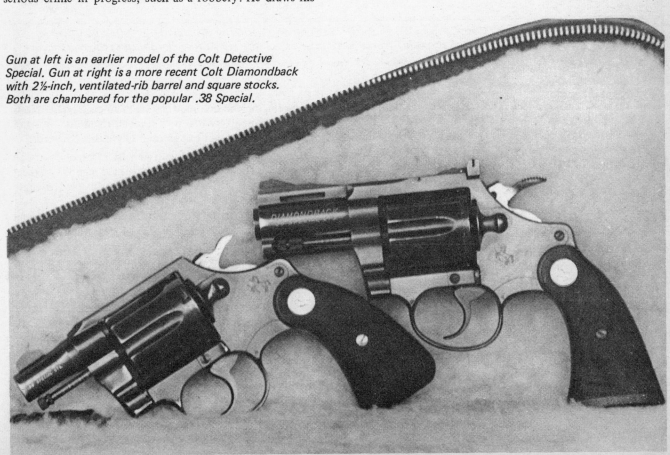

Browning Model BDA is made by West Germany's J. P. Sauer und Sohn on a design by Switzerland's SIG. Originally made in 9mm Luger, .38 Colt Super and .45 ACP, Browning soon discontinued all but the .45 ACP versions such as the one shown.

small handgun and holds the perpetrator at gunpoint. "Call the station," he yells to the distraught proprietor.

The uniformed police coming in may not have received the whole message; perhaps the frightened citizen on the phone only said, "There's a robber here! Come quick!" or perhaps they're responding to a silent alarm triggered before the off-duty policeman took armed command of the scene. But they're going into the situation with guns drawn and ready to shoot, and they're acting properly.

They're expecting to find a violent armed criminal. What they see is, perhaps, a man in Levi's and a T-shirt, holding a small handgun on a couple of other people. A few officers might open fire at this point, though most would shout a challenge: "Police! Drop your weapon!"

But that off-duty patrolman in the Levi's and T-shirt won't drop his gun. He's full of adrenalin, and when he hears that shout, he'll turn instinctively toward the sound before the words even register, and his gun will turn with him.

If there has been gunfire inside, the off-duty cop's ears will be ringing and his emotions are at an even higher pitch, making it more likely that he'll respond to another officer's challenge in a way that can be tragically misinterpreted.

He turns to face patrolmen who have responded to an armed robbery call. They know the armed man they expect to see may turn on them with a gun in his hand. They have decided beforehand how to respond.

When it is over, one of the officers may kick the gun away from the corpse and find the badge in the hip pocket of the Levi's...

Eliminating the off-duty gun is not the answer, either. In departments like New York City Police Department, where an officer carries his gun whenever he leaves his house, a huge percentage of felony arrests are made off-duty. Many officers would feel uncomfortable without a weapon, even on their own time. The thrust has not been to eliminate the off-duty gun, but to make it optional.

What remains is to make it safe, and to give every officer the same kind of training with it that he gets with his

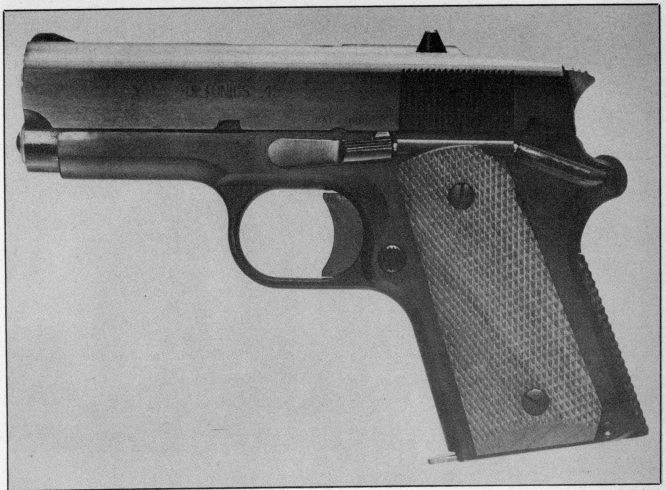

The Detonics .45 is chambered for the .45 ACP cartridge and, although it may show resemblance to the familiar Colt Model 1911 design, there are many interior modifications and it omits features such as the barrel bushing and the grip safety.

service weapon, plus specialized instruction in the subtleties of the off-duty confrontation!

The fact that the officer is off-duty means that he is usually caught by surprise, and is definitely without backup or immediate police communication. In most robbery situations, he must seriously consider staying in the background and letting the thing go down. His police expertise in assembling descriptions, etc., will be valuable to subsequent apprehension, and he also avoids triggering a firefight that might take innocent lives. When a bystander is slain, no matter by whom, people will inevitably say, "No one would have been hurt if that glory-seeking off-duty cop with the hero complex hadn't pulled his gun!"

Draw the off-duty weapon only if you are convinced that death or injury will be inflicted upon innocents if you do not interrupt.

Any officer who has his gun in his off-duty clothes should also be carrying his badge. When you draw the first, you should draw the second.

Whether or not you yell, "Police," will be determined by

the situation. If a gunman has his pistol-barrel in the mouth of a storeowner and has said, "I'm going to blow you away," your shout will only startle him into pulling the trigger. If the felon has convinced you that he is about to take life wantonly, no law requires you announce yourself; on the contrary, practicality demands that you put a bullet through his brain and short-circuit his nervous system before the trigger-pulling impulse reaches his index finger.

A shield on a belt or lapel will not be seen. We know from studying gunfights in depth that combatants on either side develop a kind of tunnel vision that focuses on the opponent and his gun, and blocks out everything else, including bystanders in the background. You want that badge where your opponent will see it: right with the gun. It is easy to slip out your wallet or badge case, flip it over your hand, and leave the shield or star hanging right under the gun muzzle.

This way, someone who turns on you and forces you to shoot him can't testify later from his wheelchair that he tried to fire because he thought you were a holdup man

Colt's .38 Special Diamondback has target sights and broad, target-style hammer spur.

Introduced about 1970, Sturm, Ruger & Company's Security-Six has built an excellent reputation for rugged reliability and all-around excellence. It's usually made in .357 magnum, though a .38 Special version is available; so are fixed or target sights.

The accuracy potential of small handguns can be astonishing. This ten-shot group was fired from a sandbag rest at fifty yards with Federal's exceptionally accurate Index No. 38A match load that carries a 148-grain lead wadcutter bullet for target work.

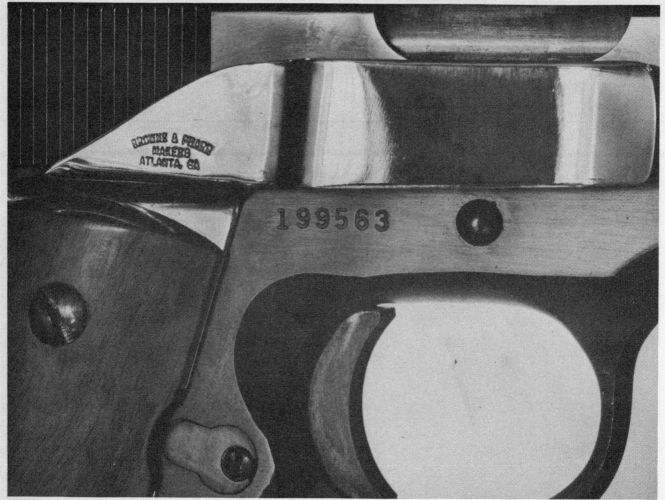

For those who carry the Colt autos, such as the Commander, or Government Model as shown here in .38 Colt Super, Browne & Pharr of Atlanta, Georgia, offer this sturdy steel spring clip that attaches beneath right-hand stock to hold gun on belt.

instead of cop. When he sees your steel, you want him to see your tin at the same time.

Once the situation is in control — the suspects weaponless and prostrate in spread-eagle positions with their ankles crossed — keep your identity clear! Holding the gun in one hand, raise the badge case in the other and rotate it over your head so everyone around you can see it; announce loudly, "I am a police officer. Please stay where you are. The situation is under control. I am a police officer."

Once the situation is under control, instruct the store manager (or an employee who doesn't seem rattled) to call the police station, and to advise that you are holding the suspects at gunpoint and describe you. Tell them to say something like, "Officer Self is holding the suspects on the floor. He is wearing jeans and a Beaver Patrol sweatshirt."

This serves two functions. First, the officers will be able to identify you on sight, even though they may not recognize your face. Second, it covers them if the suspects should overwhelm and disarm you in the interim, and be laying for the officers, who may now have their guard down when they come in. Assume that you have been disarmed: when the uniformed patrolman walks in with his gun in his holster and starts to say, "Good going," he could be cut short by a revolver blast, if you haven't done your part.

The officers responding may not be the ones who got the call in the first place, and there is also the possibility that the dispatcher didn't pass on your description. For this reason, you should instruct the store manager, or a competent-looking employee or citizen to stand by the entrance where you expect the uniformed officers. This person should be instructed to tell the incoming policemen what you look like and what you're wearing.

Studies of armed robberies over the past few years show

a dramatic increase in the use of backup teams by criminals. These indiviudals are often seeded inside the establishment several minutes before the actual robbery team moves in; their sole purpose is to blend in with the innocents, and be able to cut down any police officer who attempts to arrest the first team of robbers.

An officer who has neutralized or controlled the first team should have his back to the wall, and constantly scan bystanders for threat of hostilities. Backup-teams also frequently stay outside with the escape car, and are prepared to come in rapidly to shoot if they think their accomplices have been apprehended by a lone, easy-to-take policeman.

Some situations have occurred in bars or lounges where the officer was accompanied by his wife. The officer should seriously consider staying put in such a case, but if he has chosen to intercede with his off-duty gun drawn, he should keep his wife out of it. Many officers trained in off-duty crime intervention techniques have suggested, "Why not have my wife make the call and wait at the door, instead of an employee or bystander? I trust her a lot more!"

Good point, but remember the possible presence of criminal backup teams inside or outside the confrontation site. If they are there, they will make certain that your call for help doesn't leave the building, and that means that they will neutralize whoever you send for reinforcements, before they move in on you.

The question has been raised as to whether the kind of gun carried by the officer makes a difference. Some officers feel that the sight of a small automatic or other non-police-type sidearm can be equated with a "criminal gun," and will cause a uniformed man coming in to make a snap judgment and fire prematurely. Some departments permit off-duty officers to carry only blue-steel .38

If bulk is not a critical factor, the AMT Hardballer .45 ACP is made entirely of stainless steel on general lines closely similar to those of the Colt Model 1911 design. The one shown has a standard five-inch barrel, but a Long Slide (7") is available.

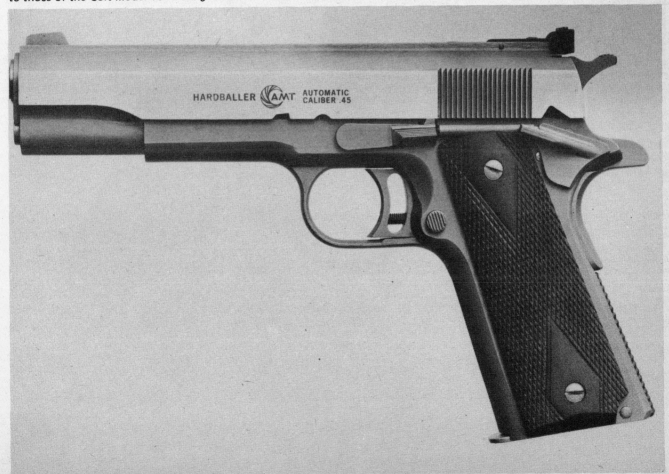

revolvers for just this reason.

One can argue the validity of this premise. Surveys of police cases show that, rather than being predisposed to shooting at someone with a non-police gun, student response was that they would shoot at anyone no matter what gun they had, if they weren't clearly identified as police. Many criminals carry Detective Specials.

The off-duty patrolman runs a great risk of being mistaken for a felon when he makes an arrest in mufti. Black officers, especially those in ghetto areas, are particularly vulnerable to this syndrome. In New York City, after an off-duty black officer was slain by white patrolmen while pursuing a robbery team, black cops announced bitterly, "They think every black with a gun is a criminal!"

"It is not my place to comment on the tragedy of that kind of thinking on the part of the white officers, but I know that if I were a black officer in New York City, I would draw my own off-duty gun only to defend my life, and would never undertake a pursuit," says Massad Ayoob, who researched this chapter.

A law officer's duties demand much, and intrude upon his own time more than those of almost any other profession. The officer knows when he takes the job that he will have to risk his life more than once, but sacrifice is not in the contract. By using the techniques outlined above when he draws his off-duty gun in the face of a crime in progress, he greatly increases his chances of showing up alive and healthy for his next scheduled tour of duty.

Charter Arms also makes the Undercover .38 Special with two-inch barrel and Bulldog grips, their Model No. 13821.

Here's another Ruger Security-Six, this time with the optional target-type rear sight and a four-inch barrel.

The original Colt Commander design featured a frame of high-tensile aluminum alloy. The Combat Commander is of the same dimensions, but with a steel frame. Both are offered in a choice of 9mm Luger, .38 Super or .45 ACP.

GUNSMITHING FOR
Greg Roberts Knows What Cops

Greg Roberts' conversion work on this Colt Lawman frame features a bull barrel and an Aristocrat sight rib. Grips were made in the Philippines.

LAW ENFORCEMENT
Want; That's What They Get!

IN SANTA CRUZ, California, a young gunsmith and shooter is carrying on what amounts to a family tradition: offering the best combat handguns to law enforcement officers that his know-how can produce.

The young man's father, Duke Roberts, was range master for the police department in Pasadena, California, until his retirement. Over and above his dayside duties, with the Pasadena department, the senior Roberts operated a part-time reloading and gunsmithing service out of the family garage, assisted by son Greg.

After the elder Roberts' retirement from active duty, the family moved to Santa Cruz and, about 1972, the father-and-son team started offering a mobile service facility to regional law enforcement agencies, traveling from department to department to provide preventive maintenance and routine repairs. On weekends, they would set up their display at matches of the California Combat Association to do on-the-spot repair, action smoothing and similar services.

The younger Roberts caught the bug for competitive shooting and joined the Santa Cruz police reserves, competing in local and regional matches. This led him to a keen interest in custom revolvers; the specialized variants often termed combat conversions, equipped with such features as heavy bull barrels, auxiliary sight ribs and the like.

Greg Roberts started producing his own custom guns and before long, added lines of other combat match needfuls such as holsters and speedloaders to his wares on display at the matches. The end effect was to move the operation out of the garage and into a shop that continues to operate as On-Sight Gun Sales (726 Water Street, Santa Cruz, California 95060). Although the store carries a typical stock of shooting supplies for the walk-in customer, the clientele is predominantly law enforcement personnel and competitive shooters specializing in the police revolver matches, also termed combat shooting.

Some time in 1977, in the midst of expanding the shop capabilities, Roberts was offered a chance to buy another company, Monterey Bay Munitions. The prime specialty of MBM is the reloading of ammunition in .38 Special, .357 magnum and .45 Automatic Colt Pistol (ACP). Due to deep present involvement in the custom gun building and ammunition reloading, Roberts is giving serious consideration to getting out of the retail store business to concentrate solely upon the two areas of his primary interest: law enforcement and custom revolver work. He does little or no work on automatics, beyond mounting the occasional set of sights on a slide and similar minor chores, not from lack of opportunity but due to the stark scarcity of hours of containing more than sixty minutes.

"I can't do everything all the time. I have to leave two or three days a week to go out and shoot and hunt, because I feel those are the things that are important, too," Roberts notes ruefully. Far from being a casual plinker, the shop showroom boasts a wall covered with trophies and plaques

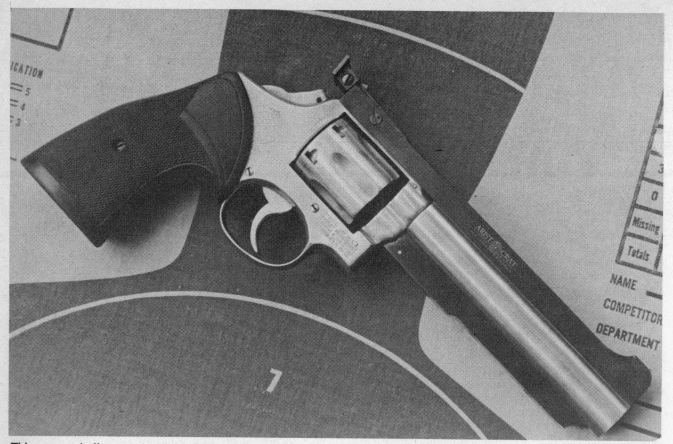

This gun was built around a Model 64 Smith & Wesson action with an Atkinson stainless steel barrel and sight rib by Aristocrat, plus Pachmayr rubber grips.

earned by the younger Roberts, including coveted berths on the California *Governor's 100* and the USA *President's 20* teams.

The one-inch (outside diameter) stainless steel barrel blanks used for conversions by Roberts are made in thirty-two-inch lengths by famed barrelmaker Bill Atkinson of Prescott, Arizona. and rifled to a pitch of one turn in fourteen inches (1:14"). Having conducted exhaustive tests, Roberts believes this to be the best barrel blank to be had, although it's comparatively expensive when priced against most available blanks. Other blanks, Roberts has found, may outshoot the Atkinson barrels with some one or two particular loads but, in the long run, the tubes out of Prescott edge well ahead of the pack and make it possible for Roberts to guarantee the capability of his guns to deliver fifty-yard groups of two inches or less out of a Ransom Rest, when using factory Western or Remington wadcutters.

Thanks to the performance of the Atkinson barrels, a shooter in any part of the country can buy one of Roberts' guns and be assured of a local supply of ammunition that

Greg Roberts has been involved in handgun work since his teens, working with his police officer father.

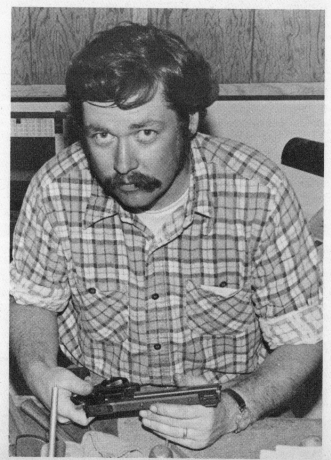

will deliver the guaranteed level of accuracy. Roberts uses Douglas premium chrome-moly stock for all of the blued barrels he makes up and finds it satisfactory on a basis of gun for gun and ammo for ammo, down the line.

An accessory popular with Roberts' customers is the Aristocrat sight rib, particularly among police revolver competitors who favor the neck-hold aiming point. In this system, the sights are aligned upon the base of the silhouette target's neck and the bullet lands several inches lower in the center of the scoring circles. The Aristocrat rib features a three-position range-changing screw on the side and three different elevation adjustment screws on top. The numbered positions on the side screw are marked 1 (seven yards), 2 (twenty-five yards) and 3 (fifty yards). Correspondingly numbered screws on top enable the shooter to fine-tune the point of bullet impact at each of the three range settings.

"As long as the shooter is as smart as the rib, it eliminates all possible errors," Roberts comments, wryly.

He uses a Bo-Mar rib on his own competition revolver, because he prefers the center hold over the neck hold and thus has little need for the three-way switching capability of the Aristocrat rib.

Roberts confesses himself considerably dumbfounded by the burgeoning popularity of custom guns for police revolver competition, both in terms of the number in current use and those being sold. There are several well-known pistolsmiths in the same line of work — Ron Powers of Independence, Missouri; Austin Behlert of Union, New Jersey; and Bill Davis of Sacramento, California, being three typical examples — and Roberts has no ambition to top them in terms of guns completed and delivered.

"I don't feel I can build any more guns than I do now and still continue to do them personally. I like what I'm doing, I like the product I turn out and I enjoy dealing with shooters on an individual basis," Roberts explains.

Although the elder Roberts may help out with some of

Duke Roberts (left), a retired police officer, works with his son in customizing projects, as well as repair and maintenance work for California police departments. In photos, they check indexing, and handgun's crane.

Arrow points to numbered adjustment screw for setting three-position cam for events at 7, 25, 50-yard ranges.

It's not likely one will use Allen wrench to change point of impact in the field, but sight is built for such quick changes in combat pistol competitions.

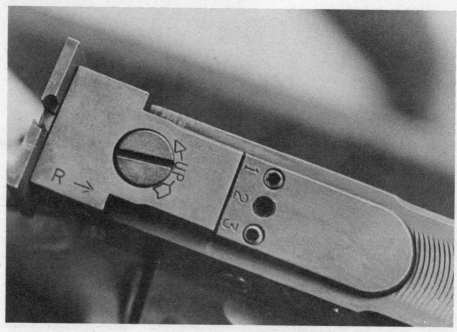

the action work, Greg Roberts' work is in every gun that goes out and that includes shooting, testing on the Ransom machine rest and rigorous inspection. If Greg is not satisfied, the gun gets further work until it meets his demanding standards.

Asked for his thoughts on matters such as coil-spring conversions to replace the leaf spring that powers the hammer, Roberts replied, "I'm kind of a purist in a lot of ways. I love the way I can make a typical Smith & Wesson double-action feel, without going to a lot of other modifications such as coil springs for the hammer and so on. I think it's a good, efficient action. As for reliability of ignition. there are a lot of guns that won't go off unless everything is done right but, when you get things the way they have to be, the guns will work."

Although the major bulk of Roberts' output consists of revolvers in .38 Special or .357 magnum, he confesses to considerable fascination for the large, non-magnum cartridges such as the .45 Long Colt and .44 Special and he has built several custom revolvers in such calibers, usually based upon the Smith & Wesson Model 28 action.

The conversion cylinders in .45 LC are made up with the case head recessed into the rear face of the cylinder, the same as the original in .357 magnum. The recessed head approach, Roberts explains, is due to the length of the Model 28 cylinder — the longest magnum cylinder available — with its clearance of but 0.015-inch between the rear cylinder face and the front of the recoil plate.

Roberts recalls that his interest in the big non-magnums stems from the first one he turned out in .45 LC for a friend in Salt Lake City. Fresh out of the bluing tank and off the assembly bench, they bought a box of Remington

Left-side view of the same handgun illustrates the overall workmanship that goes into Roberts' conversion.

factory .45 LC ammo and took it to the range for a trial, finding they could use the same hold and sight picture at one hundred yards that was needed at twenty-five yards.

"Really a socker!" Roberts marvels.

He buys his lower ribs from Sacramento's Bill Davis when the customer requests that optional feature. It adds four or five ounces to the overall weight of the gun and enables Roberts to provide a variation to the usual Smith & Wesson lockup. Instead of locking up in the end of the ejector rod, it locks between the rear face of the lower rib and a mating arrangement on the crane yoke, thereby allowing the cylinder to ride free, without interference, with a useful gain in overall accuracy potential.

In addition to Smith & Wessons, Roberts offers the same basic conversions such as bull barrels and sight ribs for double-action Colts and Rugers. The latter can be of exceptional interest to shooters with small hands and/or short fingers since the distance from the back strap of the Ruger frame to the trigger is somewhat shorter than it is on typical Colts or S&Ws, and that can prove to be a tremendous asset to the small-handed shooter in double-action work.

Arrow points to repositioned front lockup plunger which was installed by Greg Roberts during the process.

Chapter 12

A LOOK AT POLICE
SHOTGUNS

New York City's Emergency Services Unit (ESU) uses tear gas to flush out a suspect as armored ESU weapons specialists stand by with shotguns at the ready against the possibility that the suspect may come out shooting.

The Spectrum Is Less Than Broad And Each Has Its Own Advantages

*Upper gun is Savage's Model 30 Field Grade in slug mode;
Lower is Smith & Wesson's Model 916 Eastfield pump.*

A 12-GAUGE shotgun, known semicolloquially as the "riot gun," is the deadliest hand-held weapon available to the police officer. A six-shot model loaded with No. 4 buckshot can put 162 lethal projectiles into the target area in less time than it would take to empty the twenty-shot magazine of a submachine gun. It is a weapon so destructive that few victims of close-range hits survive. Many feel that it's too much firepower for law enforcement to routinely wield; others believe that without that capability, officers may be fatally outgunned by heavily armed criminals.

Should police carry shotguns in sector cars? If so, what is the safest method? What are the best types and brands of police shotgun, and the optimum ammunition? We assigned contributing editor Massad F. Ayoob to analyze the nature of the shotgun in law enforcement, and various types of ammunition:

"Riot guns" come in three standard barrel lengths: eighteen-inch (the shortest that is really practical); twenty-inch; and twenty-two-inch. All are 12-gauge. The shortest barrels are definitely better suited for fast handling in close quarters; however, they have noticeably more severe muzzle blast. This can be a more serious disadvantage than one might think, since it slows the officer's recovery

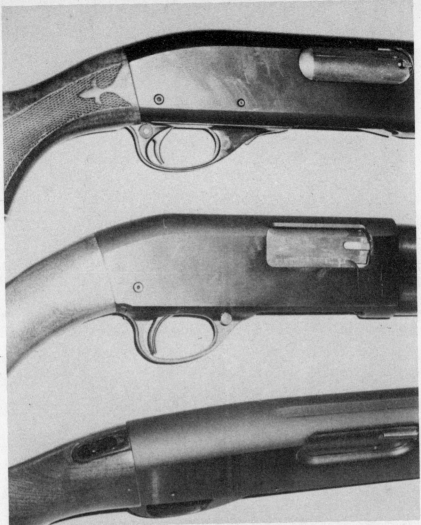

Opposite page, the short double-barreled shotgun has a place in law enforcement. This officer has the Beretta BL-2 over/under with 18½-inch barrels in 12-gauge chambering. The BL-2 was marketed briefly to police, but never became popular. Now discountinued, it has come to be a collector's item. Above, from top, Remington M870 with safety behind trigger; High Standard 8113 with safety in front of trigger; S&W 916 with sliding tang safety. Mixed brands in the same department can cause deadly confusion in their operation.

time between shots, especially at night when the muzzle flash can be blinding, and in a cramped area, where the reverberations can be so deafening that the officer won't be able to trace his hidden opponent's movements by sound.

There seems to be little difference between twenty-two and twenty-inch barrels in this respect. The real choice is between the eighteen-inch for greater convenience and quicker handling and twenty-inch for more controllability.

Magazine capacity should be maximized; many police shotguns can be fitted with magazine extensions that go all the way to the end of the muzzle. High Standard's Model 8113 used by many departments, is factory-equipped with a full length tube. This gives the officer six or seven shells, against as few as four in standard shotguns. Remember, the gun is carried with an empty chamber.

There are two other worthwhile additions to the police shotgun: A rubber recoil pad gives the officer slightly quicker recovery between shots, and by reducing the discomfort of recoil, makes it less likely that he will flinch on the trigger and miss.

Rifle-type sights are a definite advantage on a police shotgun. They allow the officer to load the weapon with deer slugs and turn it into a carbine, more than doubling the effective range of the gun. Standard sights on these shotguns consist of a simple bead at the muzzle, and a wide, shallow groove atop the receiver. A good shot can do remarkably well with such a gun loaded with deer slugs, but the average officer will perform substantially better if the gun has real, rifle-style sights. Sights make little or no difference with buck or birdshot.

An increasingly popular piece of equipment is the optional folding stock of the Remington. A pistol grip is part of the package, intended to increase controllability when shooting from the hip. The stock itself is a metal skeleton, which folds out of the way on top of the receiver in such a way as not to block the sights. A press of a

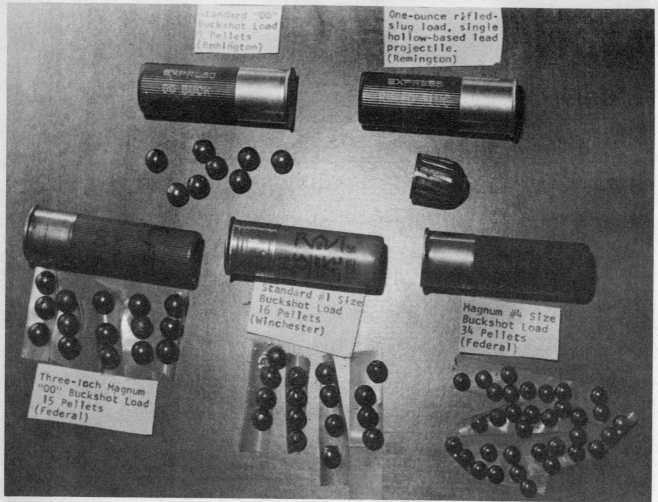

Opposite page, Remington's Model 870 with folding stock is becoming increasingly popular with police due to its maneuverability in close quarters, coupled with a high degree of controllability and excellent accuracy.
Above, this illustrates the broad variety in payload among various shotshells made up for police shotgun use.

button, and it snaps out to full length for firing from the shoulder.

It's a good idea, but it doesn't work out as well as many expect. First, accuracy is severely reduced when this or any shotgun is fired from the hip. Second, the metal stock is not conducive to proper shoulder aiming, and its hard edges have been known to slap the face painfully. Finally, it shortens the gun on one end but not the other. To conceal it beneath a raincoat, the plainclothes officer has to hold it between receiver and slide handle to prevent the muzzle protruding from under the coat; he will have to shift the weapon is his hands before he can bring it into play. With a true undercover shotgun, such as the discontinued High Standard Model 10, he could hold the weapon in firing position through a cutout pocket, and bring it into action much faster. The High Standard can be fired from the shoulder with greater accuracy than a folded-stock pump gun, yet is shorter overall.

Apart from double-barrel shotguns still in use by a few departments, the standard police riot gun is a slide-action. It is less likely to malfunction than an automatic, and if it does jam, the slide action gives the officer more leverage with which to clear the mechanism.

Another reason pump guns are favored is that when carried in a ready-access cruiser rack such as the Lecco Lock, steel jaws clamp the slide into a forward position, preventing unauthorized personnel from accidentally or otherwise discharging the weapon while in the lock. However, the Los Angeles Police Department's SWAT team is said to be using automatics, and LAPD sets a lot of trends in police equipment.

Virtually all police departments use buckshot as standard ammunition, usually 00 size. In a standard shell, there are nine of these .33-caliber balls. The 12-gauge magnum load in the 2¾-inch shell contains twelve pellets of 00 size, and fits any police shotgun.

Recoil and blast are increased slightly, but an officer who can handle the basic load can handle the short magnum. A truly "magnum" shotgun round is the three-inch shell, originally designed for long-range waterfowl shooting. Two police shotguns, the Smith & Wesson and the Savage, come with three-inch chambers,

Here's another view of the Remington Model 870 Police shotgun with stock conversion unit in position for firing from the shoulder in usual way.

and the Federal Cartridge Company makes a full magnum shell with twelve 00 balls.

Recoil is substantially sharper, enough to give a lot of officers trouble in rapid-fire recovery. Three-inch magnum ammo should only be issued to select weapons experts; the 2¾-inch magnum buckshot is a good standard load, and is currently used by many departments.

The standard size for most of this century has been 00. However, there are some authorities who feel that smaller sizes might be more effective for police work. Several Federal agencies have standardized on No. 4 buckshot, which contains twenty-eight pellets of about .24 caliber in a regular shell. The reduced potency of each individual pellet is compensated for by a denser pattern. As a rule of thumb, five of the nine projectiles in a standard 00 round will strike a man-size silhouette at forty yards; with No. 4, a single blast will deliver fifteen or more hits. Therefore, beyond point-blank range, the shotgun's stopping effect depends on multiplicity of hits. It's an argument that favors No. 4, and many departments are switching to that size. No. 1 size buckshot with sixteen .30-caliber pellets in a standard shell, is also becoming more popular with police.

At close range, pellet size is less significant, since the shot charge hits *en masse;* that close, even birdshot will create the terrible destructive effect that medical examiners call "the rat-hole wound."

Nevertheless, officers should not be deluded that the shotgun always delivers instant knockdown. In one New York City gun battle, an officer blasted a gunman in the chest at a range of fifteen feet with standard 00 buckshot. The man spun around and raced to the doorway. Another blast caught him full in the back, slamming him forward but not off his feet. As he raced through the door, a second patrolman shot him in the buttocks with a .38, breaking his pelvis and dropping him to the ground. As the first officer approached, the severely wounded felon rolled over and leveled his .32 at the cop's head. The officer fired a third shotgun charge that caught the man square in the chest, flipping him over. The officer still had to kick the pistol out of his hand. At that point, the gunman stood up under his own power, leaned against the wall, and said distinctly, "I've had enough , man. Don't shoot me anymore."

He died in the ambulance. He had taken three full loads of buckshot, any one of which should have neutralized him instantly, yet he was still capable of taking an officer's life, and quite willing to do so. It was incidents like this that led the NYCPD stakeout squad to switch to deer slugs.

The "deer slug" or "rifled slug" weighs seven-eighths to

Winchester Model 1897 pump shotguns are still in use among some police departments, despite having been considered obsolete for decades; a tribute to sound design and lasting workmanship. Note the exposed hammer.

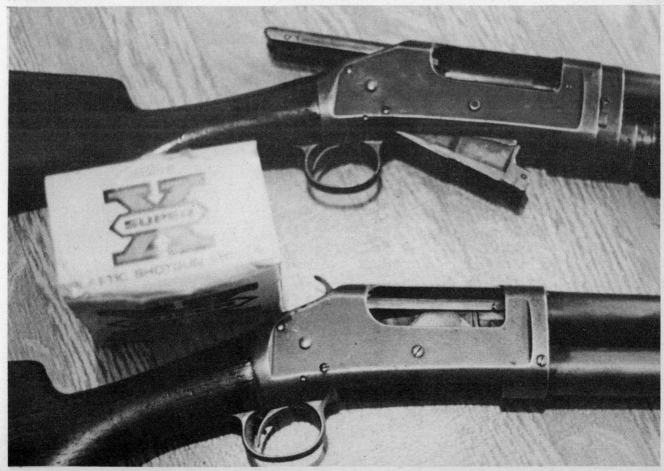

Opposite, from left, Federal 37mm tear gas gun; Remington Model 11; Ithaca Mag-10 Roadblocker and a pair of Remington 870R police guns.

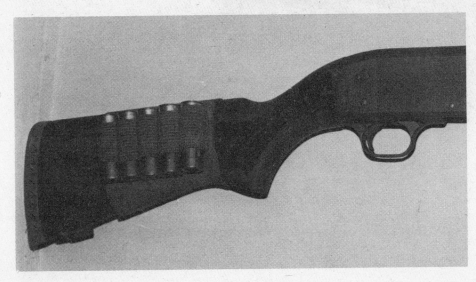

Above, Remington 870 is popular because of twin action bars; barrel removes easily for cleaning. Below, left, Perry Ammo Sling on Ithaca Model 37 riot gun carries spare shells.

a full ounce, and is the equivalent of .729 caliber. Within its range, it delivers substantially more impact than a .30/30 hunting rifle. It has the greatest auto body and barricade penetration of all shotgun rounds, yet is not likely to completely penetrate a human body, since its wide cross section packs up matter in front of it, retarding its speed. This ammunition in a shotgun with proper sights gives the officer carbine capability within reasonable urban combat distances.

Birdshot is issued occasionally. Its principal function is crowd dispersal. Theoretically, it is fired at an angle on the pavement a distance in front of the advancing mob, bouncing the tiny pellets up into their legs with just enough power to sting. The mild impact, plus the psychological fear that they are being fired on, has broken up crowds in the past. However, this is an extremely dangerous strategy for several reasons:

(a) A buckshot round could accidentally get mixed in with the fine birdshot, and the ricocheting .33-caliber projectiles could cause severe or fatal wounds.

(b) A nervous officer may fire prematurely or miss, sending his load of birdshot not against the pavement but directly into the faces of the crowd, causing severe eye damage or fatalities.

(c) Giving the crowd the impression that they are being fired on with lethal firepower may have an opposite effect, enraging them to the point where they overwhelm the police line.

(d) In the one-dimensional eye of the television camera, such an action seems the epitome of police brutality.

Birdshot has no real place in law enforcement work. Modern science has given us a far more humane and effective arsenal of crowd control weapons.

Another load to be considered is the 12-gauge tear-gas round typified by the AAI Ferret. Surprisingly effective, it still shouldn't be standard equipment unless all officers are equipped with gas masks, and are highly trained with tear gas in general and this round in particular.

There is a hot controversy in New York, Boston, Hartford, and a host of other major cities. The PBA leaders claim that they are at a lethal disadvantage when they confront increasingly heavily armed criminals with nothing in their own hand but a service revolver. Departmental administrations argue that injuries to bystanders will occur

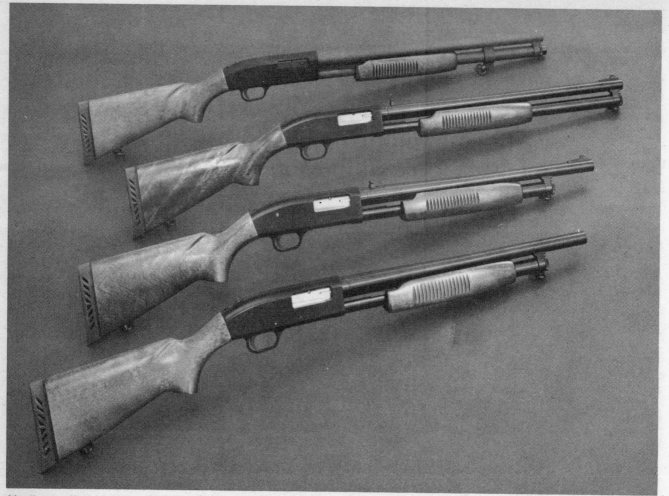

*Mossberg calls their lineup of police shotguns the Model 500 Persuaders. From the top, here are the 20",
8-shot, non-glare Model 500 ATP-8SP; the 20", 8-shot M500 ATP-8S with rifle sights; the 18½", 6-shot
M500 ATP-6S; and the M500 ATP-6, the last two differing by inclusion of rifle sights or plain bead type.*

if the officers increase the volume of firepower in an urban
shootout. Minority groups claim that the presence of a
shotgun in a cruiser is an implicit threat of brutality.

In terms of street survival capability, the working cops
have an overriding point. It is suicide for one or two
officers with .38s to challenge a three to five-man robbery
team equipped with sawed-offs and fully automatic
weapons. Reluctant administrators keep worrying about
where all that police buckshot is going to go, but a trained
officer is less likely to miss with his shotgun than with his
sidearm.

The real danger to the public is from the heavily armed
gunmen who will spray their firepower carelessly if the
officers don't have the combat equipment and experience
to stop them instantly. Moreover, a felon with a shotgun
knows he has a deadly edge against a pistol-armed cop, and
is more likely to shoot it out with him. There is an
excellent chance that he would surrender rather than trade
shots with a patrolman who commands as much firepower
as he.

On the other hand, the administrators are correct in

feeling that an accident with a shotgun is more serious than
one with a revolver and, perhaps, more likely to occur.
Easier to shoot accurately because of its length and
two-handed control, the shotgun is still more complex to
handle. Even in departments with annual or bi-annual
shotgun qualification, we still hear of officers who have
accidentally left a round in the chamber when returning the
gun to the cruiser, or who touched off a wild shot while
unloading the weapon in the street or car. These incidents
can be prevented only by constant familiarization.

The best approach is that taken by the Los Angeles
Police Department. At the beginning of every tour, the
officer checks out a shotgun, loads it, locks it in the car,
then does the reverse at the end of the shift. This promises
two things: the weapons are constantly checked and
cross-checked to assure that they're in safe conditions of
carry, and the officers handle them so often that the
movements become second nature. All departments with
cruiser guns should at least require that the weapon be
inspected at the beginning of each tour.

The complaints of minority groups may seem

exasperatingly unreasonable to the police, but are still a problem to be dealt with and can easily be solved. In such an atmosphere, the department need only install the weapons in an inconspicuous place, beneath the seat or in the trunk.

From the strict viewpoint of combat readiness, the handiest place for the police shotgun is in the front seat by the dash, muzzle up, loaded and locked. It's quickly accessible to either officer in the front seat. Quickest is the Lecco Lock, which is released electrically by a hidden button under the dashboard. A disadvantage is that the ignition must be on. Also, a subject in the front seat may be able to find the button and gain control of the weapon. The Lecco apparatus may also obstruct the glove compartment.

There are free-standing front seat racks available that solve all these problems: they lock with a key. The S&W system is an excellent example. In fast-breaking situations, however, the gun is slower to clear since the cop has to fumble for a key.

There are racks available which place the shotgun horizontally on the mesh cage that separates front and back seats. However, this position may be inconvenient to both

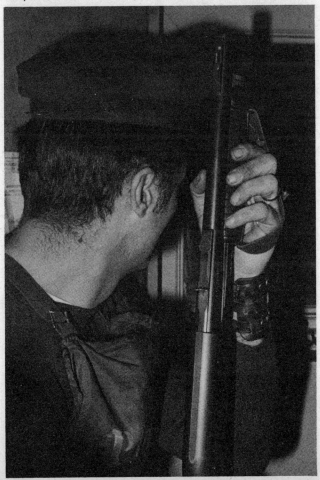

This member of NYCPD Stakeout Squad was photographed in 1972 on duty in Harlem. He's wearing a Davis bulletproof vest, carries a 14" Ithaca pump shotgun and two revolvers.

front seat cops, and is the most blatantly visible display of police firepower.

The gun may be carried horizontally against the lower edge of the front seat. Butt should be to the left in a solo patrol vehicle, to the right in a two-man sector car. S&W's horizontal key lock works well for this kind of discreet carry, and the gun is as quickly accessible as in the stand-up model. In wet weather, though, the officers' shoes may splash rain and slush onto the weapon. It can be carried in a protective boot, but this often interferes with quick removal, and the boot is difficult to lock effectively. Perhaps the best such approach would combine the horizontal S&W lock with a light, flexible carrying case, open along the top for quick clearance.

Carrying the shotgun in the trunk is the safest method, and the only one that allows the passenger compartment to be left unlocked when the cruiser is unattended. Unfortunately, it defeats one of the main purposes of putting such a weapon in the vehicle in the first place: instant equalization of firepower in sudden combat situations. When the radio is yelling for you to respond, it's hard to justify taking half a minute or more to break out your primary weapon.

Ayoob acquired a sample of every leading brand of police shotgun, and all but the Ithaca were equipped with rifle-type sights.

Remington Model 870 — Four-shot magazine capacity, crossbolt (push-button) safety located behind trigger, extended magazine and folding stock available as options, or as bolt-on accessories to departments already owning the basic gun.

The Remington was the handsomest in our test battery, probably because it was the commercial model. The recoil pad is useful in police work, and the high gloss RKW stock finish isn't just for looks: the same type of finish is used on bowling pins. Highly resistant to scratches and dents, it is worth considering in a heavy-duty police gun even though it costs a few dollars more.

Remington is known for its smooth, positive action; while most pump guns have a single slide operating bar on one side of the action, the Remington has twin bars. Our sample gun was a bit rough, though by no means objectionably so. Trigger pull was excellent: crisp, clean and light. The rifle-type sights have a white diamond on the rear leaf and a gold bead front for dim-light visibility. Accuracy was excellent, despite the fact that the detachable barrel was a trifle loose.

Ithaca Model 37 — Known as the Model 10 in police configuration, this sample was near-new, and owned by a department (all other guns in the test were furnished by the factory, but Ithaca was too heavily back-ordered to spare one.) A Parkerized gray finish seems to resist rust well, but scratches easily. The Ithaca is the choice of departments like New York City and Los Angeles and, until recently, was the standard of quality in the industry. Demand has strained production and quality control, however; recent samples don't seem up to par in fit and workmanship. The sample failed repeatedly to eject, with both standard and magnum ammo: the officer could get off one or two rounds, then the weapon would jam with the ejected shell not quite clearing the chamber. Some jams could be cleared with a very forceful pull on the slide; some required that the shell be pried clear with a pocket knife.

Although it has a great many natural advantages for police use, the pump shotgun can be awkward from the barricade.

The Ithaca ejects out the bottom rather than to the side, making it better for left-handed officers. Safety is a crossbolt behind the trigger. On the rifle-sighted models, a red plastic Raybar front sight is used for maximum visibility. Extended magazine is available; standard capacity is four shells. Delivery may be delayed, since police production over the next year or more is said to be already allocated. One danger on the Ithaca is that it can discharge automatically if pumped while the trigger is being held back. The Ithaca should be ordered with the optional trigger disconnector, standard on all other guns tested. Reputation is good; we hope our sample was an isolated lemon.

High Standard Model 8113 — This model comes standard with extended magazine and rifle sights. Along with the Remington, our sample had the best trigger pull in the batch. Safety is a crossbolt in front of the trigger, where

it can be easily and quickly released without changing hand position.

Action was the smoothest of any gun in the tests. The criterion for judging a really smooth slide action is to hold the gun vertical, cocked on an empty chamber, and press the slide release. If the action is really slick, the slide handle will drop down by itself. Only the High Standard passed this test.

Smith & Wesson Model 916 — The S&W is made on equipment that used to turn out the Massachusetts-made Noble shotguns. A lot of stampings and other production economies are used. Nevertheless, it's a rugged little weapon, unusually accurate with deer slugs, because the barrel is fixed rather than interchangeable, an attribute shared by the High Standard. The six-shot magazine is standard.

The safety is a sliding button atop the frame, in the

manner of a double-barrel shotgun. This is an excellent feature in a police weapon: on or off position is readily determined by look or feel, and the release is equally accessible to left-handed officers. Recoil pad is standard, and the gun will accept three-inch magnum shells.

The trigger is the worst of the lot in terms of sporting use, but possibly the best for police. It's a long, creepy pull that requires deliberate movement of the trigger finger.

One disadvantage was that our sample could not be emptied via the magazine: there is no shell release latch, and the gun had to be unloaded by pumping each round through the mechanism, an unprofessional procedure.

Savage Model 30 — This gun shares S&W's three-inch chambering and top-mounted thumb safety, and the Remington's white-diamond sights. The rear sight folds down, an undesirable feature because the sight can be flattened accidentally, becoming invisible when needed. Savage has a very small piece of the police market, but the Model 30 is an adequate cruiser shotgun. The twenty-two-inch barrel of the rifle-sighted model is a bit long for practicality, however, and the gun should be fitted with a recoil pad, as should any police shotgun.

Like the S&W, the Savage is a police-modified version of an economy-grade shotgun, while Remington, Ithaca, and High Standard are medium-priced lines in their sporting versions. Price spreads are not quite so wide in the police models, since all law enforcement shotguns came with standard finishes, etc.

Many feel that officers should be required to inspect their police shotguns prior to commencing tour of duty so as to maintain the intimate familiarity with the individual gun's operation that can be so vital in times of stress.

This Big Gauge Is Just The Ticket For Road Blocking In Some Areas!

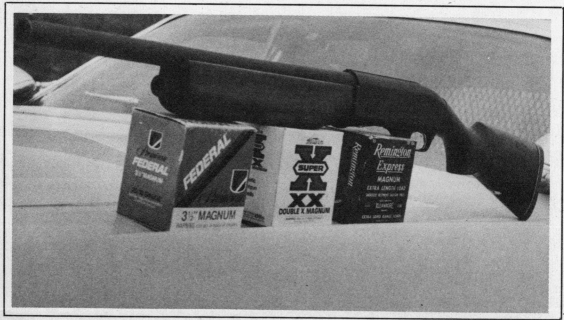

Above: The Ithaca 10-gauge magnum Roadblocker was tested with three brands of factory ammo.
Right: The Model 37 Featherlight 12-gauge (left) is compared with the 10-gauge model discussed here.

THE ROADBLOCKER is the law enforcement version of Ithaca's Mag-10 shotgun. The name tagged to the short-barrel model seems to match the product well.

Chambered for the 3½-inch, 10-gauge magnum round and fitted with a twenty-inch barrel, it is most formidable. The gun sent to us by Ithaca was well fitted and functioned well. One drawback, we felt at first, was the three-round capacity for the magazine. This problem was not serious, as field testing proved. Weight was another consideration until thoughts were given to actual use.

Ithaca touts the Mag-10 as being the first 10-gauge gas auto in the world. They also have an operational lifetime warranty which is somewhat limited but still covers a bundle and that is unusual in the times about us. Fitted with an exclusive stainless steel gas system called Countercoil and other stainless steel parts, the warranty

cards should lie dormant in the files at Ithaca. The Countercoil system does a very effective job of cutting recoil and muzzle whip. Three controlled, rapid-fire shots were the rule and not the exception. The thick recoil pad soaks up a lot of black and blue, also.

In the field, the Mag-10 Roadblocker did just what it was designed to do. Functioning with Federal and Winchester ammunition was flawless and the gun tied every bale. While in Idaho, Elmer Keith was kind enough to give us a box of 10-gauge shells and jamming became apparent. Later it was determined that the age of the ammunition itself may have been part of the problem. Fresh ammunition fed and functioned with no hitches whatever.

This gun is big and it is heavy. Overall length is one-eighth-inch short of being forty-two inches long. The receiver is nine inches long. According to postal scales, the gun weighs ten pounds, eight ounces, empty. Loaded with

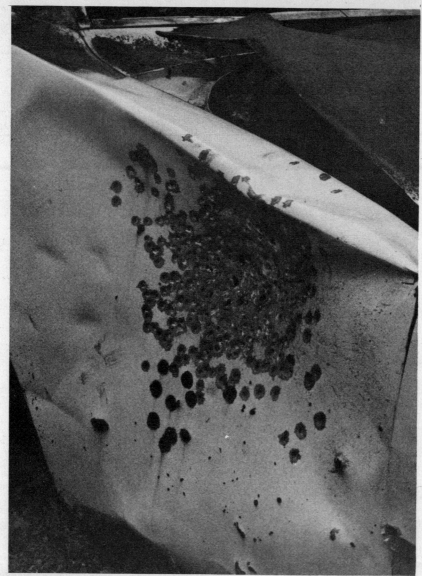

In actual tests in Wyoming, it was found that a load of Number 4 shot, fired at twenty-five feet will stop an automobile. Of note is the tightness of the pattern.

three rounds of number four shot it tips eleven pounds one-half ounce. The buttstock has a small oval sticker — which can be removed — that tells the customer that genuine American walnut was used. The wood on the test gun was tight and evenly grained. An oil finish was used and it sets off the darker, military type finish used on the barrel, receiver, forend nut and trigger guard. The charging handle, bolt, follower, bolt release and trigger guard are left polished. The buttstock is well designed to fit the average shooter and the forend is comfortable and hand filling.

The Roadblocker is designed and will fill the bill for special occasions. It was not designed to be carried by policewomen checking parking meters, although many female law enforcement personnel could use it with no problem. This gun has no function better than that for which it was named: roadblocks. The amount of shot which can be accurately placed in just a heartbeat is awesome.

Airport security could benefit from this shotgun. Barricaded subjects could be exposed easily with this gun. There are other situations which would benefit from the size, design and caliber of the Roadblocker.

Three shots, from twenty-five feet, took the entire open door off an abandoned, junked, 1959 automobile. This was accomplished with the use of BBs but number two and number four shot also proved effective. The field tests were done from many angles and distances. Never was a fourth shot needed to accomplish damage that would have stopped any vehicle. At thirty-five yards, a heavy, late model automobile still sustained enough damage to have stopped it. Three shots into the right front fender, shredded the right front tire, tore the radiator into scrap and ruined the entire carburetor system. This damage would have stopped even the most exit-minded individual.

Many police officers distrust semiautomatic firearms,

with barely an exception. In a life and death situation, any malfunction could be the last function. After 140 rounds of all available brands of ammunition were shot, it was found that the Ithaca Roadblocker was as dependable as any peat burner. It restores a batch of faith in a product that is American made and distributed. No malfunctions of any kind were experienced. Although the enclosed instruction brochure warns of fouling, this was not found to be a problem. The Roadblocker comes equipped with a brass bristle brush fitted to the gun.

Although specialized by its very weight and size, the Roadblocker does have other practical applications. One of the drawbacks is the cost of the ammunition. Most law enforcement departments are handicapped by meager budgets. Prices are nearly double that of comparative twelve-bore ammunition.

While not favorable for those who hold the purse strings, the cost of the ammunition can be offset with field tests which show the effectiveness of the Roadblocker. An adage which states that one pays for what one gets certainly applies to the 3½-inch 10-gauge scattergun.

There is a formula for finding the foot-pounds of energy delivered by a particular shot charge at forty yards. This was not undertaken but may be of benefit for some. Actual damage at various distances would seem to be the true test. Tests which determine the amount of shot which is placed on paper at forty yards, inside a thirty-inch circle were not obtained either. When a shotgun will blow the entire windshield out of an automobile, at fifty yards, the gun should be deemed serviceable for law enforcement work.

The Roadblocker must be used with 3½-inch magnum shells only. To load it, the first step is, as always, to point the gun in a safe direction. Engage the safety which is just behind the trigger, in the trigger guard itself. Pull the charging handle back to open the action. Place one shell directly into the chamber. Depress the carrier release below the ejection port to close the chamber. Two more shells may then be inserted into the magazine.

The Roadblocker is packed, from the factory, in a fitted styrofoam package. The shotgun itself is taken down to permit a small size parcel. Assembly is goof-proof. First, inspect the bore and clean it. Unscrew the forend nut and take the forend off the receiver assembly. Pull the charging handle back to lock the action open. Insert the barrel into the receiver and listen for a metallic click. When you hear this, the barrel is fully seated. Put the forend back on, replace the forend nut and screw it down hand tight. Take-down is just as easy and this system really shines when it is time to clean and inspect the duty firearms.

The Roadblocker is impressive and does have a place in law enforcement. From the brass bead front sight to the Presentation model Pachmayr recoil pad, it is every bit of mean, designed to do a job. In a 3½-inch, 10-gauge magnum, the wad alone is nearly the diameter of a 12-gauge shotshell.

The Ithaca Mag-10 Roadblocker seems aptly named, since its primary function, based upon design, is to stop vehicles that seek to crash law enforcement roadblocks. It was found that fresh ammunition should be a precaution in use.

Chapter 13

RUGER'S MINI-14

This .223 Law Enforcement Carbine Incorporates New Ideas And Innards In A Proven Exterior

THE RUGER MINI-14 carbine originally was created in 1973 for use by official police and government agencies, both domestic and foreign. A carbine featuring military sights, plus a basic military configuration, cannot really be considered a top choice for those who hunt woodchuck, coyote, wolf, fox or bobcat, the species representing the game most often collected with the .223 caliber. However, thousands also are in the hands of civilians, here and abroad.

Since we had long been familiar with Ruger's interest in the law enforcement market for the Mini-14, it made sense to utilize the help that could be provided by the personnel of an active, modern police department. Bob Zwirz serves on occasion as a consultant on matters pertaining to ordnance for law enforcement. In this capacity with the Ridgefield Police Department in Connecticut, he often seeks out their in-the-field judgments as they relate to various firearms and specialized equipment. Nothing is more pertinent than the personal opinions of officers who will actually rely upon the item in question.

Contact with Chief of Police John Haight served to release the department's firearms instructor, Sergeant Robert Brunelle, plus a fully-equipped cruiser for several periods of diversified testing with the Ruger .223. As dictated by problems of space, all equipment carried in such a vehicle must be constructed in such a manner that an item's reliability does not suffer from the need for absolute compactness.

Safe and positive securing proved no problem at all with the Mini-14, since overall length of the carbine is 37.25 inches. Barrel length in this case is 18.5 inches. This compactness of the carbine compares favorably to popular shotguns that run anywhere from 38.5 to 40.5 inches, depending on the length of barrel chosen. The only item that can better it, regarding a low-standing profile, would be a standard law enforcement smoothbore equipped with a folding stock; this device scales the unit down to a scant 30.25 inches.

During evaluation sessions, Sergeant Brunelle and Zwirz found that the carbine's weight, with its magazine empty, was exactly 6.4 pounds. Loaded, with twenty rounds, it tipped the scale at 6.9 pounds. There were no problems encountered with hang-ups during the time an officer disengages the carbine and the time required to be out of the cruiser, ready for action. In the case of low-profile cruisers, ease of handling and exiting can prove a more significant problem than with a number of vehicles used in the past — particularly for taller, heavier-framed personnel.

The Mini-14 represents the perfected result of over five years of intensive engineering and testing. And, as you have possibly surmised, it is a gas-operated, box magazine-fed, semiautomatic carbine. It has been designed around the caliber .223 (5.56mm) U.S. military and commercial cartridge.

At a rapid glance, some might feel the Mini-14 is a look-alike of the World War II M-1 Garand, but that is where its similarities end. The Ruger was developed entirely by this group's engineers and is produced solely in the Ruger factories in Connecticut and New Hampshire. However, design of the Mini-14 does incorporate certain basic principles as applied to the Garand breech-bolt locking system.

Above: Police Sergeant Robert Brunelle makes adjustments on the Ruger Mini-14 during initial tests back in 1973. (Below) Others are making magazines for the Mini-14.

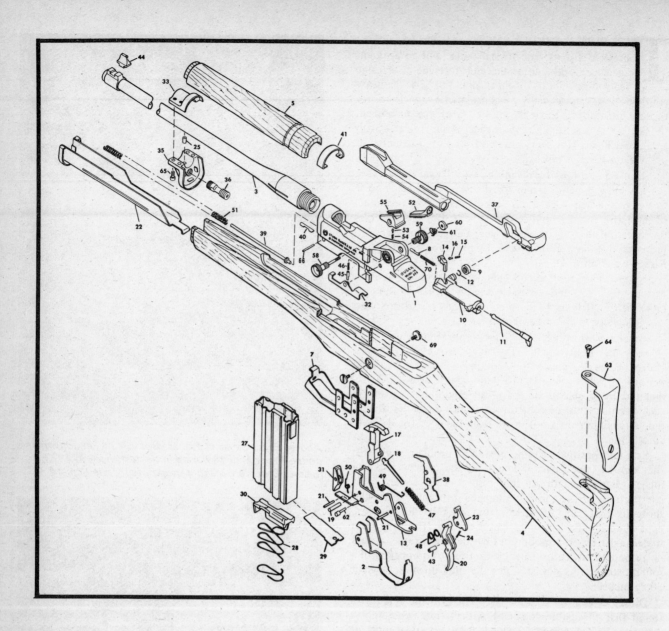

When the Ruger engineering group began laying out drawing board plans for their carbine, they not only restricted themselves to compactness, but to simplicity as well. Sophistication, if you will accept this term as an apt description, lies in the fact that this special purpose carbine is composed of relatively few, extremely rugged components. When field-stripped, you have but eight components laid out in front of you. This is no small bonus when we consider the maintenance problems that often confront a police department armorer.

For those who may ask why Ruger chose to design their system around the .223 military and commercial cartridge, let us answer it with several thoughts.

First, the .223 is readily available as a military load, both here and abroad. Second, it is a commonly available commercial loading. And third, characteristics of the cartridge itself make it a sound choice for specialized situations that apply to such a firearm's use.

Ballistically speaking, the .223 can be classified as an efficient cartridge. It boasts satisfactory flat trajectory, plus

exceptional energy retention at two hundred and even three hundred yards.

Using Remington's 55-grain Power-Lokt hollow-point, you have a muzzle velocity of 3200 feet per second (2010 way out at three hundred yards); foot-pounds of energy at the muzzle gives a reading of 1251. This is still going for you at two hundred yards (700 fpe), and at three hundred yards with around 490 fpe.

Trajectory-wise, when the 55-grain is on at one hundred yards, it will be just 3.5 inches lower at two hundred yards and only a little over a foot low way out at nine hundred feet. When you consider these ballistics facts, bear in mind that our old war-horse, the .30/06, gives us a figure of 2700 fps against the 3200 figure for the .223.

One other especially desirable characteristic of the .223 centers around that matter of high velocity — due to it, a bullet normally can be expected to disintegrate when it strikes a hard surface. Such a characteristic virtually eliminates the bugaboo of ricochet or undesirable penetration. To go one step further, like it or not, recoil with certain calibers is a genuine problem with a great many

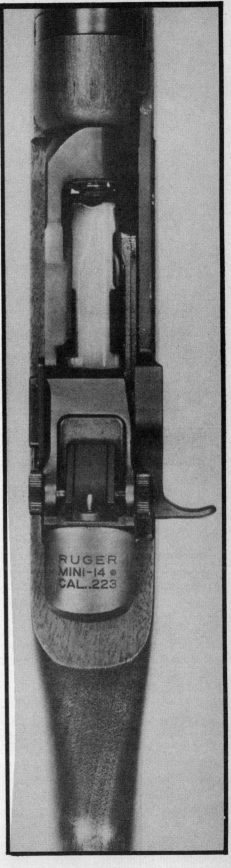

Above: The Mini-14 bears a resemblance to the Garand M-1 rifle of World War II vintage in some respects, but the innards have been simplified. (Below) Ruger's Steve Vogel checks out the carbine with Brunelle during test.

Intricate workmanship of the Mini-14 is visible in this top view of the receiver with the slide retracted.

From top: The Model 20GB was designed specifically for military use; the version just beneath also is for use by the military, but features a ventilated fiberglass hand guard; standard Mini-14 in traditional blued steel; the stainless steel version at bottom affords the carbine more versatility, protects it in bad weather situations.

more shooters than are willing to admit to it. In the case of the .223, the low recoil impulse of this cartridge greatly reduces both shooting and training problems. In fact, the overall conventional appearance and operating features of the Mini-14 go a long way in that department.

From an internal design viewpoint, the Ruger has much going for it. All important are such attributes as minimum breech mechanism length, maximum strength of the breech lock-up, plus, of course, the previously mentioned minimum number of parts and ease of field maintenance. We've also learned that Ruger tests durability repeatedly by standardized test of 10,000 rounds for their Mini-14; all components have been engineered and produced to withstand this test without either experiencing breakage or measurable wear.

Other pertinent construction details of interest to the more knowledgeable gunowner include the following:

1. Magazines for the Mini-14 are available in five or twenty-round capacities.

2. The carbine's gas system is of the fixed piston type. It features low stress and a long stroke slide. It also provides maximum reliability and accuracy and the lowest apparent recoil factor.

3. The 18.5-inch barrel calls for six grooves, right twist;

one turn in twelve inches.

4. Regarding sights, the rear is of the peep type adjustable for elevation and windage in increments of one-minute of angle (one-inch at one hundred yards) by means of readily grasped knobs which produce audible and tactile clicks. The unit is mounted on the rear of the receiver. The front sight calls for a gold bead on a post, mounted in an integral barrel band.

5. As for the safety, which Sergeant Brunelle and Zwirz both liked, it is mounted in front of the trigger guard so that it may be set to Fire position without removing the shooter's finger from the trigger guard. When the safety is set to Safe, the hammer and sear are blocked. However, the slide can be cycled while the safety is on.

6. You'll find that the firing pin is retracted mechanically during the first part of the unlocking of the bolt. Thus, the rifle can only be fired when the bolt is safely locked.

7. The bolt has two massive locking lugs located on either side of the bolt head. An extension of the right locking lug forms the integral bolt roller pivot. The rear of each locking lug mates with a matching gradual camming surface in the receiver on closing, thus providing great force on bolt closing and powerful, non-abrupt primary extraction.

8. The receiver, as mentioned, has a short overall length.

Above: The longer magazine available from Ruger offers greater continuing firepower and is favored by some law enforcement agencies. (Below) Arrows point to the cases that have been ejected during semi-auto fire by Bob Zwirz. The carbine has found broad acceptance both in this country and abroad with police agencies adopting the gun.

The clean lines of the original Mini-14 Ruger carbine have found wide acceptance with collectors and sportsmen, as well as with law enforcement agencies. The addition of other accessories have increased this interest.

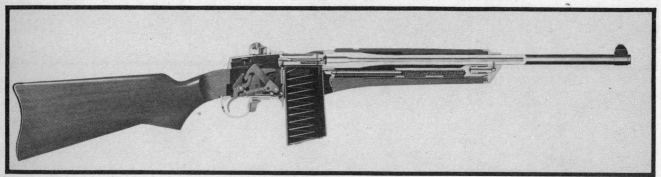

The simplicity of the carbine's design is reflected in this cutaway drawing, which shows the various components of the gun. Comparison with the Garand M-1 and the M-1 carbine ends with the exterior appearance.

The carbine takes on a much more lethal look when it is outfitted with a telescoping stock, hand grip and banana clip. This type of configuration is being sold to military forces in a number of foreign nations today.

It is adequately vented to allow for safe gas escape in event of cartridge failure.

9. The stock is one piece with pistol grip, turned from American walnut. It is reinforced with a steel liner at stressed areas. The wooden handguard and forearm are separated from the barrel by an air space to promote cooling and prevent the possibility of any charring under prolonged rapid-fire conditions.

10. The bolt is held in the open position upon firing of the last round, a feature which is all-important for rapid reloading. The bolt can be closed by either depressing the bolt release, or by pulling back on the operating handle, then releasing on a fresh magazine.

On one of the days when Brunelle and Zwirz were looking over the Mini-14, conditions were close to perfect for some extensive target sessions. These included firing from both kneeling and offhand positions, as well as firing from partial concealment behind the cruiser and other

marginally protective natural screens. Accuracy with the combination of easy-handling rifle/low-recoil cartridge proved to be excellent. There is little recoil. This is a decided plus feature in any kind of firefight. The accuracy of more second and third shots at moving targets is lost, due to poor recovery time on the part of the shooter, than as a result of any other built-in problem.

There was absolutely no disagreement between Sergeant Brunelle and any of those present during the field evaluations when the subject of comparison between the M-1/.30 caliber military carbine and the Mini-14 came up. That there is much similarity in handling and manual operation is at once obvious to both the shooter and the onlooker. However, it cannot be classified as a copy of any earlier rifle.

In both Brunelle's and Zwirz' opinions, it is far more efficient for the purpose intended than would be, as an example, the M-14 military rifle in caliber .308. The Ruger

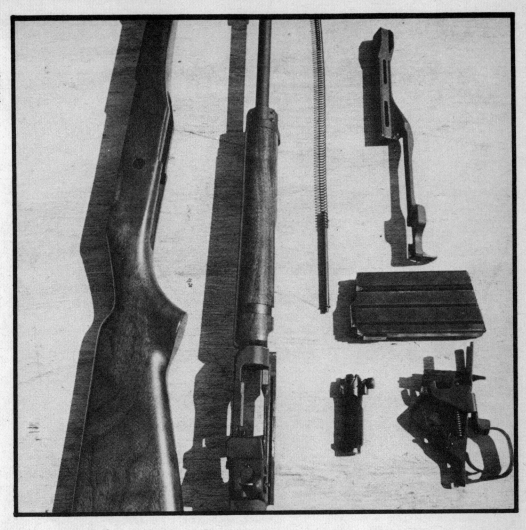

The Ruger-made carbine field strips quickly, illustrating simplicity of the major components.

product tends to make training a minimal chore; that, as stated, includes the speed with which someone new to the Mini-14 can field strip, then reassemble the rifle. Even the trigger pull of the rifles tested made for a no-flinch day. Set for around 4.5 pounds, it lets off the way it should. Law enforcement types should also keep it in mind that, in 5.56mm, they can call out special needs — this includes ball, tracer and blank ammo.

Though some five hundred rounds were run through the carbine, there was never a malfunction of any type.

The year 1979 marked the thirtieth year of existence for Sturm, Ruger & Company. As an innovation in celebration, Bill Ruger introduced a stainless steel version of his Mini-14 carbine. It is a handsome arm available with magazines that hold five, ten, twenty and thirty rounds.

"I can't tell you that shooting a stainless model is different from firing the standard version. And no firearm, whether made of stainless or not, can take saltwater baths for long without showing discoloration. All firearms require care if they are to keep their excellent finish and continue to function freely. Stainless, however, does resist and live a far safer life in the constant vicinity of salt water, high humidity, or bad weather," Zwirz reports.

When several companies began offering scope mounts and other accessories for a sporter-type Mini-14, following

initial introduction in 1973, the carbines were scooped up with a vigor that amazed even Bill Ruger, Sr. At the same time, large orders were being confirmed by several European countries.

The Mini-14 production line has never stopped. Neither have the special configuration designs slowed their pace on the drawing board of Ruger's engineers. Sales have spread to a number of countries that instantly recognized the compactness, effectiveness and dependability. The same is true on this side of the Atlantic. The sale of .223 ammunition (5.56mm) escalated so quickly that factory producers of that caliber had to increase production substantially.

Since its initial introduction, the Mini-14 has shown all manner of special innovations from a steel folding stock and heat resistant, ventilated glass fiber handguard, to a model that some consider a first class infantry arm. This model, the 20GB, is equipped with a rifle grenade launcher, flash suppressor and bayonet stud. The folding stock model, AC556K, has proved ideal for aircraft and armor crews, paratroops, patrol vehicles, dignitary protection and similar applications. With the exception of the standard Mini-14 in semi-auto mode, the selective fire weapons utilize a positive three-position selector lever offering semi-automatic fire, a three-shot burst, or fully automatic fire.

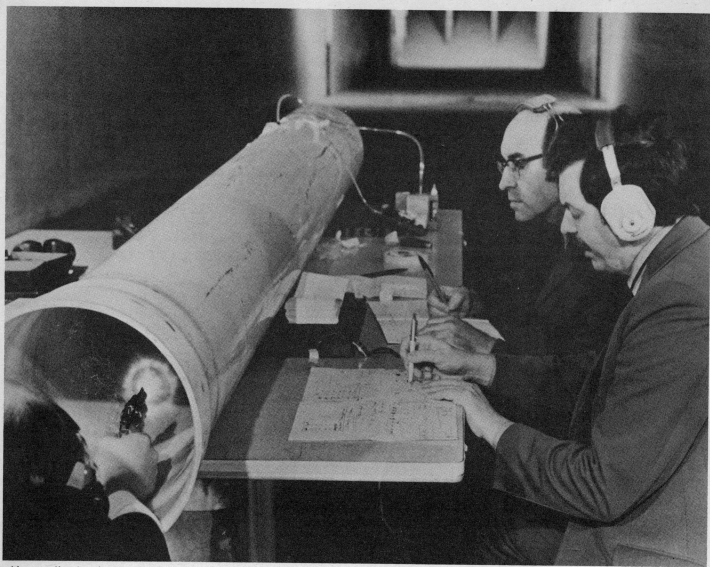

Air sampling by the Mount Sinai School of Medicine found that the Nyclad ammunition emits from 61 to 89 percent less lead and lead components into the air than was the case with comparable samples of standard .38 Special ammo.

WHAT ARE WE DOING ABOUT LEAD POISONING?

Chapter 14

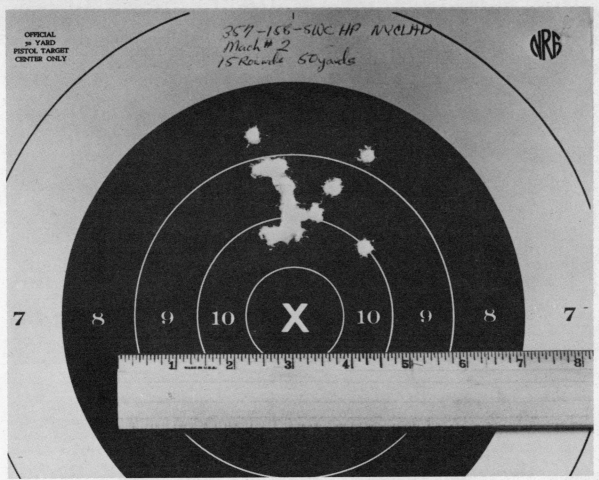

357-158-SWC HP NYCLAD
Mach #2
15 Rounds 50 yards

In factory tests from a machine rest, Smith & Wesson's new Nyclad .357 magnum 158-grain bullet in semi-wadcutter hollow point construction was found to offer accuracy that was considered comparable with standard bullets now being used.

A Serious Threat
To Law Enforcement Instructors,
S&W Has At Least A Partial Solution!

THROUGH AN IN-DEPTH STUDY, researchers have discovered that indoor range air pollution poses a clearly defined health threat to personnel who work in shooting ranges.

The first move has been to close a number of police ranges due to the known health threat. Many civilian ranges have been forced to take the same step, disastrous as it is, financially.

Conducted at the request of Smith & Wesson, the study was undertaken by the Environmental Science Laboratory of the Mount Sinai School of Medicine in New York City. It now is recognized that lead oxide fumes, generated by gunfire, can cause an accumulation of lead in the blood of firearms instructors, maintenance men and shooters. Studies by the National Institute for Occupational Safety and Health found a number of indoor firing ranges in

Recovered after being fired into water, the S&W Nyclad bullets were found to have expansion characteristics that were almost identical to those of conventional lead bullets.

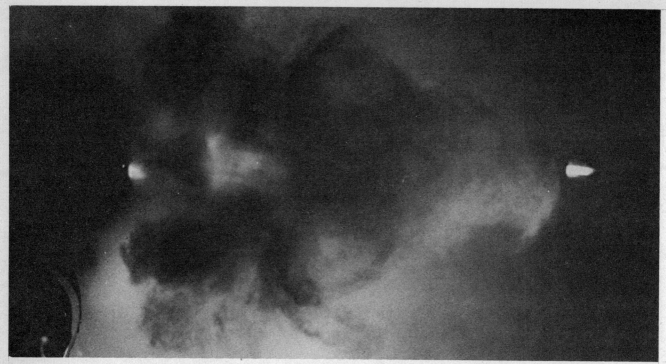

Stroboscopic photo halts bullet in flight, shows amount of smoke generated in firing conventional lead bullet.

violation of existing guidelines relating to exposure to lead in the work-place.

In studying the health effects of exposure to lead in police training ranges, Dr. Alf Fischbein of Mount Sinai found more than half of the eighty-one law enforcement employees tested to have elevated blood lead levels; more than forty micrograms per one hundred milliliters. A series

of tests on sixteen firearms instructors showed eighty-seven percent had blood lead levels below this figure before indoor training began. Afterward, fifty-four percent showed blood lead levels above that figure. Five of six firearms instructors with multiple lead-related symptoms had clear biochemical lead-induced abnormalities.

Environmental surveys of three indoor firing ranges in

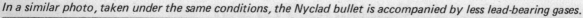

In a similar photo, taken under the same conditions, the Nyclad bullet is accompanied by less lead-bearing gases.

This artist's rendition of a cutaway of the Nyclad cartridge shows that construction is the same as the standard round.

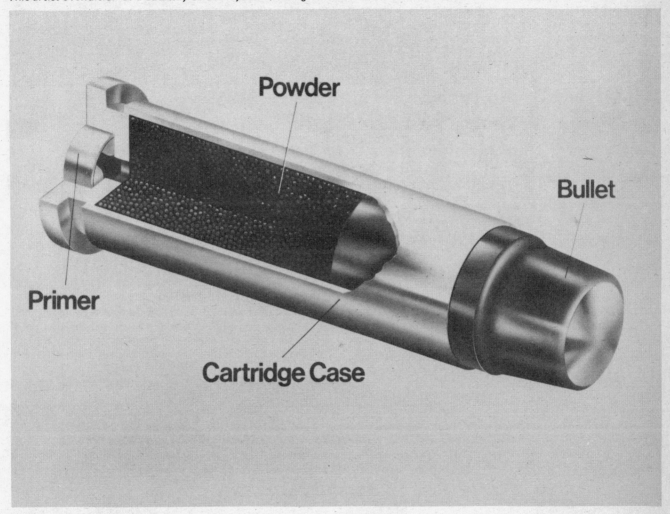

the New York metropolitan area indicated that insufficient ventilation can lead to excessive exposure. In one case this was 4½ times the current standard set by the Occupational Safety and Health Administration. In some cases, such exposure has resulted in clinically observable lead disease.

"Anyone working in an indoor firing range should be tested for lead," Dr. Fischbein says. "Our studies found a strong correlation between blood lead and zinc protoporphyrin (ZPP) levels over the total group. Blood lead levels reflect recent and current lead absorption and may vary considerably with the prevailing exposure. However, ZPP levels represent biological events occurring in the bone marrow. ZPP remains in the red cell over its life of 120 days, so short-term exposure has little effect on ZPP concentration.

In Dr. Fischbein's study, two categories of symptoms were found: Central nervous system symptoms include headache, dizziness, fatigue, weakness, nervousness, irritability and sleeplessness. Of eighty-one individuals examined, twenty-six percent reported such symptoms. Gastrointestinal symptoms were reported by sixteen percent of those tested, and ranged from loss of appetite and weight to abdominal discomfort and pain.

Dr. Fischbein recommends that blood lead and ZPP determinations be included in a medical surveillance program for firearms instructors. He adds that good personal hygiene, work practices and housekeeping are necessary parts of a lead prevention program.

To combat the now-recognized serious hazard, Smith & Wesson has developed a new type of nylon-jacketed bullet that significantly reduces the emission of lead oxide fumes that pollute the air of indoor firing ranges. Nyclad ammunition, in preliminary tests by independent researchers, cuts airborne lead contamination by more than

Nyclad ammo is being packaged in distinctive box. Sample rounds (from left): wadcutter, round nose, semi-wadcutter.

sixty percent when compared with the cleanest of conventional lead bullet ammunition tested.

"These preliminary tests indicate that a police training range, closed because it marginally failed to meet new OSHA standards, might reopen if Nyclad ammunition is used exclusively," says S&W marketing vice-president Robert Hass.

Smith & Wesson Nyclad ammunition prevents much of this lead pollution by shielding the bullet from the hot, expanding gases of the burning powder and the friction of the bullet against the bore as it is pushed through the barrel of the handgun. Lead and lead compounds are emitted into the air when a cartridge is fired. A small part comes from the primer, but most is traced to the effects on the lead

Firing Nyclad bullets into cotton waste material allowed recovery of undamaged samples. Rifling marks are visible on the nylon jacket, with no lead being exposed either on the side or base. Fibers are from the cotton waste material.

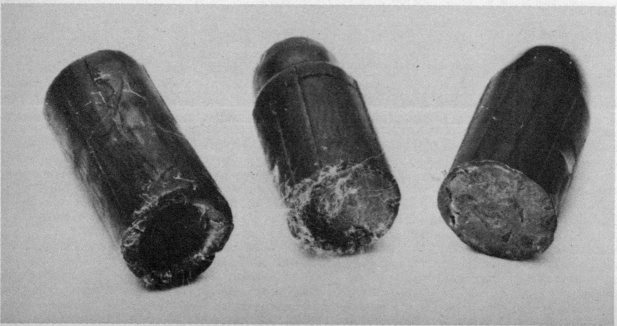

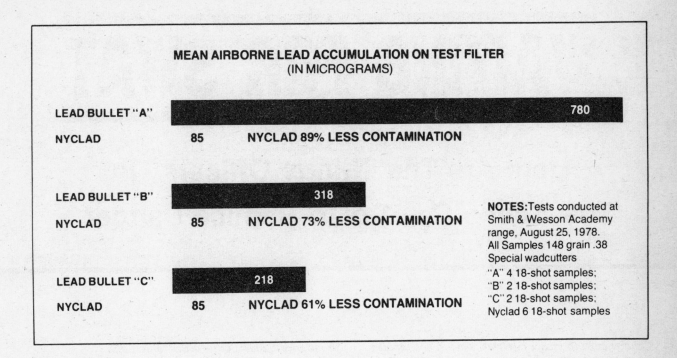

MEAN AIRBORNE LEAD ACCUMULATION ON TEST FILTER
(IN MICROGRAMS)

LEAD BULLET "A"   780

NYCLAD   85   NYCLAD 89% LESS CONTAMINATION

LEAD BULLET "B"   318

NYCLAD   85   NYCLAD 73% LESS CONTAMINATION

LEAD BULLET "C"   218

NYCLAD   85   NYCLAD 61% LESS CONTAMINATION

NOTES: Tests conducted at Smith & Wesson Academy range, August 25, 1978. All Samples 148 grain .38 Special wadcutters
"A" 4 18-shot samples;
"B" 2 18-shot samples;
"C" 2 18-shot samples;
Nyclad 6 18-shot samples

projectile itself.

Hot gases push against the base of the bullet, oxidizing the surface of the lead. Some gas escapes as the bullet passes the gap from the cylinder into the barrel carrying lead contaminants into the air. More escapes as the bullet exits from the muzzle. Some lead is smeared inside the bore as the bullet is pushed down the barrel through the rifling. The hot gases of later shots react with this accumulated lead to add more contamination.

Smith & Wesson engineers knew that metal-jacketed bullets reduced lead contamination, but they were not an acceptable alternative; they are considerably more expensive and more damaging to range facilities than unjacketed lead bullets.

Smith & Wesson developed the process of jacketing the lead bullet with a protective coating of inert nylon that resists the effects of abrasion and hot gases. Ballistic tests showed that the nylon jacket remained intact on the base of the bullets recovered after firing, and that the rifling lands did not cut through the jacket. Recovered bullets consistently showed *no* exposed lead. During these tests it was noticed that the firing of Nyclad ammunition produced little smoke when compared with conventional lead bullet ammunition.

Tests at the independent H.P. White Laboratory in Maryland confirmed that "S&W Nyclad ammunition produces considerably less smoke in both clean bore and fouled bore condition than either of the lead cartridges tested."

Dr. Fischbein, with other scientists, tested emissions of S&W Nyclad ammunition at the S&W Academy range in Springfield, Massachusetts. Firing through a tube from which controlled air samples were taken, Dr. Fischbein found that Nyclad ammunition emitted from sixty-one to eighty-nine percent less lead and lead components than the three comparable samples of conventional .38 Special 148-grain lead wadcutter loads tested. With these early indications, Smith & Wesson hopes to participate in more comprehensive testing at an actual police training range.

In side-by-side tests by Smith & Wesson ballisticians, it is claimed that .357 magnum 158-grain semi-wadcutter loads, fired in identical guns, showed that Nyclad ammunition reduces bore fouling at least seventy-five percent, even at high .357 magnum velocities. It virtually eliminates the problem of bore fouling in .38 Special loads, S&W spokesmen contend. In tests of accuracy and bullet expansion, they found that Nyclad ammunition performs equally as well as comparable conventional loads.

Smith & Wesson is introducing Nyclad ammunition with nylon-jacketed bullets in .38 Special and .357 magnum calibers. Initial production responds to the immediate needs of law enforcement agencies. Additional high performance loads for revolvers and semi-automatics will be added to the Nyclad line in the near future.

Chapter 15

WAITING FOR SWAT

Here Are The Things Officers On The Scene Can Do To Reduce Danger

Counter-ambush tactics rarely involve just one problem. In this instance, a plainclothes officer at left pins down suspected felons in a shopping mall, while patrol officer drags wounded bystander out of the line of fire.

A N INCREASINGLY common tactical problem in law enforcement today is the barricaded felon who has taken hostages. "This is a job for SWAT," you say. It is, but SWAT won't be there until they're mobilized. During that terrifying interval, the officer on the street is the man who has to handle this extremely sensitive and dangerous job.

We discussed the situation with nationally known police weapons and tactics expert Massad Ayoob. His article in *Trooper* magazine titled "What to do While Waiting for SWAT" has become something of a standard training guide in this area. We debriefed him for pointers on how the first patrolmen on the scene should handle such emergencies.

LEHD: To keep it simple, let's take a hypothetical situation: an officer in a patrol car responds to an armed robbery in progress call. When he pulls up to the liquor store where it's going down, the bad guy inside pegs a couple of shots at him and yells, "Stay back, I've got a hostage!" Where does our patrolman go from there?

AYOOB: First behind cover; and second, to his transceiver to call for assistance. Obviously, this is a situation that warrants a specialist team, specifically a Special Weapons and Tactics Unit, and one or more trained hostage negotiators.

But while you're waiting for the specialists, you've got a bombshell ready to explode on you. Analysis of these situations shows that the immediate first moments of the confrontation are the most dangerous. This is when the perpetrator is most excited, most confused, most angry at having been thwarted and cornered by the police.

Practically speaking, the responding patrolman doesn't have the authority or the opportunity to do a whole lot. The patrol supervisor who responds to the officer's call for help is the guy who's going to have to set up the containment ring, the perimeter, the...

LEHD: Wait a moment! Those terms may not be familiar to all our readers.

AYOOB: The containment ring is a circle of strategically placed officers who are ideally under solid cover, well armed and armored. Their function is to closely observe the premises, and to act if the felon attempts to escape. In some departments, this first line is called the "inside perimeter."

Sometimes called "outside perimeter" is the farthest area back from the scene which has been cleared of innocent bystanders. Your case problem involves a liquor store. Unless it turns out that a person inside will have access to a higher floor in the building, it is safe to assume that the hostage-taker inside will be stuck on the street level. This is an extremely important consideration, because how far back you place your outside perimeter is largely dependent on the field of fire the bad guy has. Of course, the higher up he can situate himself, the farther he'll be able to hit someone.

The containment ring should consist of squad car personnel initially, the first to respond after the officer's call. If it develops into a siege, they'll gradually be replaced with properly armed and armored tactical people, if enough are on hand. At least, it's likely that support personnel will make their way up to bring them vests and shoulder arms if they don't have them already.

LEHD: But you say most of this deployment will be made by the patrol sergeant?

This SWAT team, practicing maneuvers, has allowed itself to bunch up on a staircase landing prior to sweep-search of a building. An ambusher with an automatic weapon would have a field day, undoubtedly downing them all.

Two weapons with definite use for SWAT members are H&R Ultra rifle in .22/250 with a high-power telescopic sight, an excelent sniper rifle, and short barrel Dan Wesson .357. Latter compact, versatile and a hard-hitting handgun.

AYOOB: Most of it, but in the initial moments, responding units will be acting on what information they get from the first officer at the scene. This is one of many reasons why the first officer should stay with his vehicle, or someplace where he can observe and relay intelligence on his portable.

If he tries to be a hero and runs in to take care of it himself, he's not only likely to get himself and some innocent people shot, but his backup officers won't know what the hell is going on. It'll wind up looking like a Chinese fire drill, and a lot of officers will be put in the line of fire unnecessarily.

The first officer is the eyes and ears of the whole police response to the problem in those vital moments. He should speak calmly and clearly into the transceiver, and give directions as to how incoming backup should approach. But there are questions he must ask himself: Where will they be in the line of fire? What exits are there behind the target building that must be sealed immediately? How far out from the target building should responding patrol cars block intersections and begin to seal off the outside perimeter? No one is in a better position to dispense this immediately vital information than the first officer.

LEHD: What about evacuating the innocents?

AYOOB: True evacuation is a large-scale effort. Once the supervisor arrives, he can assemble the manpower to coordinate it just as the police do at fire scenes.

It's a touchy question as to whether the first officer should attempt to do this with his squad car public address system. Depending on the circumstances, he might wish to go on the public address mike and say, "Take cover. This is a police emergency. If you are between X Street and Y Street, go inside and take cover immediately."

The trouble is, that big voice coming from nowhere might just drive another frightened bystander into the liquor store to be taken hostage. It's up to the officer's own judgment as to the location, how many people are around, whether he feels more gunfire is likely. You don't want to add to the confusion and create panic.

LEHD: Should the initial officers on the scene attempt to make contact with the hostage-taker? Should they try to cut his phone lines so he won't be able to make any grandstanding calls to newspapers and television stations? Or should they just wait for the negotiators?

AYOOB: Once the scene is under control — that is, a containment ring and outside perimeter are in place — several minutes have probably elapsed. The feeling among the experts is that the sooner the police make a positive contact with the felon, the better.

I say positive contact because a negative contact can cost the lives of every hostage inside. Such would be the case when some cowboy gets on the horn and tells the felon, "Come out with your hands up or we're coming in," or maybe, "If you kill the hostages, you die, too!"

LEHD: Why are such warnings negative?

AYOOB: Because you're probably talking about a real loser in there; a frightened, angry, unstable person who is in a very strung-out emotional state. He sees all these police cars outside, he has these terrified people inside whimpering while he holds a gun on them. It may be the first real sensation of power and importance he's ever had in his life, and here you are challenging him to use it. There's a good chance he'll kill a hostage just to prove he's as much a man as the big-mouth cop with the megaphone.

LEHD: What's a positive contact, then?

AYOOB: Don't use a loudspeaker if you can avoid it. Your message can get garbled, and that bigger-than-life voice is threatening and frightening. What you want to do is get this guy calmed down.

Your best bet is to get to the nearest telephone and dial right into that liquor store. Don't ask to talk to "the punk with the gun," ask for "the man in charge."

LEHD: Isn't that something the hostage negotiators can do?

AYOOB: It depends how quick they're going to be there. The New York City Police Department has an extensive staff of trained negotiators, so one will usually be on the scene in a matter of minutes. But most departments

In a training problem, the pseudo felon overpowers the police officer during a standard check-out situation.

Once free of the officer he has overpowered, the pseudo villain in this exercise flees, firing as he runs.

After the felon has escaped, he has taken cover in an old house for purposes of the problem in police work.

have only a few people with training, and it can take an agonizingly long time to get one to the scene. In the meantime, you've got an unknown quantity stewing in there, waiting to blow up.

An initial contact can usually be made safely, so long as the discussion is kept very gentle, and very general.

In this way, the police can help to freeze the action, to calm things down until the professional negotiating team arrives. It can also give the officers a better and quicker handle on whom they're dealing with, how many criminals and hostages are inside, and whether anyone is injured. Besides, it distracts a panicked robber from any acts of violence he might have been about to commit on the hostages.

LEHD: How do you feel about the philosophy of severing, or at least controlling, phone lines from the hostage site, to frustrate the hostage taker's efforts to get publicity, say in a terrorist situation?

AYOOB: Frustrate is the right word. This used to be a standard tactic, but they're getting away from it now. Dr. Harvey Schlossberg, the now-retired NYCPD police psychologist who is the father of modern hostage negotiation work, is now of the opinion that letting these people talk to the media is a *good* idea. It's a safety valve, and it's one more thing to bargain with. Besides, once phone lines are cut, it's a hell of a job to reestablish them for the negotiators. It's best to have a police supervisor call the phone company and have it done from their end, which takes a minimum of half an hour.

LEHD: A lot of people think that it's bad police work to let a hostage-taker talk to the press, because it results in publicity that could trigger some other nut to go out and do the same thing.

AYOOB: There's something to that, but the individual officer's main responsibility is to control the situation at hand. Besides, Schlossberg makes a very interesting point on this: when someone does get on television holding a hostage, he usually makes such a complete idiot of himself that even the sickies don't want to emulate him.

LEHD: Let's get back to how the responding officer should negotiate with the barricaded gunman.

AYOOB: Well, he shouldn't negotiate per se; that's a job for experts. What he's doing with that initial contact is just calming things down, and opening the door for the hostage negotiators who, hopefully, will soon be arriving.

LEHD: What about situations that occur in small towns or rural areas, where this sort of thing hasn't been anticipated, and there are no hostage negotiators or SWAT teams?

AYOOB: When the SWAT concept first became popular in the early Seventies, a lot of little departments tried to form their own, and found that a small agency simply can't support such a unit, either tactically or financially. Since then, there has been a trend toward more reliance on county and state police for this service, or a mutual assistance pact with the nearest large force that has a tactical unit. You're also seeing "cooperative" teams being formed by three to six or more contiguous small departments, using one or two men from each. This brings its own set of logistical problems, but at least is more affordable in terms of dollars and manpower.

LEHD: What about training a hostage negotiator for the small department?

AYOOB: NYCPD has the best training available. Lt. Frank Bolz, head of their hostage negotiation unit, has done more of these jobs than anyone else in the world, and he's never lost a hostage, nor has one of his people ever had to kill a perpetrator. Schlossberg, who trained Bolz, is now going across the country lecturing to police departments. Smith & Wesson Academy has just introduced a hostage negotiation program. I believe it's now part of the SWAT training program at the FBI Academy.

LEHD: Should the SWAT unit itself have a negotiator on the team?

AYOOB: All members of a well trained SWAT team will have some training in negotiation, and very often, one of their people will be the main negotiator. The problems with that are, one, you're taking a man away from another function on the team, and two, it's likely to wind up that the negotiator will also be the SWAT team squad leader. You're pulling that pivotal officer in two directions with two sets of responsibilities: you're asking him to try to convince the suspect in one breath that he is his friend, while at the same time he may be waving the "green light" signal at the sniper to blow this guy's head off.

I do tend to feel that the negotiator should be a police officer instead of an outside psychiatric professional. At the same time, a small town chief may be better off going with a local psychologist with whom he has made a previous agreement to consult in such cases.

LEHD: What advice do you have for the patrolman out there manning the containment ring?

AYOOB: He should remember that he is in as much danger of getting killed as the hostages. Experience teaches us that the longer the bad guy is cooped up with his victims, the more rapport they'll develop and the less likely it is that the hostages will be killed. The bad guy develops no such warm feelings for those cops outside. In the Siege of Brownsville in New York, where terrorists had taken over a sporting goods store, one well equipped officer peered out from behind his patrol car once too often, and one of the gunmen put a rifle slug through his head.

The biggest single mistake patrolmen seem to make at a barricade scene is to assume that the gunman is locked in the same place where he was last spotted. On the contrary, that guy is going to be moving around inside as much as he possibly can. If he can go higher, he will. The officer who wants to keep his head on his shoulders should constantly scan every window, every door, every shrub around the foundation of the building. And he should stay well behind cover, just darting his head out to peek, and from a different angle each time, if that is possible.

I really wish someone would come out with a decent hand-held periscope. It would keep a lot of policemen's heads out of a lot of criminal gunsights.

Again, it's extremely important for the first officer to

With the practice felon holed up in the abandoned house, officers use tear gas projectiles to bring him out.

Members of the New York City Police Department took part in this actual stakeout in Harlem. Officer partially hidden by support post carries two revolvers, a 14-inch Ithaca pump-action shotgun, and wears Davis bulletproof vest. All were standard equipment for the department's stakeout squad, which since has been disbanded.

request backup teams to seal off escape avenues. There are numerous situations where a SWAT team will arrive at a scene, sweat it our for hours, and finally break in to find that the bad guys sneaked out the back moments after it all started, while all the patrol cops were parked out front where the action had been focused.

It is vitally important that all police personnel at the scene, especially those in close, be either uniformed or readily identifiable as law officers. The situation is probably going to wind up with a lot of cops drawn in from other agencies or precincts, and you can't rule out a tragic shooting caused by mistaken identity.

There are little tricks, too. For instance, the topography may be such that ground floor on the east side of the target building is the lobby, but ground floor on the west side is the basement. Thus, if an officer covering the east side says into his radio, "There's movement on the third floor," the officers in back will be focusing their attention on what is actually the second floor. It's better to count floors down from the top of the building when transmitting such information.

LEHD: What about special weaponry for barricade and hostage-type sieges?

AYOOB: The first thing you do is rule out certain weapons. You don't want pyrotechnic-type tear gas delivery, because if the gas only drives the criminals and hostages deeper in the building, it's soon likely to be on fire. I think AAI's nonflammable 38mm Ferret barricade-penetrating projectile with an invisible-vapor CS gas payload is as close to ideal as you're going to get.

Shotguns are tricky in any situation involving hostages. Buckshot spreads too much and ricochets too much, and rifled slugs have a nasty tendency to exit the felon's body

with enough power to kill a hostage behind him. Ditto the .308 sniper rifle. The .223 with soft points is probably ideal. New York City has had excellent luck with it, and so has the Los Angeles Police Department SWAT. In fact, one of two cases I know of in which a SWAT officer actually shot a suspect out from behind a hostage, was done by an LA team member with one round from an AR-15 at medium-close range from the front. The other was in Texas, and the SWAT officer's weapon was a Browning Hi-Power pistol with a 9mm Glaser Safety Slug, from behind. These were classic examples of professional police marksmen using special purpose weapons in situations where there was no other way to save the hostage's life, which both these officers did.

LEHD: What about armor?

AYOOB: Most SWAT officers have shell-type vests, heavy units designed to stop .30/06 armor piercing. I personally think that a standard Second Chance is often a better bet. The New York cop shot in Brownsville was wearing a heavy vest, and it's possible that the sniper spotted it through the crosshairs and shot him in the head for that reason.

With the Second Chance, you can get a K-47 insert that stops anything short of black-tip .30/06 armor piercing. It slips right into the vest, and the advantage is that the first officer can shove it into his regular vest through his shirtfront, and a SWAT officer making the final assault can have it on under his fatigues or coveralls where the bad guy won't see it. The majority of barricaded felon and hostage situations involve handguns and shotguns that are defeated by conventional Second Chance or equivalent soft armor, which a wise patrolman will already be wearing anyway, before he even gets that first call.

LEHD: Any final advice for that first, responding officer?

AYOOB: His greatest contribution to the overall effort is going to be the way he directs the initial police response to the situation. He should make a point of knowing the entrance and egress points of every building in his patrol sector, so he can direct the first wave of backup officers to the proper containment ring positions. He should already be wearing concealed armor, because he'll probably never have time to don a vest once he gets there.

One problem that should be faced up to before it ever happens involves the rural or small town agency. As you know, there is often a bit of rivalry between state and local and county police, and there have been some very frightening situations that went down because a local officer was too proud to call on a bigger outfit for help. As one commander told me after he had royally screwed up an operation because he hadn't called for state police assistance, "Those damn troopers grab all the credit; *that's* why we didn't call 'em!" Only a miracle kept a young officer from being killed in that botched operation, which would have been handled much more smoothly by the state police SWAT team that should have been called in to deal with it.

Admittedly, that's not something the individual cop has much control over. In a big department, the decision to call SWAT normally emanates from a patrol supervisor, and in small agencies, it usually takes the chief's request to mobilize a state or county SWAT unit.

The main thing is to know your turf, know your procedure, and make a careful approach with constant hard cover when you're coming up on anything that could escalate into a full-fledged siege. That way, you live long enough to do your part in the operation!

An M-16 rifle, equipped with a Starlight night vision scope, in the hands of a SWAT trooper, gives officer a decided edge. Note body armor which he also wears.

Submachine guns still have a place in law enforcement. Indiana officer demonstrates house-clearing techniques, wielding a Model 1928 Thompson. The submachine gun is used against multiple opponents who have no hostages.

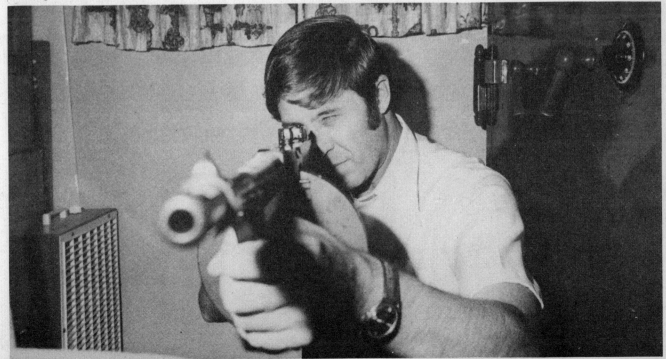

One of the law officer's most dangerous moments is when approaching a suspicious vehicle and driver halted on the street.

Chapter 16

Chapter 16

THE
.41 MAGNUM LIVES

OFFICER RAMIREZ pulled up behind the van, turned off the siren, but left his dome lights on. He'd stopped the van, because it matched the description of a stolen vehicle, and the rear plate was completely mud covered.

Opening the door of the black-and-white, Ramirez walked forward toward the driver's side of the halted van. Suddenly a thought flash back to his training brought a momentary shiver and a slight pause. This was one of the deadliest of all situations for an officer — the moment in which he approaches to investigate a strange vehicle.

Ka-boom!

There was a flash with the sound of thunder. Ramirez felt as though he had been kicked in the left side at belt level. He found himself sitting on the pavement, his left arm useless, his whole middle suddenly numb. As he began to realize that he had taken a shotgun blast at close range, he also became aware that the van had started up, was moving away. Instinct born of training is a strong factor. Forgetting everything else, Ramirez drew his revolver and fired six careful shots after the escaping vehicle.

A passing citizen put in a radio call for help and reloaded Officer Ramirez' empty revolver for him. He was still conscious when the ambulance arrived.

Ted Ramirez was a lucky man. His involuntary pause probably saved his life. Most of the shot charge missed, and he will enjoy a speedy recovery.

Later that same day, a local hospital emergency room reported the admission of a gunshot victim. The man had been struck from above on the shoulder and the bullet had

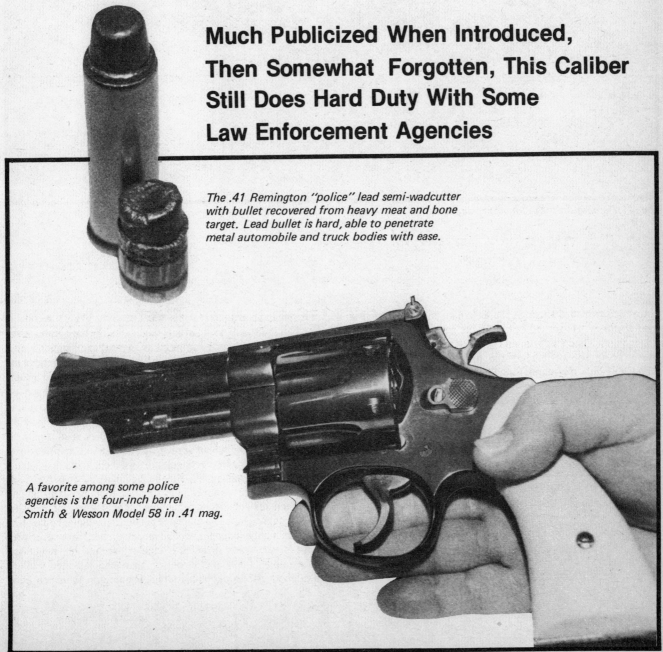

Much Publicized When Introduced, Then Somewhat Forgotten, This Caliber Still Does Hard Duty With Some Law Enforcement Agencies

The .41 Remington "police" lead semi-wadcutter with bullet recovered from heavy meat and bone target. Lead bullet is hard, able to penetrate metal automobile and truck bodies with ease.

A favorite among some police agencies is the four-inch barrel Smith & Wesson Model 58 in .41 mag.

The .41 Remington magnum, right, surpasses the .357 magnum in every type of test conducted by handgunner Claud Hamilton.

coursed downward through the length of his torso lodging near a kidney. He turned out to be the passenger in the van, the man who had shotgunned Officer Ramirez. He was bent over, facing the officer, at the time the van sped away, which explains the manner in which he had been hit by one of Ramirez' shots.

The officer is real, although Ramirez isn't his name. The incident happened, too, and not too long ago. It made a profound impression, because the bullet which hit the shotgunner penetrated the steel van body, then went on to pass nearly through a man *lengthwise.*

The gun and cartridge that did the job seem much like a cross between a buzz saw — like the .357 — and a sledge hammer, such as the .45. That's the .41 Remington magnum. The city was San Antonio, where they issue the S&W Model 58, and the load was the Remington factory police load carrying a flat-nosed lead semi-wadcutter bullet weighing 210 grains.

One of the things about which so many law officers have

written in recent years is the need to avoid over-penetration by handgun bullets in urban situations. Yet we know that the automobile is becoming an ever more present and important element in our daily lives and more frequently involved in urban crime. Officers need the ability to attack automobiles and their passengers effectively without having to resort to special weapons or ammunition.

Remington's choice of this bullet for their police loading of the .41 has been criticized. The bullet is of the well known Keith type lead semi-wadcutter, and it is something of a paradox. In recent loads worked with by Claud Hamilton, he has tested the bullet in really massive meat and bone targets bigger and tougher than any man and it has been his consistent experience that it does not upset to any notable degree. Yet, he reports, the bullet's brutal flat nose is highly damaging to a fibrous tissue. More surprising yet is the fact that this bullet seems to penetrate automobile body metal better than the jacketed bullets available! All things considered, Remington seems to have

Light loads are possible for reloader using tufts of polyester pillow stuffing to hold powder firmly against primer to ensure uniform ignition.

Neither the homemade .41 wadcutter nor the hollow point bullets proved especially accurate in tests.

made a better bullet choice than many believed.

The .41 magnum and the Smith & Wesson Model 58 have made a real name for themselves in San Antonio, despite objections to the gun in other areas. We have it on excellent authority that one solid body hit has been all that has been needed to settle matters — usually fatally — when the .41 has been involved. It has been reported that the SAPD began to get so much bad press that they started using deliberate leg shots to take it a little easier on the bad guys. Unfortunately, the .41 bullets allegedly passed through the target in every case. Fortunately, there have been no reports of innocent bystanders hit.

The .41 magnum is, frankly, a happy marriage of the hot velocity characteristics of the .357 magnum with the frontal area effect of the larger .44 and .45s.

There have been complaints about the accuracy of the

Commercially made bullets and factory-loaded ammunition in several weights and configurations are available in .41 Rem mag.

.41, probably based upon some early lots of commercial ammunition which were undersize and of excessively soft lead. A bullet of .408-inch is not likely to give the best accuracy in a .410-inch tube, and this is what we have been told the San Antonio police had to put up with. Hamilton's experience with commercial loads has been that they have been uniformly .410-inch in diameter and they have given good accuracy in his Model 57 Smith & Wesson, with little or no leading.

"Of course, I have not gone out and fired several hundred rounds of .41 through my gun, so I am not really in a good position to pass judgment on leading," Hamilton admits.

Granted, commercial loads are limited, but for the shooter able to recognize the .41's potential, the bullets available commercially include Speer, Sierra and Hornady in weights from 170 to 220 grains. If you cast your own, you can add to that Lyman 212-grain lead semi-wadcutters and Lee's in 195 and 240 grains. About all that is missing is a good lead hollow point and a good lead wadcutter for low velocity anti-personnel and target work. With a little ingenuity these can be made up by hand. A much better job can be done if you have access to a fine bullet-swaging press such as the Mity-Mite system made by Dave Corbin (D.H.

Available factory-loaded ammunition includes lead bullet, left, and jacketed soft point, at right.

At left: The .41 magnum revolver has proven to be an excellent hunting handgun in addition to its more familiar law enforcement duties. Below is the S&W Model 57 with six-inch barrel; four-inch and 8-3/8-inch also available.

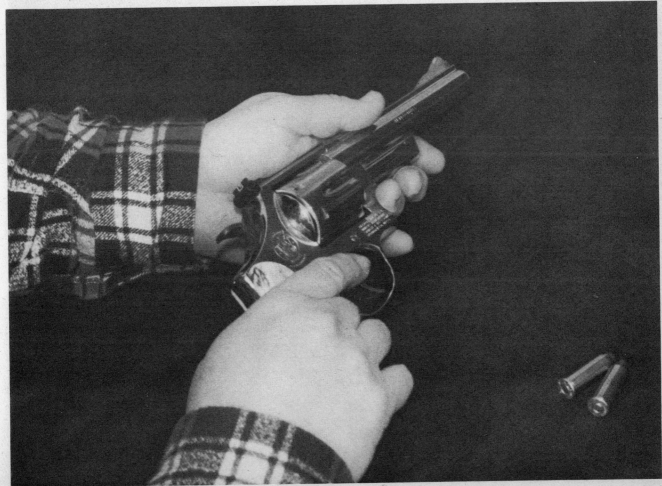

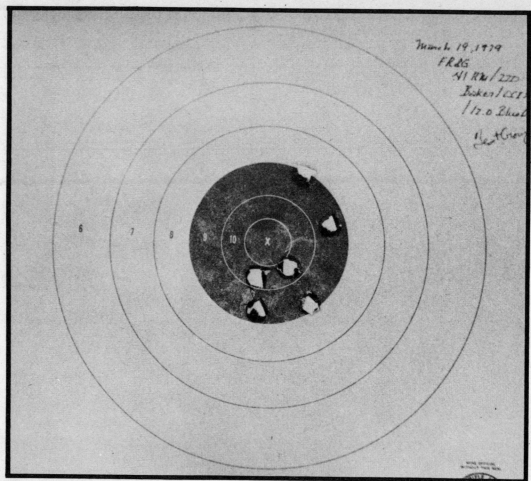

Best target group tested was produced using 220-grain Baker lead semi-wadcutter bullet pushed out by 12.0 grains of Blue Dot powder. All six in the black!

Corbin Manufacturing & Supply, P.O. Box 758, Phoenix, Oregon 97535).

With a friend, Hamilton took his four-inch Model 57 S&W to the range to learn how well it would do with fresh Remington police loads and some of his own handloads. Hamilton experienced good accuracy particularly with his lighter loads and a hard lead 220-grain semi-wadcutter made up by Baker.

"For some reason I seem to get best accuracy with lead bullets in lesser powered loads...better, that is, than I get with similar weight jacketed bullets," Hamilton reports. "Also, I seem to be able to get fifty to a hundred feet per second better velocity with the lead bullets for the same powder load without much leading trouble, as long as I stay well down in the 1000 to 1100 fps range.

"I make no special case for my loads, but I do believe they merit consideration by a serious admirer of the .41. There are lots of good bullets available. The ones I chose perform well, I know, in the lower velocity range."

As with so many things in life, eventual choices are based upon the likes and dislikes of the individual as much as on sheer merit. The .357 has its strong advocates. So do the .44 magnum and the .45 ACP.

"The .41 Remington magnum seems to be a happy combination of the better qualities of both," Hamilton feels. "It has the frontal area needed to do damage and yet is not so large that it cannot be driven to respectable velocities without too much noise and recoil. There have been many .41s over the years of our history. Most have faded but now I think we have one that will be with us for a while!

"My lead hollow point and wadcutter bullets were made by hand, not swaged as I would have liked them to be. I believe that carefully home-swaged lead wadcutters can be at least as accurate as the good Baker LSWCs I used and probably a shade better off a Ransom Rest. Hollow-base wadcutters at somewhat lower velocities yet — in the 700 fps range — may prove optimum," Hamilton says.

Hole in door of Volkswagen is proof that .41 magnum lead semi-wadcutter will pass through automobile metal. Other bullets of unknown caliber did not manage to penetrate.

LOAD DATA FOR .41 MAGNUM IN 4" MODEL 57 S&W

800 fps	900 fps	1000 fps	1100 fps	1200 fps	1300 fps
200-grain cast wadcutter 8.0 grains Herco	200-grain cast hollow point 9.0 grains AL-7	200-grain cast hollow point 9.6 grains AL-5	210-grain JHP (Hornady) 16.2 grains 2400	220-grain JSP (Speer) 12.8 grains AL-5	220-grain JSP (Speer) 17.8 grains 630
220-grain cast SWC (Baker) 8.8 grains Herco	220-grain cast SWC (Baker) 9.2 grains AL-7	220-grain cast SWC (Baker) 10.3 grains AL-8	220-grain JSP (Speer) 15.3 grains 630	210-grain JHP (Hornady) 17.8 grains 2400	
200-grain cast hollow point 8.5 grains AL-7					

Chapter 17

THE HOW OF POLICE WEAPONS TRAINING

New police recruit is taught techniques of the kneeling position by experienced shooter Bill O'Brien.

Trooper Fred McKinnon, rangemaster for the Illinois State Police, fires Behlert Custom Mini-Combat Model 39 auto. While range work is important to every police officer, classroom knowledge is becoming of importance.

This Instructor Impresses Upon Officers That Their Lives Are On The Line Constantly

THE MAN IN the front of the classroom isn't a teacher by trade, even though his W-2 form for this job lists him as "assistant professor." He's wearing a police uniform — navy trousers, light blue shirt with badge and emblems, a black leather patrol jacket he just took off — but there are other things about him that only another trained policeman's eye can recognize: the customized Colt .45 automatic in his black Bucheimer Police Auto Breakfront holster, or the spot on his shoulder where the ripple of fabric is not a small wrinkle, but the top edge of a hidden, bullet-resistant Kevlar vest.

His name is Massad F. Ayoob. He's a cop who teaches weaponcraft when he isn't doing patrol. To readers of gun magazines, he's somebody who writes a lot about handguns. But to the men in this classroom, every one of them full-time, in-service police officers, he is a man who may be able to teach them how to stay alive in a moment when their most frightening occupational nightmare comes true.

And they are all listening.

The scene is a spartan classroom in New Hampshire, the State Vocational-Technical College at Nashua to be exact.

The students are here as part of the Advanced Police Training Program of New Hampshire, an entity created several years ago with Federal funding to bring a new dimension to that tired term, "police professionalism." The courses include psychology and human relations, police photography and accident investigation, and a host of other subjects of vital interest to the cop on the street. The head of the project is Norman Philcox, an ex-FBI man.

Philcox was brought in to head the outfit because the New Hampshire Police Standards and Training Council, which administered the program, wanted nothing but the best for their instructional staff. Philcox carries that philosophy into his selection of instructors. For patrol and self-defense training, he selected Arthur Lamb, who heads that area of instruction at the Boston Police Academy, and who is recognized by police agencies throughout the free world as the man who developed the simplest, and perhaps the best, technique of self defense with the baton. And, for teaching firearms and teargas, Philcox went with Ayoob.

Back in the classroom, tonight's lecture is the first three of six hours on counterambush tactics; the course itself

Technique often starts in the classroom with experienced instructors. These shooters later take to the range to develop their shooting capabilities, including the use of the barricade as a protective device in shootout situations.

lasts for thirty-six hours lecture time alone, never mind range work. In the latter field, Ayoob guarantees that each student will come up at least one level (that is, sharpshooter to expert, or expert to master) once he has completed the course, and no one has ever asked for their money back.

"We all have the fear of ambush in the back of our minds," he begins, "and it's a valid fear. The problem is, we haven't defined the thing that we're afraid of, and learned how to cope with it.

"When an ambush comes, it's only a chance in a thousand that it will be a choreographed murder attempt by trained killers who deliberately have set out to assassinate policemen. Instead, it's what we in the trade call a 'hasty ambush.' You walk in on a domestic disturbance. The nut inside sees you coming, and he thinks, 'They're coming to take me away.' He grabs his gun, gets into a corner, and waits. Or you go in on a burglar who didn't

realize he triggered a silent alarm. He knows he's got no place to run, so he hides in a corner, and he cocks his arm with the crowbar and waits for you to come near where he's hiding, 'cause if he can't sneak past you he's perfectly willing to go out over you.

"And there's not a man in this classroom who didn't have a veteran cop tell him, on that first day of patrol, 'Kid, you never know when the car you pull over for a defective tail light is gonna have a cop killer behind the wheel, who thinks you've caught an alert on him, and is ready to kill you before he lets you take him in.' What we're getting at is, ambushes usually are done quickly by unprepared people, and a cop who is prepared has gone a long way toward evening up the odds."

The instructor walks toward the first row of seats, and stops in front of a big, uniformed cop. Without warning, Ayoob's hand lashes out in a karate backfist strike, stopping an inch from the cop's right eye. The latter instinctively jerks his head back, and raises a hand defensively. Ayoob's fist moves again, and this time, the officer doesn't duck as violently. By the fourth move, the policeman knows he isn't going to get hit, so the fifth time, he sits there resolutely and hardly blinks.

When Ayoob snaps his fist the sixth time, lightly clipping the officer's right eyebrow, the latter almost falls from the chair. "What did you learn from that?" the instructor snaps.

A hand rises hesitantly from the back, and the instructor nods for the student to speak. "You faked him out," a young policeman answers. "You got him so used to being feinted at, he wasn't ready to get hit."

"Right," the instructor answers. "And that's just what happens to all of us on the street. We walk into potential danger scenes so often, that going into a fresh burglary site is like walking into our living room. Most of the time, nobody jumps us, and we get complacent. After a while, we walk in there like it was our own living room.

"Tell me," he says, turning to the officer who just experienced five feints and a skimming impact, "why didn't you block my hand when I hit you?"

The officer looks sheepish. "Well, you did it a few times, and didn't hit me, and I felt pretty stupid trying to block a punch that wasn't a real punch."

"Exactly," says Ayoob. "You pull over a hundred cars, and none of the drivers give you a hard time, so you feel like Dirty Harry if you walk up ready to draw your gun. You go into a hundred fresh break scenes, and nobody's ever there, so after a while you feel like a cowboy if you go in with your service revolver in your hand. That's where complacency comes from. Your own job sets you up to be a sucker that 101st time.

"Everything you were ever taught in the Police Academy told you that complacency would get you killed, but they made complacency sound like being fat and stupid, so you thought it was something *you* wouldn't ever have to worry about. They never told you that complacency is the occupational hazard. They never said you'd spend so much of your working life in danger, that danger would be the norm, and after a while, you'd get used to it.

Famed police combat champion Bill O'Brien of Hartford, Connecticut, shows a young officer the proper two-hand hold for the revolver. The gunfighter techniques of the Old West are frowned upon in today's training.

"An aggravated assault or coming onto a fresh burglary is something that happens to civilians so seldom, that when it does, it becomes a high point of one's life to tell their grandchildren about. For you, it's a routine part of the job, and you literally have to make 'notes for court' to keep from forgetting the details. For cops, danger comes with the territory. It gets to be like breathing. And we get routine about it.

"And that," the instructor concludes, "is what gets so many of us killed."

Few policemen ever get shot at. Ayoob understands this. Something like one-third of his classroom work is pure audio, with the students listening to tape recordings that make their blood run cold. The men talking on the tapes are the policemen that Ayoob travels around the country to debrief; cops who have "been there," who have shot it out with hoods, and sometimes won and sometimes lost. But the words the student hears are those of the man who was there, either taking the bullets in his own body, or watching another man die by the narrator's own hand in the disastrously violent moment of a kill-or-be-killed shootout. shootout.

When you talk about cops and guns, you are talking about death. Ayoob reinforces this basic truth with both the tapes, and color slides of shootout scenes and gunfight victims. Sitting through one of those classes, you come to understand the awesome destructive power of heavy ballistics, and you realize that terms like "gaping wound" and "head blown off" aren't just catch phrases used by mystery writers.

The instructor flicks on the Panasonic, and we in the classroom hear the horror story of a metropolitan patrolman gunned down from ambush. It isn't nearly as clean as syndicated reruns of *Adam-12* would have you believe.

The patrolman on tape is young, 26. You hear him make the two incredible mistakes that put him in the way of gunfire, and later he tells you the two mistakes his partner made, that contributed to both of them getting shot.

The patrolman speaks of no red badges of courage. He just tells you how it feels to stop a .38 slug: "Like a pickax being driven into your chest." He tells about firing back, and missing, because he shot from the hip and couldn't coordinate with his target, even though the man who shot him down was only four feet away. He tells of the unbelievable pain, and of how the people on that inner city street ran away when he called for help, and how it felt to watch his blood flowing down into the gutter, knowing he was going to die.

The young officer tells how a passing police cruiser

found him and his partner lying in puddles of blood...how the surgeon in the emergency room told him, "Son, you've lost so much blood you're going into shock. I can't knock you out for what I've got to do." And you hear the patrolman say, "Doc, hurt me as much as you want, just make me live!" Then you watch the police students cringe in their seats as the voice on the tape explains how they shoved tubes into his nose, his arms, his penis, then cracked his chest open with something that looked like a T-bar, as six orderlies held him down.

Ayoob flips the tape. The faces of the police students are white. They have just heard thirty-five minutes of horror, and everyone of them pictures himself on that gurney in the emergency room.

"What did that cop do to get himself shot?" Ayoob says softly.

"He should've had his gun out!" yell two or three.

"He should have aimed, then fired," cries another.

"He should have called in his location before he did anything, so he wouldn't have laid there hemorrhaging for ten minutes," adds one.

When the discussion is over, Ayoob reaches for the button to play the next tape. It is a New York state trooper, and he tells of the moment when he and his partner were scuffling with two suspects next to a pulled-over car, and heard the other trooper scream, "He's got my gun!"

The trooper flings his man aside. Then, he tells Ayoob's students over the tape, "I saw the flash of the .357. I felt the impact, over my heart. It felt like a strong man poking me with an outstretched finger. Then I had my own gun in my hand, and I fired three times, and it was over."

Abruptly Ayoob shuts off the recorder. "What do you guys think of that?"

"I don't believe it!"

"What kind of vest did he have?"

Ayoob looks at the last student who spoke and lets his smile grow wider. He presses the button again, and we hear Ayoob's own voice asking in the distance, "Skip, what kind of vest did you have?"

"I was wearing a Second Chance super featherweight," the trooper answers on tape.

Ayoob could have spent three hours showing films and talking theory about body armor. He does, in fact, bring in sample vests for his students to shoot at outdoors. But this approach — more than half an hour of vicarious horror, from the viewpoint of an officer shot through his unprotected chest with a .38, compared to the vest-wearing trooper hit with a magnum over the heart, with only a burn scar from the heat of the trapped bullet — does more than

Crouch-and-point shooting is seldom taught today. This officer, knowing he has 25 seconds to qualify, has placed weak hand on knee for body support. If rules permit, it would be better to use the two-hand hold!

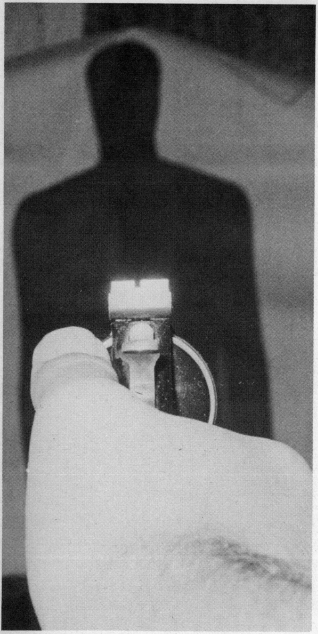

On night patrol duty, sights that have been painted white give the officer a deadly edge against an attacker. Better yet are Julio Santiago's glowing Day-Nite sights being used by some police agencies.

any verbal lecture or dry ballistic demonstration ever could. When the seventy-two students for this semester came in the instructor polled them on the hardware they carried, and asked if any wore vests. Five had armor when they came to class. Before they leave, nearly half will be wearing vests under their uniform shirts.

The students in Ayoob's class break at a different hour than others in the day or night courses at the Vo-Tech College, because their uniforms and off-duty guns tend to frighten the other students. "It also keeps us from waiting in line in the cafeteria during the coffee break," Ayoob smiles. We sit with him at a separate table, and ask about the subtleties of teaching guns to cops.

"The full-time police officer is the hardest guy in the world to teach. It has nothing to do with intelligence; they're brighter than average by far. The problem is, they see a lot, and they get cynical. That's another of their occupational hazards. To convince a working street cop you know what you're talking about, you better give him a dramatic demonstration, and let him know every minute that what you're giving him came off the street, not out of a classroom. These guys have been there. They may not all have killed, but they've all had to go up against street people hard, and they come out of that with a fortified learning experience that makes them question anybody who comes on with just words.

"These guys read a lot of articles telling them how to do their job, written by people who never wore a uniform, never made an arrest, never responded to a lethal danger scene. I *have* done these things, but that doesn't make me good enough to teach them, it just makes me *one* of them.

"What I teach from is that I'm a part-time cop, but a full-time writer for police professional journals, and those magazines pay me to go all over the country and find out what's happening in the hot spots of law enforcement. I debrief the bosses, the instructors, and the guys on the street who go through it. When they consent to let me tape their experiences, they do it because they want other cops to know how to stay alive if they face what they went through. I'm not teaching this course; a hundred street cops who've been caught up in kill-or-be-killed death scenes are teaching it, as far as the tactics. All I teach from my own authority is how to shoot fast and straight, out of the leather with a hard-hitting gun; the rest is a distillation of what I've learned from the professionals around the country who've been there."

Back in the classroom, into the meat of the counterambush course, the pens are moving fast and furious to keep up with the notes.

"One thing that gets cops killed, is trying to move wounded partners out of the line of fire," says Ayoob. "Experience teaches us that the best thing you can do for a wounded cop is leave him there until you can neutralize the guy who shot him, then roll in a full paramedic unit that you'll have already ordered to stand by. A sniper wants to kill; the man who's down probably won't draw any bullets, and by running clear of your wounded buddy, toward cover, you'll draw fire away from him. Try to drag him out, and you'll draw a burst of fire that will kill you, and finish off your buddy if he isn't dead already.

"A lot of people on our job get shot going up staircases. Again, it's the complacency problem. When you move on a staircase, keep your back to the wall, eyes going right and left, gun in your hand. Don't ever forget that your killer can come up behind you.

"When you go around corners, take a quick look with your head low, then duck back before you move around it.

If you even feel danger, have your gun out and ready to fire. If you're making a building search and you run across a door that won't open, try to lock it shut before you continue down a corridor. Take a minute to shove a trash barrel in front of it or something. That way, you won't turn your back on it, and have the guy inside pop the lock and shoot you in the back when you're halfway down the hall."

Ayoob cuts things short ten minutes before the class bell rings, and opens it to questions.

There aren't many; most of the classroom stuff has been covered. Some want to talk guns and gear; he tells them to wait 'til after class and do it over coffee. Then he adjourns the class five minutes short of what the state says he's supposed to, because he knows these are cops, and cops have little time with their families, and he wants to give them a running start to clear the parking lot before the rest of the college breaks night class.

The after-session lasts for almost an hour before the last student leaves. Ayoob is on his own time, but he gives it freely because he says, "Every cop who asks me a question teaches me something. I teach on the state's time, but it's worth it to me to learn from these guys, if they can spare the time."

Johnny Robbins, 13, set new match record in Second Chance shoot. Youth weighs 100 pounds but was able to handle recoil of .45 with crouch stance, two-hand hold.

Chapter 18

COUNTER-AMBUSH TECHNIQUES

AMBUSH IS A fear that haunts every policeman's mind. Military tacticians teach counter-responses, but some of them don't always work in the law enforcement context; the job is different, and even the enemy is different.

In police academies across the country, a standard training guide is the article, "Ambush!" by Massad F. Ayoob, reprinted from *Law And Order* magazine, an independent police professional journal. Some also use Ayoob's "Ambush II," printed originally in *Trooper* magazine.

Ayoob does law enforcement for a living, but police work only part-time. That's a seeming contradiction that needs explanation. He is a part-time patrolman and weapons instructor for a New Hampshire police department, and an assistant professor of police science teaching weapons and chemical agents for the Advanced Police Training Program of New Hampshire. He also is a guest lecturer at the Smith & Wesson Academy and the New Hampshire School of Self-Defense.

He has developed a body of authenticated, tape-recorded information that reflects, not what people think, but what *happens* when policemen are fighting for their lives against the most dangerous people in society — the people from whom they protect the innocent.

Based on this background, LAW ENFORCEMENT HANDGUN DIGEST interviewed him regarding counter-ambush measurements in law enforcement.

LEHD: When you look at police ambushes today, what is it that gets cops killed?

AYOOB: Lack of preparedness, and not believing that it will ever happen to them. Nobody would spend his life working in a job where they thought somebody was really waiting around the corner to kill them. Cops are no exception. They know it can happen, consciously, but they have to subdue that knowledge subconsciously. Otherwise, every time an officer had contact with a human being — five people, ten, a hundred a night — it would intrude on how he dealt with the public, and it would rot his mind. When a cop gets poisoned for people, he's all done, because the job *is* people.

LEHD: You do your own studies on this, and you debrief others in law enforcement who do such studies. Are you all in agreement?

AYOOB: Yes and no. One of the top instructors in the country told me, "Cops get shot because so many of them are decent human beings instead of killers. A man tries to kill them, and these cops don't *want* to kill another human being, so they hold off. Sometimes the bad guy drops his gun, and my cop is a hero. Sometimes the bad guy shoots, then my cop reacts from training and from outrage, and at least he usually takes the other guy with him. I can train them to shoot...but no one can train a decent human being to kill with a reflex like Pavlov's dog."

He is right. I go in after these situations have gone down,

Most Ambushes Are Not Planned, But They Are Nonetheless Deadly For The Officer!

Patrolman has silhouetted himself in doorway and will not be able to see an opponent in the shadows. He is prime for an ambush.

and you see cops who died, who had two or three seconds or more to shoot and drop the other man before he could fire the shot that killed the cop.

I differ with some of the others on this. Mind-set is part of it, being prepared to drop the hammer on the opponent, but so is the plain, physical ability to draw the revolver quickly, and fire a well-placed shot. There is a terrible trend in law enforcement today, to get away from quick draw. "Judgment shooting," in and of itself, is fine, but if the officer needs to respond to a killer in less than a second, I think we should train him to do so. The equipment is there, and the administrators could find the training time.

LEHD: Why don't they find the time?

AYOOB: The service handgun is the biggest and bulkiest piece of equipment a lawman carries, but it is also by far the least often used. You can count on your fingers the number of police departments in the country that have gunfights often enough to even develop their own statistics. Most departments rely on statistics they get from outside sources. Since most cops who die are caught by surprise — killed in hasty ambushes — statisticians conclude that these cops died because they didn't have their guns in their hands. This much is probably true, but they go on to conclude that, because they didn't have their guns drawn, they died from a mistake, so it would be pointless to teach them fast draw.

In many ambushes, the cop would have been dead no matter what he did: he walked into a deathtrap, and it was sprung on him. But you look at others, like Foster and Laurie in New York. I've seen the autopsy pictures and the official shooting reports that followed the deaths of those two ambushed cops. Al Seedman, former NYCPD chief of detectives, stated that they were shot in the back, then shot again after they were down and pleading for their lives. Others in NYCPD theorize that both were dead before the gunmen kicked their bodies over and shot Laurie in the genitals and Foster through both eyes. We don't know.

But Seedman was in charge of the investigation, and he says each officer went down with .45 hits in the back of the torso, and then would have had a few seconds before their assassins administered the *coup de grace*. If Seedman is right, then we can assume that, had Foster and Laurie been wearing Second Chance vests, and had they been wearing fast draw holsters, they might have been able to absorb those hits harmlessly, roll over, and kill their tormenters, and would have survived! But Foster and Laurie are dead, and all that theorizing is guesswork.

LEHD: Unlike some instructors, you teach hardware as well as tactics.

AYOOB: I tell my students that a powerful handgun with a carefully designed anti-personnel load can mean the difference in surviving or not, after they shoot an armed man who is full of adrenalin and on a kill trip. I favor the .45 automatic, or the .357 magnum with a 125-grain hollow

Officer has gone to the prone position behind the front wheel of his unit. Note how small a target he presents.

In answering disturbance call, the officer keeps his back to wall, and is scanning behind and above, the directions from which an ambush is most likely to come. His hand is on .45 service auto, holster unstrapped.

point. For the guy who's stuck with a .38, input from the street indicates that a +P hollow-point load is the way to go.

LEHD: What else do you teach in hardware?

AYOOB: Vests and backup guns. Second Chance alone has sixty-four cops who've been shot on the street, and are alive because they had the vests on. You look at the statistics before 1972, when Rich Davis brought out the Second Chance vests, and now; assaults on cops haven't gone down, nor has crime, but cop kills have taken a radical drop. I attribute that purely to the fact that so many cops are wearing Second Chance or equivalent armor. The reduced number of police fatalities shows a marked increase in percentage of head shots, a clear reflection that a high number of cops who get shot in the belly or chest are surviving, because they're wearing armor.

Cases have been reported all over the country wherein a cop is kidnapped and slain later, or disarmed and killed on the spot. The backup gun lets the cop surrender his service weapon to the attacker, thus putting the latter off guard. If

he was going to kill the cop right there, he would have done it without asking for the gun, and we have the statistics to confirm that. Once the kidnapper feels safe and secure, the cop with a backup gun passes the fifty/fifty line into situational dominance.

LEHD: That term "situational dominance" comes up again and again. What does it mean, exactly?

AYOOB: When Jeff Cooper's students ask him, "How do I know when I've mastered combat pistolcraft," he answers, "When anyone who tries to take your life is in more danger from you than you are from them."

I try to take Jeff's concept one step further, and impress the opponent to the extent that he realizes that this is the case. If I am going into a killing situation, I want the other person to know that while he may or may not be able to hurt me, *he* will surely die if he threatens me with lethal force.

This has worked for me, and for my students. I have held a dozen people at gunpoint in my life, not counting routine procedures, and eleven froze when they realized that I had this situational dominance. The twelfth tried to bluff me out, and I reinforced my position with a verbal warning: an armed robbery suspect, he then realized he was about to be killed, and put two empty hands against a Volkswagen bus. That one was close, and I lost some sleep over it, but I daresay he lost more.

LEHD: And if that one had drawn his gun? What would have been the difference?

AYOOB: I was locked on his groin with an Ithaca riot gun. He reached under his coat, and I said, "Don't touch it," at the same time that my finger was tightening on the trigger. I was shooting a lot of PPC tournaments back then, and that killing situation in that parking lot was like a match: Shoot when the target turns. I knew the guy was supposed to have a nickel-plated .38, and I was waiting to see metal before I pulled the trigger. "If the target turns, you fire." "Shoot, don't shoot." I stayed up all that night, because I had been ready to kill a human being on reflex, without thinking about it. But whenever I was feeling maudlin, I remembered what he told me later: how he would have killed me. If he *had* drawn his gun, he would have died, and knowing that robbed me of a night's sleep, but at least I would have been alive.

LEHD: Apart from officers failing to exert that situational dominance, what else gets them killed in ambushes?

AYOOB: Dispatchers can get our people killed. They get a call and tell us, "There's trouble at 125 Maple Street, see the woman." An officer gets out of the car and gets blown away, because nobody told him the trouble was a man with a gun inside that house.

Dispatchers on police radio networks aren't trained nearly as well as cops. They work for a lot less money, and the city or the state usually wants to keep costs down. There are exceptions: Illinois, North Carolina, and a few other states are busting their humps to make sure the police dispatchers are real professionals. But in most places, the cop is taking his cue from somebody who isn't trained to find out what's going down at the trouble scene, and relay that information adequately to the policeman who is responding there. "Unknown trouble" turns into "man with a gun," and by the time the responding officers realize that, one or more of them may be dead.

A classic case occurred in the Northeast. A teenager gave a party for his friends while his parents were away. A neighbor called and told him to keep the noise down, or "I'll call the cops." The kid said, "Any cops come up here, I'll blow their brains out."

The woman called in a noise disturbance complaint. She didn't mention what the teenager had said, but that was partly the dispatcher's fault for not drawing it out of her.

They sent a two-man car to answer a routine noise disturbance complaint. The woman who had complained called back to tell the dispatch center about the kid's threat, but it was too late. About the time that call was coming in, one of the responding officers took a fatal .308 rifle bullet through the chest.

If the call had been taken by a radio dispatcher trained to extract the last drop of information from the calling party, perhaps a 26-year-old policeman with two kids wouldn't have been shot down.

It goes the other way, too. In the Southeast, not long ago, a policeman pulled a car over for a routine stop, and ran the license number through his radio. Dispatch center came back with a computer "hit" on a stolen car, and the officer was so warned.

He then made a felony-type stop, ready to shoot it out with a car thief, and when the driver made a wrong move, the cop shot him dead. It turned out that the driver had been a local citizen driving to his father's funeral, which accounted for his erratic behavior. The licensed number had been punched in wrong at dispatch, because it wasn't a stolen car after all. An innocent man had been killed by mistake. Was it the officer's fault or the dispatcher's?

LEHD: What are some of the other ambush-type things cops should watch out for?

AYOOB: They should keep their eyes up; the natural position for ambush is above the victim. Talk to any cop who ever did the 41st Precinct in New York City. Talk to any veteran street cop who ever worked a tenement district. Even talk to any Vietnam-trained sniper: the attacker's advantage comes from above.

Officers should have in the back of their minds that *any* trouble call could be a setup for an ambush. It is rare that this is done intentionally. Usually, it's a domestic disturbance situation: the wife calls the cops, because she's in fear of her life. Maybe the drunken husband has been threatening her with a butcher knife, and he's passed out long enough for her to make the phone call.

She's just going to say, "Send some cops to this address quick." If the dispatcher isn't on the ball enough to debrief her on whether the person has a gun or is a mental patient, or any of a dozen questions a trained radio person should ask, the cops are gonna go in thinking it's just another family beef. They have no way of knowing that there's somebody in there who is ready and able to take human life. But maybe that drunk heard the wife call in the request, and he's gonna be standing there waiting by the door, with his butcher knife or with his shotgun, and the first cop who walks in is gonna be dead. This is your classic "hasty ambush," and it kills more cops than any carefully laid-out police assassination plan ever did.

This trooper has taken cover position behind open car door, with vehicle angled so engine block will shield him from any gunfire that situation brings.

Officer at left has shotgun, but should be using door for cover, have gun in firing position. Driver has angled patrol car to prevent rundown attempt by suspect. Engine block will shield him in event of a shootout.

LEHD: You say dispatchers can foul up and lead cops into what you call "death scenes." Since you say this is predictable, how does the cop *you* train respond to such a call?

AYOOB: En route, I instruct them to have the dispatcher call back to get all the information they can, while it will still do them some good. When they get to the door, every cop knows not to stand in front of it, *but* every street punk in the world has seen enough television shows to know cops don't stand in front of doors.

Unless there's some steel protection, I teach my cops to take a whole step back and away from the door after they rap on it. The casing of the door may or may not stop a slug, but in any case, it isn't big enough to hide your whole body behind. When I do a door number, I'm six feet away from a through-the-wall line of fire, on a forty-five-degree angle.

LEHD: Is this routine calls, or places where you have good reason to believe there are felons?

AYOOB: That's routine! If one knows there are armed felons inside, make sure to control the entire building. That will include a debriefing of someone who knows the premises, then evacuate the rest of the place before hitting the target apartment. Go in with an armored and heavily armed assault team, with the exits covered and a four-man unit hitting the main door. All should have gas masks, and CN or CS tear gas grenades, plus tear-gas rounds immediately available for the shotguns the assault team carries.

About the only times one would force entry, instead of sealing the place off and running a delaying action, would be a heavy drug bust. Even then, if it's an apartment house, seal off the drains so they can't flush anything down the toilet without it getting caught in evidence traps. Don't create a killing situation if you don't have to.

A barricaded gunman involves a waiting game. I belong to a fairly small department, and we have three of us trained in hostage negotiation. That's a lot more than average, but we're a better than average department. If we have to go in on a scene with rabid hostage takers, we have the armament and training for it, but we know we'll be writing off at least some hostages the moment we make an assault. Time is on our side, so we wait it out.

LEHD: What happens in a situation where you know they will kill the hostages?

AYOOB: We stand by with masks, our snipers controlling the containment ring, or the number one perimeter. We move in. The negotiators would make the last ditch effort to talk them out. We'd have a key code — which would generate from us inside, and nobody else — that would make the officers on the perimeter lob in the heavy chemicals, probably with 37mm Flite-Rites or Ferrets, using CS gas. The lead four-man team would hit the door, two to take it off its hinges then dive prone, two more backing them with shotguns or assault rifles. You don't use more than four to keep your own people out of a crossfire.

When cops hit doors, they don't swing inward; they go down like drawbridges. This we know from having done it. The first two cops, who may have had to use a battering ram to take the door down in the first place, follow in with the momentum and go prone, drawing their sidearms and covering the left and right sides from the lower tier as their backup men cover opposite sides with their shotguns or assault rifles, creating a potential crossfire that will go over the heads of the incoming (prone) officers harmlessly, while placing all hostiles within the police gunsights. Because hostages may be inside despite the best prior intelligence, never hit apartments with full automatic weapons.

LEHD: What happens when you get inside?
AYOOB: We own what we see. Smart street people take cover behind the heavy appliances, refrigerators and stoves.

LEHD: That shields them?
AYOOB: Only temporarily. Mainly, it isolates them.

LEHD: Which means they're yours.
AYOOB: When trained street cops make a final assault, with proper training and equipment, they *own* it!

This officer, if under fire, can use both the engine block and tires for maximum cover and he is mobile.

Chapter 19

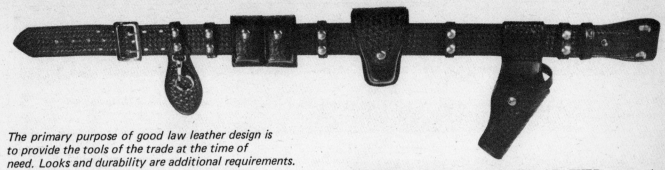

The primary purpose of good law leather design is to provide the tools of the trade at the time of need. Looks and durability are additional requirements.

LEATHER FOR LAW ENFORCEMENT

Hard-Working Leather May Make Law Work A Bit Easier

HOLSTERS AND OTHER LEATHER accessories for law enforcement personnel have taken giant leaps in design and style within the past two decades. The pace of refinement continues unabated. New designs are under test and prototypes are being built as this is written. New models are introduced each year by the larger and some of the small police holster manufacturers. Each would seem to be an improvement on previous designs as most users would agree.

The original design for a police holster probably can be traced back to the days following World War I when most city departments had access to plenty of surplus military gear, especially holsters and belts; including the Sam

The Don Hume Leather Goods' Agent 9 concealment holster is a veteran performer, popular with many officers. Holster will accept small or large guns, most barrel lengths. Badge case, above, has recessed space for badge, ID card window, handy small size.

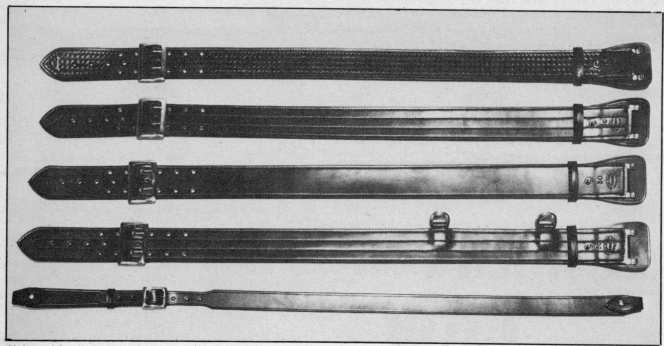

Plain and fancy designs of Sam Browne belts, such as the several offered by Don Hume, are typical of most leather manufacturers. Shoulder strap is at bottom. Below: Bianchi Model 16L full flap holster is popular for large autoloaders. However, with many law enforcement agencies, the full flap has lost some favor to lighter, moulded design holsters.

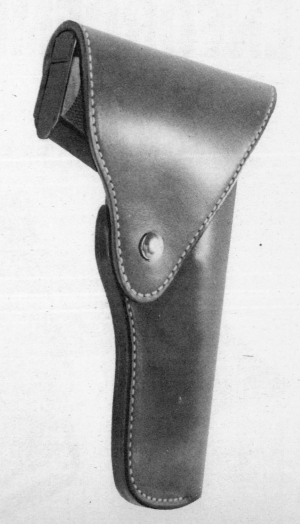

Browne, intended for the saber-carrying cavalry soldier. The military influence may have carried over even further to the idea that a police uniform should, in fact, be uniform; all the members should dress alike and their leather gear should be the same. Before that time, most police departments utilized a sort of leather-lined pocket with soft pouches in which to carry the small-frame handguns popular in those days.

At about the same time the surplus military gear became available, so did the larger frame police revolvers. The larger guns simply no longer fit in police uniform pockets. Military belts and holsters were cut down, flaps were trimmed and various other expedients were tried. Officers were beginning to travel by automobile as much as by shoe leather in some departments and the first swivel holsters were soon developed. Most departments had no real standards for the wearing of handguns, and most officers took to the swivel style for both vehicle and desk wear. The long barrel, heavy revolver was placed deep in the holster for security. The swivel was necessary for movement in and out of autos and around desk chairs.

As the handgun came to be hung on the belt in the holster, so too did various other police accessories. The billy club, key rings, handcuffs, extra ammunition, batons and flashlights were recognized as essential items for urban police, to be carried close at hand on the belt. Today, it is not uncommon for officers to carry seven or eight different items on their uniform belt. As this trend continues, most officers agree that the weight of all that gear is an important factor in their work.

Holster makers, individual one-man custom makers or the largest of the factories, recognize the need to reduce the weight of the leather product without reducing the security

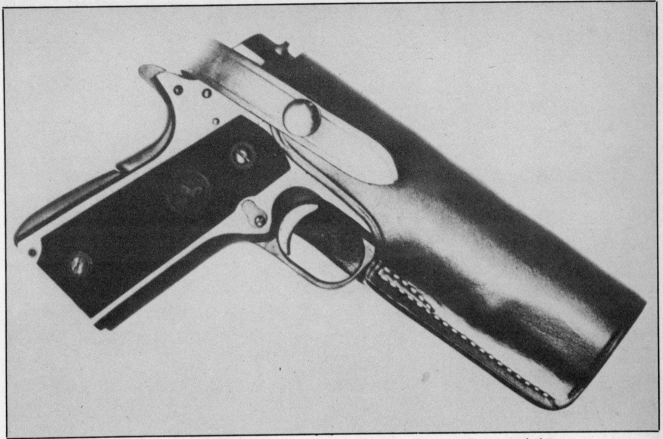

Bianchi's .45 Speed Scabbard, available in plain or basketweave, is one of the more modern compact holsters for .45 autoloaders. Design has minimum of bulk, exposed trigger guard, safety strap, and open muzzle. Gun is carried high, butt canted forward, popular with officers armed with .45 autos. Safety strap holds hammer down.

of the sidearm carried while not lessening the protection and retention of the gun. Maximum accessibility for the officer with minimum accessibility by an assailant is recognized as a most important consideration. The gun must be easily and rapidly available from any or all positions, riding in the front seat of a car, running down a dark alley or wrestling with a suspect on the street. The cop has to get the gun fast; the suspect, not at all.

Along about the 1950s, the gun holster safety strap was universally adopted for most law enforcement work. As holsters became smaller and lighter to carry, there was some danger that the upper part of the gun as well as the trigger

guard were dangerously exposed. Designers began to include a sheet metal shank in the drop loop holster to hold the holster in place so that the gun handle tilted away from the body for the fastest draw. The basic Jordan Border Patrol design is still hard to beat for many types of duty.

Not only is the design of the holster improving, so too is the quality of the basic holster ingredient; leather. It will come as no surprise to anyone recently purchasing a new belt, pair of shoes or boots, that the price of leather goods is skyrocketing. Good, top quality leather hides are becoming increasingly dear and the price rises to unheard of heights. The large makers must scour the markets for the

For those cops who do not wear the Sam Browne, there is the familiar cartridge belt, such as this George Lawrence No. 18.

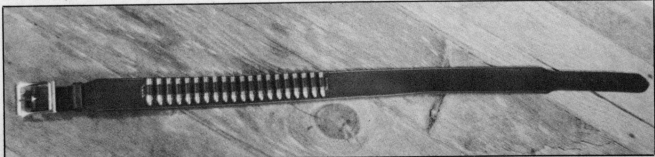

The basic incredient of police or any other leather product is leather; the hides of cattle. Top quality hides are decreasing in supply, increasing in price, ultimately affecting the price of belts, holsters and accessories for all consumers.

better hides. The price of high-grade leather has at least kept pace with the rising inflation rate at home and abroad. Each holster, belt or other accessory is clearly visible and is subject to minute examination by the maker and the customer. Most holster makers try to buy the highest grade hides on the market — hides with the least number of flaws and of uniform, specified thickness throughout.

The practice of buying from the lowest bidder may not be the best policy when it comes to leather hides. Leather is a commodity which may take as long as two or three years to reach the market and supply is dependent upon several non-controllable fluctuations such as demand, price and availability of beef, weather, feed supplies and prices, international trade agreements, and so on. The result is that each large or small leathergoods manufacturer is forced to stockpile quantities of hides, well in advance of need. Warehousing costs money.

Unless the holsters and belts used by police officers are turned out on a custom order basis by one or two persons,

another factor which leads to higher prices is the cost of skilled help. The leather industry is not as large as the firearms industry or the automobile industry so there is virtually no backlog of skilled help which may float from one factory to the next. Most of the design, construction and assembly operations are accomplished by hand and nearly all of the workers must be trained and supervised from within the individual production facility. This too, has a tendency to increase the price of good leather products.

Quality has improved as costs and better designs have been developed, however. The buyer is getting more for his money today than he was, say ten or fifteen years ago, even though he may be laying out more actual dollars. It is the quality of the product that counts and many law enforcement agencies supply their personnel with top-grade equipment which is expected to last for an entire career on the force. Most of the quality items on the market today will do just that.

Lining a holster with suede or cowhide leather may add

an ounce or two to the total weight of the item but would seem to be well worth it. Aside from the fact that cowhide leather or some other man-made material lining adds to the security of a duty or off-duty firearm, the soft finish offers good protection for the gun's finish. The sueded material will absorb any latent moisture from the metal while the gun is holstered, a plus in most climates and in situations where the officer is entering and exiting various buildings and vehicles during his tour of duty. The outside temperature changes from minute to minute, causing water vapor to condense on the gun metal, which may be detrimental to the finish. Good lining goes a long way toward reducing the risk of corrosion.

The thread used to stitch together the parts of a fine holster, belt or boot must be strong when it is sewn and remain strong for years of hard duty. There is still a question as to what is the best kind of thread, waxed linen or nylon. Safariland uses nylon almost exclusively on its belts, holsters and other items. Bianchi uses a number of strands of heavy, waxed linen thread on most of their models, although nylon is substituted at some points of extra stress. Both have their own merit and it is a matter of personal choice as to which is the better. All use a lockstitch, similar to that used on good saddles. Each stitch is individually locked. If a few stitches somehow become cut or broken, the whole seam will not simply unravel causing the holster to fall apart.

Modern police duty demands that the equipment carried must be functional, comfortable and convenient. If it isn't that, it isn't worth carrying; in fact it may be downright dangerous to have. Rigid, low-hanging holsters are almost ruled out in today's smaller, tighter patrol cars. A four- or six-inch revolver hung up in the car seat or caught in the car-door armrest can cost a cop his life, even if it was easy to carry hanging down his thigh. The evolutionary changes in holster design have gone a long way to alleviate the situation.

The primary trend in the leather industry is that leather and holsters are continuing to become more expensive. The amount of money somebody is willing to spend on a holster is proportional to the amount of money he will spend on a handgun. Back in the days when guns sold for about $65, a $65 holster was out of the question. Now a person will spend more than $200 on the same gun, so a price tag of more than fifty dollars for a holster is not too far out of proportion.

Holster parts are cut from the best quality leather available to the manufacturers. Attention is paid to thickness, strength, surface, and color of the leather as powerful machines assist skilled hands.

After the holster has been cut, assembled and sewn, the leather must be treated to minimize wear, maximize appearance, long life.

Handgun competition has had its influence on law enforcement holster design. Pistol champion Ray Chapman examines production of unfinished holsters bearing his name at the Bianchi factory in Temecula, California.

The customer is willing to pay more for quality. He is interested in features and high performance, he has been educated toward two innovations: One is the silicone suede lining for the holsters and the other is the moulded fit. Twenty years ago, people thought that holsters were supposed to be soft. You could read articles on how to treat the leather to make it soft and pliable. If you wanted the gun to go in and out easily you put graphite on the inside. However, a soft leather holster rubs on the gun and rubs on the bluing. It has now reached the point where customers accept the fact that a well-fitted holster is hard and stiff.

Concealment holsters and shoulder holsters are in the same general category but are not considered together because shoulder holsters have a definite non-law-enforcement market, i.e., for hunters as a backup or for handgun hunting. The shoulder holster is an easier way to carry a handgun in the brush. Shoulder holsters are not always concealed; they are often, by design, in plain sight.

The process of designing any holster begins with some one beginning to accept and assimilate information from potential buyers, "Why don't you make one of those?" "We like this but it should have..." or "We saw a holster that somebody made by hand and we didn't like it but it had this or that feature which would be good."

It is up to the manufacturer to recognize the trend and the future demand and market for a certain type of holster or other leather item. Before the decision is made to make the design, somebody must decide if there really is a market for it. Is it actually needed?

Here is where several features may come into the design. Will the new model have a thumb snap? Depending upon the potential market, will the holster have a suede lining or be just plain leather on the inside? The addition of a lining adds some cost to the finished unit but enhances the holding and protection of the gun considerably. What sort of finish will the holster have; plain or basketweave? What colors; brown, black, Clarino? Open muzzle or closed muzzle holster? What sort of stitching? Put all those features together at one end of the process and out comes a best-selling holster, according to the designer. Obviously, the whole process is much more complicated than that.

There is even the consideration that some holsters made for guns with short barrels, may possibly be used for concealment by police and others. In that case, the size of the belt slot is important. In other words, for two- or three-inch-barrel guns, the slot should be 1¾ inches wide because the lighter gun will be carried on backpacks or concealed as a backup and not worn on the uniform belt. The holster for four-, six-inch and longer barrels get heavier and should be worn with a wider belt so the slot is cut 2¼ inches.

The problem the large holster manufacturers have in simply producing and stocking all the sizes and colors of a single holster design are staggering. For instance, if the holster is made in twenty sizes — a not unusually large number — and in two colors, forty different combinations must be produced and warehoused. If the number on hand is to be a hundred of each size and color, it is an easy calculation to come up with four hundred holsters in stock. And that for only one holster design.

Once the design and included features have been decided, the guns that the holster is to fit must be determined. Two- and three-inch revolvers on light or medium frames are the most obvious choices for the concealable holster. Large and small autoloaders must also be accommodated with the design. The problem with that step comes with the newer, not-yet-popular guns. Nobody knows yet if it will be a big seller and if there will be a demand for holsters for the gun.

If there is a demand, a prototype holster must be made. It is tested extensively. The holster must ride on the belt at the right height, has to be at the right angle, the stock has to hit the user in the right place, the holster, in some cases, must not interfere with the safety or the magazine button.

Turned out by the thousands or produced one at a time on a custom basis, each holster must fit the gun for which it was designed. The larger factories produce aluminum gun moulds around which the leather is formed. Replicas are retained at plant to check each finished holster for proper fit during production. Size and variety soon become vast.

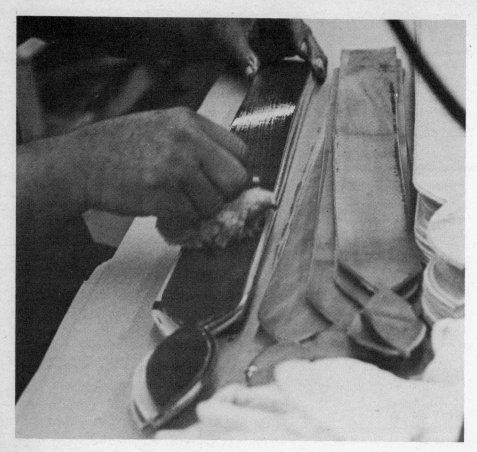

Leather dye and oil finish is important to appearance and life of belt parts. Modern economics demands lifetime use for police leather products.

Choice of thread material for holsters seems restricted to multi-strand waxed linen or nylon. Each has its merits and some producers use both. Regardless, the stitching must last as long as the leather.

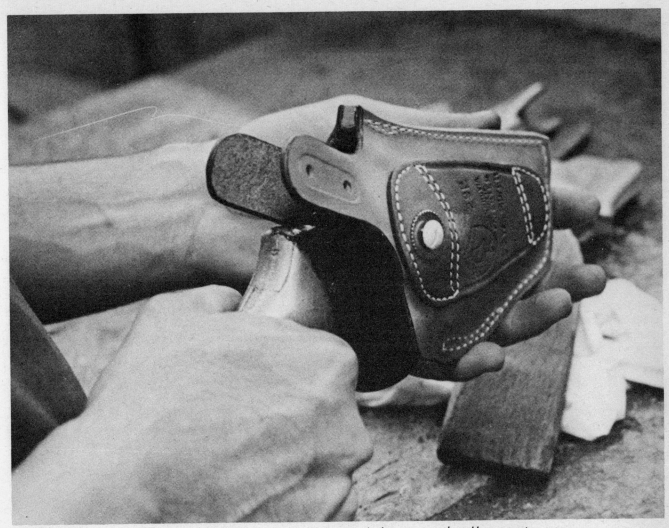

Handgun fit of production holsters is carried out at specified stops during construction. Here, a cast aluminum revolver replica is slipped into a Safariland leather holster after sewing but before installation of snaps.

The holster and gun cannot be topheavy or ride so low that when the officer reaches for the handle, he gets a thumbful of belt at the same time. The holster must be big enough and yet small enough; it must be just the right size for carrying the gun but not so small the holster's components cannot be handled efficiently in the factory.

For a recent design by Bianchi, the designer produced five prototypes for each size, twenty sizes. It takes about a year to evaluate one hundred prototype holsters before actual production may begin.

Crossdraw belt holsters may be at the forefront of current trends in design. This includes spring-loaded crossdraws. Also popular, with Bianchi and Safariland at least, is the feature of hand-moulded fitting for the holsters. Customers recognize this as a definite added protection for the gun carried. The same may be said for suede leather lining; many of today's law enforcement holsters are lined as a standard feature. A safety strap is not only accepted, but is actually demanded, by most police agencies today. Four or five years ago, the Los Angeles Police Department accepted the thumb-strap safety strap as standard for their members.

The inside safety strap not only looks neat, it tends to keep the gun in the holster during heavy physical activity, and the placement of the snap, next to the body makes it all the more difficult for an opponent to reach the officer's gun and draw it from the holster. The hammer cannot be cocked during a struggle with a criminal as long as the thumb-snap safety strap remains fastened.

Many police agencies standardize the issue handguns as well as the issue holsters to match. In many areas, the Occupational Safety and Health Agency (OSHA) requires the department to purchase and issue to the officers holsters, belts, guns, and associated gear as safety equipment. The tools of the trade are required for the job, and the cop should not have to purchase them for himself, is the current philosophy. Guns and holsters fall into the same category as safety hats and goggles on other jobs. Also, most police chiefs want continuity throughout the department. Each officer must have the same gun, same ammunition and same leather equipment. They must all look uniform at inspection. The holsters all must be black or all brown, all plain or all basketweave.

For most police gear, the style and color remains basketweave in black. For duty equipment, black is ninety-nine percent of the market; basketweave is about sixty percent. The traditional Sam Browne belt with large, heavy buckle seems to be maintaining its popularity, although Safariland, for one, offers a variation featuring no visible metal and a Velcro fastener in place of the traditional buckle.

Law enforcement agencies are continuing to emphasize quality, heavy-duty, long-lasting holsters which are required to do more than they used to. However, there are still many agencies around who have the philosophy of spending as little money as possible for holsters and leather products for their officers. It shows. Many officers buy their own top-quality gear out of their own pockets.

There is at least one agency in the United States which became tied up with their local fire department budget. The fire fighters were to receive a $45 pair of shoes and the police department was granted the same amount for leather goods. They didn't care how good or bad the quality, but they were determined to go out for bids on a complete Sam Browne belt set-up for $45. Friends, there just ain't no such thing in this day and age; not with any quality which will last past a couple of years.

Some of the smaller police departments have a better chance of getting top quality holsters and other equipment than the large forces which have a complicated budget/purchasing process. The smaller agency doesn't have to fight city hall and can convince the holder of the purse strings that the officers need a certain holster with specified features because it might save a life and the cop can do a better job because of it. It can even save an officer's life. The best does not come cheap. On the other hand, some of the largest agencies — though certainly not all — have been through the trial and error and educational process, insisting on only the best product for the taxpayer's dollar.

There seems to be a geographical trend of holster styles in the United States. Clarino is popular in the South, basketweave is a big seller in the West. There are, of course, local variations to this pattern but it seems generally to hold. Breakfront holsters enjoy considerable popularity in California and the West but as you move farther east, the agencies are less familiar with the breakfront.

For the American holster manufacturer — and for many American gunmakers too — the European law enforcement

The holster industry is not so large that a backup supply of skilled labor exists for the factories to tap. Most employee training is done at the factory with the traditional older, more experienced worker assisting the newer hands.

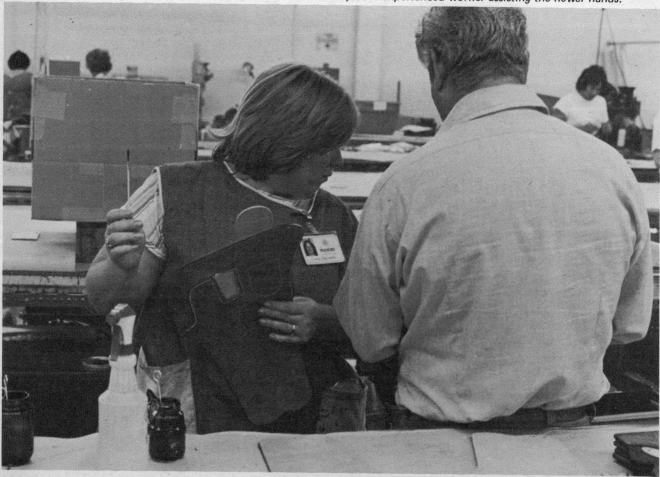

Alessi Concealment Holsters of Tonawanda, New York, specializes in the law enforcement market. Moulded concealment model rides high and close on the belt. Single-action autos are carried with leather under the hammer, cocked and locked.

Shoulder rig by Alessi features all-leather harness, ammo drop pouch carried under opposite arm.

market is singularly undeveloped. There is some design progress in Europe but not much. There seems to be little in the way of holster designing in Europe. Most large agencies overseas use Walther and H&K autoloaders rather than the typical American revolver.

There is a trend evident in recent years that more and more police officers are carrying a backup gun on duty as well as a concealed handgun while off duty. The concealed gun holster business is a large part of the industry all over the country. The primary principle of the concealment holster is, of course, concealment. The other important considerations are accessibility and protection of the gun. The industry is moving into the area of sophistication

which permits the manufacture of a holster which is super-concealable, has certain desirable features such as spring loading and body-hugging ability and the gun is carried convenient to reach.

Bianchi's most popular duty-model holsters are the front-opening design. Some years ago, Bianchi introduced his Model 27 Break Front holster which proved to be a big seller and continues in popularity today. The Break Front has gone through more than a dozen evolutionary changes during the past two decades but is the same basic design prototyped in the 1960s. The holster is designed primarily for the S&W Model 19, S&W Model 29 and Colt Python, guns with barrel lengths of four or six inches. Internal

Crossdraw holster by Bianchi is available in tan or black, plain or basketweave, as shown. Holster is leather lined, rides high and features spring opening for fast draw.

recesses lock the revolver in place with the spring-loaded front providing security while allowing a fast draw when necessary. The holster rides relatively high on the wearer's hip with a steel reinforcing loop to keep the rig in position. The Break Front, or Model 27 holster, features a safety strap with false snap on the outside to foil would-be gun snatchers.

The other front opener is called The Judge by Bianchi, available in three styles: The standard, low belt loop mounting style; the swivel model designed to ride lower while swiveling for certain situations; and the newest, The Judge Hi Ride. The latter has a flat belt slot design to pull the holster close to the body, placing the bulk of the gun above the belt line.

For those officers armed with autoloaders, some of the newer holster designs seem to reflect the experience gained among competition shooters around the country. The leather encloses less of the barrel than designs seen only a few years ago, while allowing fast, easy access to the gun handle. All have 2¼-inch belt slots for wear on the Sam Browne belt. The various designs allow the buyer the choice of open or closed muzzle and most are available in black, plain or basketweave. Some models may be ordered in Clarino finish, the most popular in the South, as mentioned earlier.

"One of the most popular Alessi holsters is the Hideout, an in-the-pants style designed for maximum concealment. In my opinion this is the most comfortable inside-the-pant holster I've had the opportunity to use. It's designed to ride high and close to the body, positioning the butt for a fast, safe draw while standing or sitting in a vehicle. The belt loop utilizes a one-way directional snap that prevents the

Colt Commander is shown in cocked and locked mode, in Alessi's inside-the-pants holster.

holster from unsnapping off your belt during the draw. On revolvers, a pull-through snap is used for natural withdrawal of the handgun," researcher Roger Combs notes.

When a holster rides as close to the body as this model, a thumb-break is not feasible, Alessi feels. The pull-through snaps are an asset in that the hammer and adjustable rear sight are covered with leather. This prevents worn clothing and holes in suitcoat linings. This holster also incorporates a cleverly moulded hip pad at the front to distribute the bulk and weight of the gun, giving the feeling of a wallet. The holster is unusual in that it is folded around the trigger guard. This allows a proper grip when drawing and also acts as a deterrent to anyone from snatching the gun from behind.

Their ankle holster was a year in planning and testing. Alessi wanted a rig that could be worn easily with comfort and security, yet would allow a quick natural draw without hangups, keeping in mind the concealment aspect. Many

patterns were cut and tested along with various methods of attachment to the ankle. They found that a two-inch-wide band of Velcro sewn to the ankle band is a very secure and convenient method of attachment that is completely adjustable. The Velcro is rated for approximately 50,000 closures, plus or minus ten percent, depending on the amount of strain applied.

When worn properly, this holster is comfortable and conceals well under all but tight slacks. This ankle unit also is constructed from top-grain russet leather. No vinyl or synthetic materials are used in place of leather.

The shoulder rig, known as their Bodyguard, is possibly the most comfortable, concealable rig in production today. The rig comes complete with a provision for spare ammo, and a handcuff carrier is an added option for police. Adjusted properly, this rig can be worn for long periods without any discomfort. The harness does not utilize any nylon or elastic which most of their testers have found to

Another method for fastening Sam Browne rigs is this one by Bucheimer Clark. Belt is without buckles or Velcro, fastening by means of a three-stud system which fits into matching holes at back of other end of belt. The system is adjustable for size and is held in place with a sliding keeper. Various accessories are available to match black or Clarino finish.

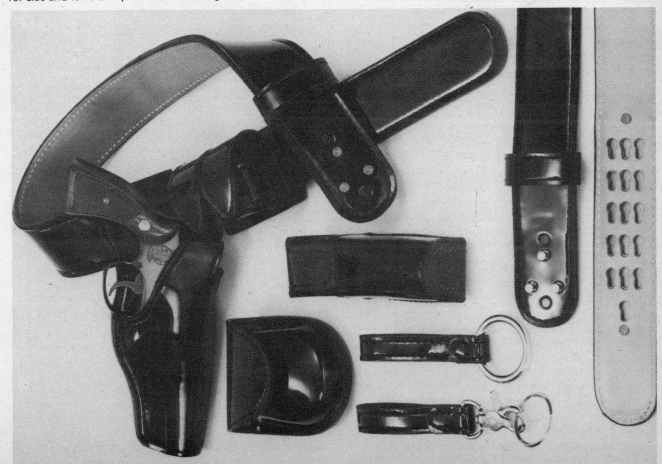

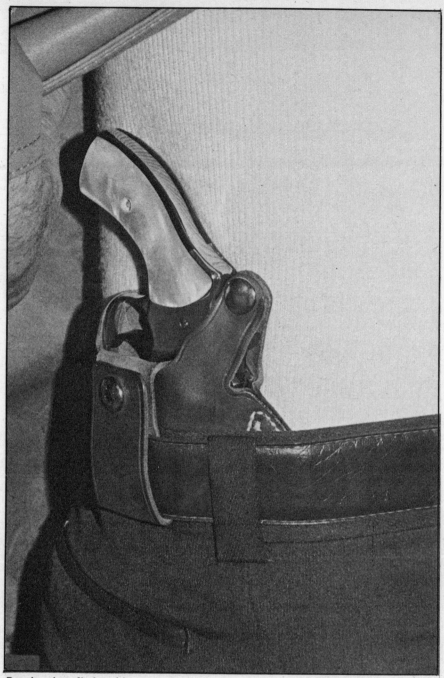

Despite close-fitting shirt and trousers on this officer, no revealing bulge is evident from this Charter Arms .38 Special in Alessi Hideout holster.

be uncomfortable after long periods of wear.

The holster is positioned semi-horizontally (butt down in the hollow of the body) for a fast natural draw. Standard on the small frame revolvers and autos, and optional on the large weapons, is a unique snap release system whereby the snaps close through the trigger guard. To withdraw the gun, just pull. Nothing to fumble with, no elastic or springs to wear. The only way for these snaps to disengage is to pull the gun. Holsters for the larger frame handguns are supplied with thumb-breaks as standard. This is mostly for peace of mind for the customer. Colt .45 autos may be worn cocked

and locked with leather under the hammer or hammer down with leather over the hammer. The trigger guard snap release system is available for these guns, also for the officer who doesn't mind carrying a fully loaded auto cocked and locked without the thumb-break under the hammer.

Their shoulder rig, when used for a small frame auto or revolver, may be worn effectively under a loose-fitting shirt, such as a backup for a uniformed duty officer. If need be, the ammo containers may be removed and another weapon can be carried under the opposite shoulder. The harness is supplied in two sizes. Regular, to fit size 38 through 42,

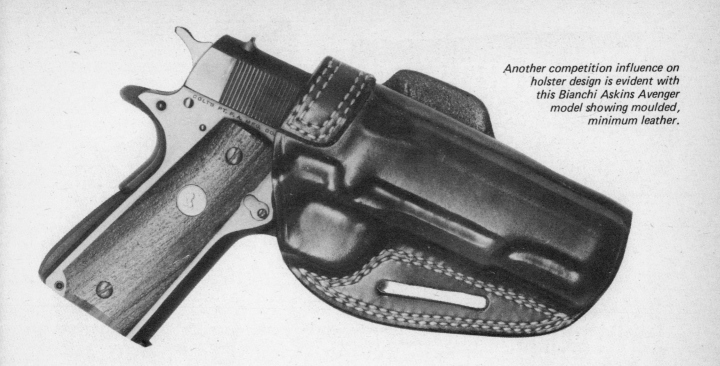

Another competition influence on holster design is evident with this Bianchi Askins Avenger model showing moulded, minimum leather.

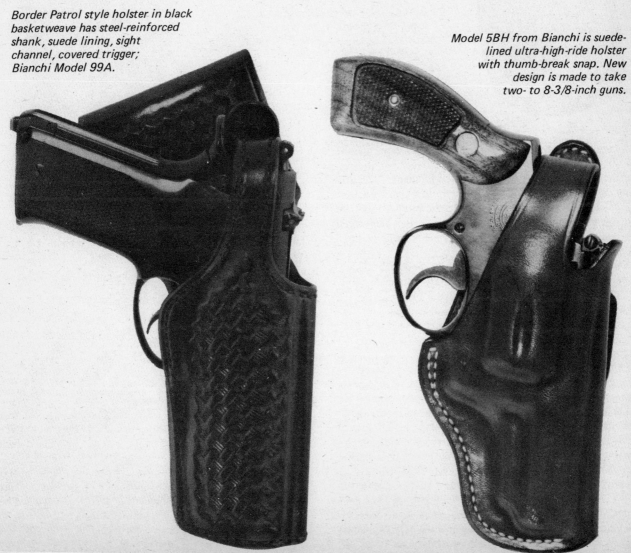

Border Patrol style holster in black basketweave has steel-reinforced shank, suede lining, sight channel, covered trigger; Bianchi Model 99A.

Model 5BH from Bianchi is suede-lined ultra-high-ride holster with thumb-break snap. New design is made to take two- to 8-3/8-inch guns.

Police officers with prior military service will realize that, while cop leather evolved from the old GI holster, military holsters have changed, too. Bianchi's Breakfront design, right, features false safety strap, thumb break safety snap near body.

and large to fit size 44 to 48. Extra-large harnesses may be had upon request.

One of the most welcome developments recently introduced into the design of many holsters is a track or groove built into the holster to guide and protect the front sight blade of the handgun. In some cases, it is reinforced with another layer of leather, in others, a channel of lined plastic or metal is built into the holster.

Safariland calls their model the Safariland Sight Track, Bianchi terms theirs a Sight Channel. By whatever name, the innovation is intended to protect the front sight blade from wear and maladjustment. It also facilitates the insertion and withdrawal of the sidearm. The sight blade itself is untouched by leather, plastic or metal in the holster, a feature welcomed by all shooters.

Safariland also offers a full line of law enforcement leather gear, including a number of Border Patrol style holsters in swivel and thumb break configuration, for autoloaders as well as revolvers. One of Safariland's innovations recently has been a Sam Browne belt system which eliminates the large, heavy, shiny metal belt buckles and snaps. The belt closure is with Velcro material rather than metal. Safariland points out that the system is lighter to wear, presents a neat appearance and does not present a reflecting, bright target for opponents in low-light conditions. The company offers matching accessories for the Velcro Sam Browne, including trouser belts, handcuff cases, key rings, magazine pouches and other items; all

Small autoloaders are carried in Bianchi's Model 17 Right Guard holster at 45 degree angle. Front opening is spring loaded, muzzle is closed.

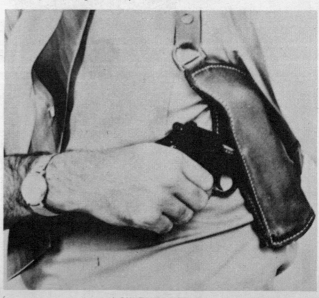

Pocket holster by Bianchi may be worn in or outside of belt or trouser band, for left- or right-hand draw. Worn in small of back, small auto is virtually invisible.

accessories are available with either brass snaps or Velcro fasteners where appropriate.

Smith & Wesson leather goods has a new holster with a concealed thumb break behind the grips. This, says S&W, protects the safety strap from accidental opening from bumping or snagging, and places it away from prying eyes and hands. The release is in a natural position for the user as the hand moves to the draw. The thumb snap release is the leverage type; the officer presses a button on the inside of the strap near his body which leaves open the safety snap

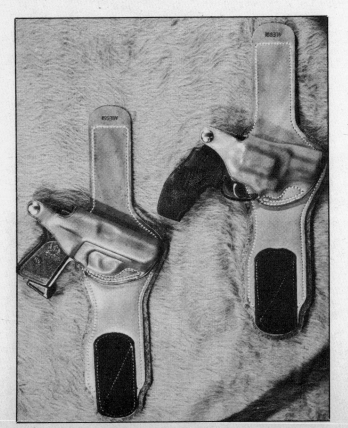

Alessi's ankle holsters fasten with Velcro for full adjustment potential. Small autoloaders or revolvers may be carried left or right ankle, inside or outside of leg.

to allow gun draw. There is a metal reinforced drop loop included which keeps the holster and gun at the proper angle for easy accessibility. Smith & Wesson also offers a line of concealable holsters as well as a complete Sam Browne belt with accessories.

Lawman Leather features a design they call the Dirty Harry shoulder holster, modeled after the holster worn by actor Clint Eastwood in his series of films. The original design was for Eastwood and specifically for the S&W Model 29 .44 magnum revolver. The object of the design is to provide durability, comfort, and ease of draw for the wearer. The patented holster utilizes two separate straps that go fore and aft of the off arm, and join together on a belt assembly that snaps to the trouser belt. The design has proven successful enough that Lawman is now building it to fit most small and large revolvers with barrels up to eight inches.

Don Hume, while not entirely restricted to law enforcement sales, is definitely oriented toward that market. Most of the Hume designs and styles have a law enforcement use in mind. Hume features a series of designs called the Jordan style, after Bill Jordan of Border Patrol fame, with different features such as a safety strap, a thumb break design and a new holster with rear sight guard to protect linings, sleeves and sights. Hume also offers a breakfront design with metal-reinforced shank and sewn-down belt loop. The trigger guard is completely enclosed to prevent the gun from being drawn from the rear. Concealment holsters, shoulder holsters for most guns, leather belts and other police accessories are included in the Don Hume line of leather goods.

Bucheimer Clark offers yet another version of the Sam

Roy Baker introduced his first Pancake several years ago,
branched out to include models for large and small handguns.
Three belt slots allow three wearing positions, all high.

Old West Leather offers an inexpensive shoulder holster
for up to eight-inch barrels with sight cut out
and belt strap. Rough-out cowhide leather
is suede lined for gun protection.

Lawman Leather's Dirty Harry
shoulder holster handles
largest handguns, including
S&W Model 29 .44 Magnum.

Modern holster design permits guns as large as Smith & Wesson Model 29 with 8-3/8-inch barrel to be carried undercover, completely concealed. This example is produced by Custom Guns & Leather, Inc.

Browne belt without either a Velcro fastener or the traditional large metal buckle. Their answer is three-stud system of fastening, with a choice of size holes to lock the belt. The system is available with a complete set of leather accessories to match the black or Clarino finish.

Roy Baker originated the Pancake holster design, since followed by many imitations. The Pancake is still popular with police off-duty or in plain clothes, offering maximum protection with minimum visibility. From the first basic design, Roy's Leather has branched out to more than two dozen varieties and sizes of Pancakes, including autoloader models. They are available for small frame, large frame, double action, single action, even sporting models for the Auto Mag and Thompson/Center single-shot pistols. Barrel lengths of two to 8-3/8 inches may be accommodated by Roy's products.

Old West Leather offers a shoulder holster system in six

components which may be converted from a normal configuration to a form-fitting upside-down concealment shoulder holster. The six parts are the holster itself — for either automatics or revolvers — left harness strap; elastic connecting strap; right harness strap; double drop clip or cartridge case; and the cuff case. The system has no rivets or fastening screws, relying on wide shoulder straps and adjustable buckles for conformation and fit.

If the uniform lawman's rig is properly matched and fits him correctly, he will wear it with a reasonable amount of comfort without being constantly reminded that he has the assembly on by a holster riding in the wrong place or being prodded by the butt of the handgun. The rig should fit so comfortably that the officer can go about his duties without being conscious of the hardware on his hip. Concealed, the gun remains out of sight and secure, accessible only to the officer immediately upon need.

Chapter 20

A HARD LOOK AT THE AUTOS

Smith & Wesson's Model 39 And Model 59 Arouse Pros And Cons Among Law Enforcement Types

THE SMITH & Wesson Model 39, and its high-capacity twin, the 59, are modern legends among American gun fanciers, including police officers.

Some call these instruments the ultimate defensive combat handguns, citing their double-action trigger mechanisms, great firepower, safety features, and general design and function. But a handful of well qualified gun people maintain that these guns, interesting though they may be for students of the development of firearms designs, are overrated in terms of their performance.

Is the 9mm, double-action S&W automatic the greatest advance in handguns since the self-contained cartridge? Or is it a pistol that has been puffed up out of all proportion by gun buffs and lawmen simply because it was new and different when it was introduced as a "modern" military pistol twenty-odd years ago?

One who has been close to these questions is Massad

Hung up with its slide halfway to the rear, this Model 39 has been tagged with its carrier's name to await attention of the departmental armorer to restore it to service mode.

Ayoob, police officer and instructor in combat handgunnery. We asked him to check out the controversy and offer his thoughts.

Look at the documented facts and decide for yourself...

Firepower: The 39 carries eight in the box and a ninth in the chamber; the 59, supposedly fourteen-and-one. We say supposedly because you'll occasionally find a 59 clip you can stuff fifteen rounds into and still lock it into the butt. At the same time, to prevent magazine spring fatigue and to keep the rounds at a proper and uniform feeding angle, it's best to carry the gun with one round less than factory-stated magazine capacity. Some users apply the same practice to their 39s. Most experienced users find the 59 more reliable than the 39, since the feed-angle of the Browning-like magazine lines the round up more squarely with the chamber.

Firepower is the *raison d'etre* of the combat automatic, and the 59 therefore obsoletes its predecessor. Before, the argument between S&W and Browning was double-action vs. workmanship and firepower. Now it's down to design versus quality — and price.

There are still people who will tell you, "If you can't do it with six shots, you can't do it at all," but what we know from studies of modern police gunfights proves them wrong. In a confrontation with an armed robbery team, for instance, it is not at all uncommon for upwards of thirty rounds to be expended. The fat magazine in the 59, backed by spares on the belt, can be a lifesaver.

This is particularly true for the officer (or, for that matter, the law-abiding citizen) who is not hardened to gunfighting. Such people tend to empty their weapon at their assailants in the first few seconds of the duel. This is not limited to panicky first-timers, either; a cardinal rule of armed combat is that you keep firing until your opponent can no longer fire back. Considering that the 9mm, in its most common loadings, is a notoriously poor manstopper, and considering that you may be firing at multiple opponents, and not forgetting the fact that in the heat of combat you may just miss a few — all this can add up to a dead cop or citizen with an empty revolver, or a live one with a half-full autoloader.

But all this is standard "six-gun versus autoloader" commentary. How does it relate to the 39/59 in particular?

The Smith 9mm is probably the most common

S&W Model 59 is a development of the M39 design, with a staggered-column magazine holding 14 or 15 cartridges.

high-power automatic to be carried in plainclothes by detectives and citizens. In that context, we're comparing the Smith Parabellum with the snub-nose .38 — and there is no comparison. Firepower, controllability, and practical accuracy are all far superior with the 39/59. In those departments that issue it, the 9mm S&W has become the most effective issue, plainclothes weapon extant.

Against the service revolver carried on a belt that can be adorned with cylindrical speedloaders since bulge is less of a problem, the Smith Nine doesn't fare so well. Its light weight doesn't mean that much in this context, and a trained man with a speedloader can recharge his six-gun every bit as fast as his partner with the auto.

But the automatics, in particular the Browning P-35 and the 59, have an insurmountable edge over any revolver reloading system: while the revolver-cop is reloading, even if it only takes him three seconds with a Dade, the cop with the auto is still shooting. In any case, the double magazine pouch is more compact on the belt, and a single spare in an inside-belt pouch, as produced by Bianchi and Safariland, gives the auto a particular edge in firepower for the plainclothes user.

Combat-Fire Control: Accuracy is a relative thing. You can theoretically build a shooting machine that will put all of its projectiles through the same hole, but if it isn't "human engineered," its precision won't matter because the user won't be able to take advantage of its intrinsic accuracy as opposed to practical accuracy.

Automatic pistols of this size are human engineered for maximum controllability. It is generic to the breed. The flat-sided grips, and the tang that goes over the web of the hand, prevent any service automatic from twisting in the hand upon recoil the way a revolver will without modified grips. Likewise advantageous is the trigger system. The hardest part of mastering the service revolver is learning to control the double-action trigger pull, which involves twelve to fourteen pounds of pressure on a 2½-pound gun, exerted over perhaps three-fourths of an inch of movement. In the 39, 59, P-35 or 1911, this is reduced to five or so pounds and a fraction of an inch of trigger travel after the first shot. Result: anyone, but particularly the novice, can deliver more accurate shots faster with the service automatic than with the service revolver.

Illinois State Police, who conducted the pioneer experiment, found that their best shots scored a few points lower with the 39 instead of their familiar target-sighted revolvers, while the poorer shots scored the same few points better. In most experience, a good revolver man will shoot substantially lower with the 39 or 59 than with a Model 15 or 19 or Python. At the same time, a poor or untrained shooter will shoot far better with a Smith & Wesson 9mm than with any revolver, whether the latter is in target or service configuration.

This is an undeniable strong point of the automatic pistol in general, and the Smith & Wesson 39/59 in particular, since it is the one type of autoloader most commonly issued to police. The mediocre shot who makes up the vast majority of those who will be carrying the gun will shoot better with it than with a revolver, because the grip shape and trigger simply make it easier for him to hold and squeeze on target. If that squeeze turns into a jerk in the savage heat of a gun battle or in the tense atmosphere of "qualification day," that non-expert officer will probably hit with the S&W automatic where he would miss with the service revolver because the mechanical control of the weapon and its firing mechanism is easier for him to accomplish.

Safety Safeness: That innocuous little thumb-latch on the rear-left side of the Smith Parabellum is a focal point of any argument, pro or con, involving the weapon. It *is* necessary to engage it to prevent the gun from going off if dropped, unless you can find some other way (like a good holster and men trained to use it properly) to prevent the gun from falling to the pavement.

The main advantage of the thumb safety on this or any service automatic is that an assailant who catches you off guard and grabs your weapon can't simply pull the trigger and snuff you as he could with a revolver. I know of two cases where the locked thumb safety of Smith & Wesson Model 39s saved the lives of police officers.

One occurred in Salt Lake City, the first major metropolitan police department to adopt the Model 39. An officer was jumped by two or three assailants and knocked down, and his gun jerked from its holster. After a vigorous stomping, the punk who had grabbed the gun leveled it at its fallen owner and pulled the trigger. Nothing happened. Realizing that it was an automatic with a safety on it somewhere, he fumbled for the first metal lever he could see — the slide release. Nothing happened. He then found a

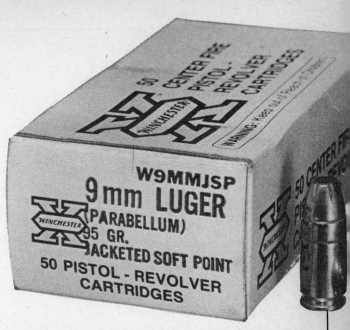

W-W 95-grain JSP has nose form similar to 100-grain on facing page, but puts less unprotected lead nose in contact with feed ramp of autoloader for improved reliability.

button and pressed it. The magazine fell out and bounced off his foot. In a rage, he found the third and least obtrusive lever, the thumb safety. He flipped it over and pulled the trigger, but with the magazine out, the internal disconnector safety prevented the gun from going off. The exasperated thug threw the useless gun at the prostrate officer and walked away, leaving him battered, but alive.

An Illinois trooper tells of the apparently harmless suspect who, when the arresting officers in the post headquarters had turned their backs, reached surreptitiously for the drawer in which he had seen an officer place his issue Model 39. The lawmen heard a metallic scraping sound, and turned to see their misdemeanant with the automatic in his hands, trying desperately to drop the hammer on the policemen. They pounced and disarmed him before he found the safety release.

A similar incident ended tragically. The safety had been left "off" on this particular Model 39, and an Illinois State Trooper was mortally wounded before the gun-grabbing felon was subdued.

Like many of the arguments presented here in favor of the 39/59, this factor would be equally true of the 1911, the P-35, or any of several other service automatics. We cite them here as advantages for the 39/59 series simply because these are the automatic pistols most in use among law enforcement personnel.

Safe Handling: Smith & Wesson has called their Model

This Model 39 has been fitted with a rear sight adjustable for both windage and elevation in place of standard factory sight adjustable only for windage, effecting an improvement.

39 the safest police type autoloader made, and the same presumably applies to the 59. Aside from reservations about the double-action thumb safety mechanism, and the magazine disconnector safety, we'll buy that.

"What?" scream irate fans of the 1911 .45 automatic. "Don't you know that the hammer-drop safeties of guns like the Smith Parabellum and the Walther can fail, and that when you flip that safety lever after jacking a round into the chamber, and drop the hammer, the steel block that's supposed to separate it from the firing pin may crystallize or otherwise fail? Don't you realize that these guns have been known to go off when someone applied the safety to a cocked specimen?"

Possibly so, but a lot more 1911s have gone off when someone who wasn't totally familiar with the mechanism tried to ease the hammer down and it got away from him.

We are talking about a defense/service automatic; that means a gun that is carried largely, if not exclusively, by non-experts. Such a person, and all those around him, are safer in trusting the skill and the metallurgy of Smith & Wesson than trusting those nervous, often inept hands.

Say what you will about the stories of 39s going off when the safety was applied. But ask whether it has happened to you, or someone you knew, or someone who knew someone you knew, or who knew a patron of your favorite gunshop. In any case, it is far more likely that a cocked revolver would go off under such circumstances when the up-tight user tried to lower the hammer than if he just pointed his 39 or 59 in a safe direction and flipped that safety lever.

Beloved of amateurs, the Smith Parabellum has fewer fans among enthusiasts who are into both the mechanics and the top-level performance of the guns they use for recreation or serious business. To them, the 9mm S&W is a flawed weapon, and they list a number of complaints that go beyond the well-worn "revolver versus auto," "single-action vs. double-action autoloader," and "9mm vs. .45" debates. They focus on the weapon itself, its design and its execution.

Poor Accuracy: The majority of police departments that have adopted the 39 and 59 qualify at no farther than twenty-five yards. This is because, at fifty yards, the weapon simply will not group. The degree of the problem seems to vary markedly between production runs.

It's a sloppily fitted weapon, with no real forward lock-up. I've seen batches that would just about stay on the black of a silhouette at fifty yards, with an occasional flyer that even experts couldn't call. But I've also seen production runs that would barely do the same at twenty-five yards, these in the hands of men who could shoot palm-sized groups at that distance with a Model 52, a Browning Hi-Power, or a good service revolver. The latter specimens, at seven yards, could not direct all their shots into one hole in the hands of combat masters.

Now, a one-hole group is no trick for anyone who has spent a lot of time on the twelve-shots-in-twenty-five-seconds stage of the Practical Pistol Course. Any two-inch .38 will perform that well, and so will any GI .45. A mid-frame automatic, with its comfortable hand-filling grip and easily manageable trigger, should do better. Those dismal close-range groups betoken a gun that often has severe accuracy problems.

To say that accuracy doesn't matter in a combat gun is to fail to understand the dynamics of gunfighting. Real life opponents don't stand upright and still, like the paper dummies on a range: they duck behind cover, and when they lean out to shoot at you, you have a small target to hit if you are to terminate their fire. A gun that can't do this can't do the job. A 39 or 59 can do it, but barely, unless you have a good sample.

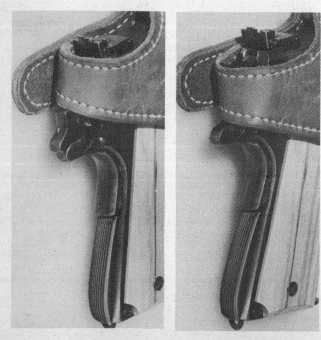

Some holsters, such as Model 55 Safariland, offer option of carrying with safety strap behind or under the hammer.

As discussed, placing safety catch of the Model 1911 in firing mode involves a quick, convenient and positive downward sweep of the thumb as shown here upper/lower.

"How can the 39 be a poor performer," many ask, "if its sister gun, the Model 52 is conceded to be the best factory-produced center-fire target gun in the world?"

One can only answer that the two are different guns, built to different specs from different materials. Ask anyone who has tried to accurize a 39 to Model 52 capabilities, the way 1911s are routinely modified to equal or better Gold Cup .45s. Pistolsmiths and S&W gunmakers alike answer, "It can't be done, and if it could be, it wouldn't be worth the expense."

In some early combat pistol matches, Model 52s stole top honors. The 52 is a superbly accurate pistol with minimal recoil transmitted through its steel frame by the mild mid-range wadcutter .38 for which it's chambered.

But when such guns were banned from most competition because they didn't represent weapons carried for real-life combat, 39s didn't take their place. They couldn't. They weren't accurate enough, even in the context of fast silhouette shooting.

Magazine Disconnector Safety: Any gun buff into automatics knows that a pistol which cannot fire the round in the chamber if the magazine has been removed is a liability in a gunfight. This prevents the user from taking one of the auto pistol's main advantages, which is that it can be fired instantaneously if the user is attacked while reloading.

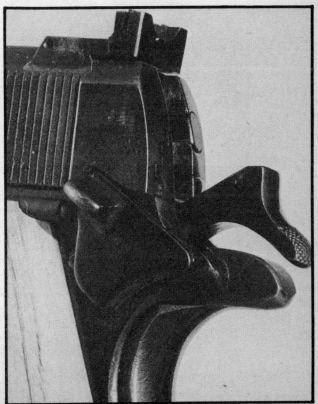

Even in cocked-and-locked mode, as here, a heavy impact on muzzle of the M1911 or M1911A1 can drive the inertia firing pin forward hard enough to fire a chambered round.

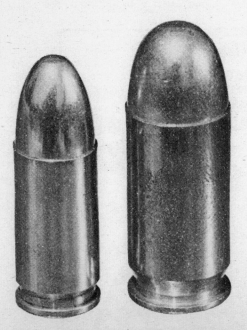

Comparative size and contours of the 9mmP and .45 ACP FMJ or hardball loads shows why the latter usually is considerably more effective in quickly disabling the target.

Super Vel high-performance loads, developed by Lee Jurras in the early Sixties, drastically affected thinking on handgun performance. The brand remains in production in a variety of popular calibers and loads by current plant.

The illusion of safety with this device is dangerous. For one thing, it may fail. For another, no man qualified to carry a gun is going to feel any safer with one that has the magazine out but a round still in the chamber than with a fully loaded piece. It breeds the bad habit of leaving auto pistols with a round in the chamber when the gun is supposed to be "empty." That means that when such a person handles another type of automatic, he has set the stage for a terrible mistake.

A gun-wise cop — indeed, a competition shooter — of our acquaintance, has the scars of a .380 slug on his hand from a double-action auto. Accustomed to 39-type pieces with magazine disconnector safeties, he took liberties with a gun that didn't work quite the same way. The result was a loud noise in his department locker room, a lot of blood, and a lot of embarrassment. He got off cheap.

Police officers who carry 39s and 59s often are encouraged to "deactivate" their sidearms by removing the magazine when escorting a prisoner into a cell block or other secured area. This, supposedly, keeps them safe from a disarming attempt without stockpiling guns in some clerk's booth on the way in.

The fallacy of this is threefold: (a) anyone who overpowers him will have access to the spare magazines on the unconscious officer's belt to reload with, and checking two to three magazines is more bother than checking the gun itself; (b) many officers, regulations notwithstanding, may have removed the magazine disconnector from their service pistols, and an officer facing a stolen service auto can't be sure it hasn't been so modified; and (c) an officer who borrows a service auto from a brother officer or the department armory probably won't know whether the gun in question has the disconnector intact.

Some feel that disconnector safeties should be taken out of all issue Smith autos and made into tiepins. That way, they can at least, perform some kind of useful function, and the guns themselves can now give the men who carry them an extra edge in high-volume shootouts where reloading becomes necessary. Checking isn't that rugged a problem, even in small departments where there may not be a secure vault in which to store the checked-in weapons.

Favored military carrying mode for the M1911 is with the hammer down on an empty chamber, cycling the slide to make it ready to fire. As discussed, it can fire, even in cocked-and-locked mode (below) if dropped on its muzzle.

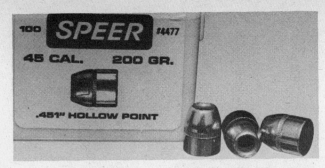

Speer's 200-grain JHP for the .45 ACP is an excellent performer, available also in factory loads from Speer. Right, Browning Model BDA offers an expensive but very reliable double-action auto chambered for the .45 ACP.

When Ayoob checks the customized 1911 he usually carries on duty, he simply takes spare cuffs and closes one bracelet over the pistol, one side under but not through the trigger guard, the other between the cocked-and-locked hammer and the firing pin.

Safety: The thumb safety must be engaged if the 39 or 59 is to be carried fully loaded without fear of accident, and while a locked safety can be top insurance against a gun-grab, it can jeopardize an officer's life in a fast-draw-and-shoot situation if it isn't designed right. And the 9mm S&W's isn't. It requires an upward stroke of the thumb, as opposed to the downward stroke that unlocks a Colt-Browning type auto. A downward stroke is a natural part of the drawing action, performed as the hand closes over the butt, which is why cocked-and-locked on a 1911 or P-35 is every bit as fast for the first shot as a double-action revolver. The upward stroke required on the Smith (and the Walther, and many others) requires the shooter to break his grip just at the moment when he should be clamping down for maximum control in the presumably imminent crisis which is making him go for his gun. Result: a slow, perhaps fumbling draw that delays that vital first shot, and when it does go off, it may be awry because the hand may not be locked solidly into a control position.

If the officer has a good, fast-yet-secure holster — one that releases quickly with a thumbbreak yet prevents the

Upper right, Browning P-35 Hi-Power carries Seecamp DA conversion, Pachmayr grips and target rear sight. Lower right, Benelli B76 is a single-column 9mm DA recently introduced. Below, Walther DA, such as this Turkish-made copy, offer DA, but only up to .380 auto.

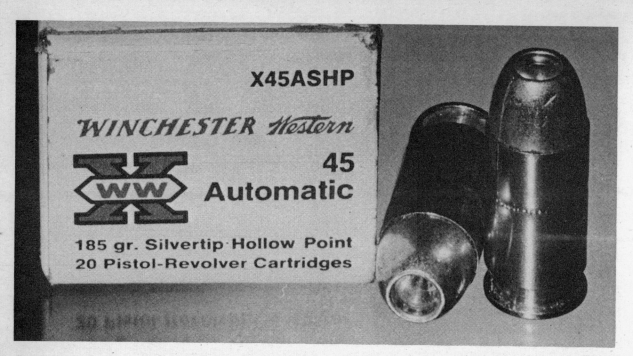

Recently introduced by W-W, in both 9mmP and .45 ACP, the Silvertip hollow point load carries bullets having a lubricated jacket of special aluminum alloy, combining accuracy, feeding reliability and good expansion potential.

gun from dropping out when the officer falls or runs — the safety may be left off. The Wrentham, Massachusetts, Police Department has the best policy seen: the officer reaches down to his holstered 59 and locks the thumb safety when going into a crowd or brawl situation but keeps the gun ready-to-go at all other times. It's the best compromise I've seen yet in terms of carrying this weapon practically.

Aluminum Frame: The handful of early steel-frame Model 39s are fetching prices on the collector's market right now that are about equal to what your father would

Although FMJ hardball loads for the 9mmP have been made in 124-grain bullet weight, the current trend has been toward the 115-grain version, such as this by W-W.

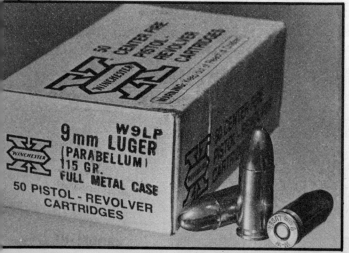

have paid for a Paterson Colt when he was young. If there were enough of them around, they'd be valued for practical reasons as well as scarcity.

S&W says they stay with the aluminum frame because the cops like it. No doubt that's why Colt still sells aluminum frame Commanders. The fact is that the few ounces you take off with the duralumin superstructure are noticed only in a gun like the Chief Special Airweight, which may frequently be carried in pocket or ankle holster. Here, the small weight saving makes a definite difference in comfort. But 39s and 59s are carried on or in the belt. Supported by the wide band of leather, the added weight of a steel frame gun becomes so insignificant as to be virtually unnoticeable.

If the light alloy frame does nothing for the better, it does a lot for the worse. Recoil with an aluminum Nine like the Smith is roughly equal to that of an all-steel .45. The relative effectiveness of the two calibers is considered elsewhere in this chapter. Steel construction would bring the 39/59 down in recoil, and make it as controllable as they easy-to-shoot P-35 and Combat Commander 9mms. This would be in keeping with the generally good controllability that is one of the advantages of most other 9mm Parabellum service automatics.

Reliability: In one test by a large state police agency, two brand new test 59s went full automatic within two hundred rounds. With a police department that had purchased 59s for all its men, the guns all fouled up so horribly (more than one jam per magazine in each gun) that the department angrily sent them all back to the factory. In fairness, some attribute that disastrous performance largely to the S&W ammo that had been purchased with the guns: the semi-wadcutter training rounds and the stubby, light, high-speed soft-nose duty loads were both too short and untapered to feed reliably in *any* 9mm. Still, an early random survey of seven guns out of the boxes showed one defective magazine release, and two filled with rust-colored gunk. Yet the first 59s were beautiful guns, showing better workmanship and better shooting capability and reliability than the 39s that had preceded them. In any manufactured product, quality varies between production runs.

Jams have been reported on 39-equipped firing lines with guns built from the Fifties to the Seventies, in various state of tune, and even with hardball. In the last analysis, we must say that a good 39 or 59 is a very reliable auto pistol, but that they are not in quite the same class as the Browning and Colt 9mms in terms of reliability.

Much of the mystique of this gun has been built around several concepts that those who spend a lot of time with combat handguns consider fallacious. Let's examine them one by one.

The Double Action S&W Auto can be carried ready-to-go like a revolver, in perfect safety.

S&W has publicly admitted that a Model 39 or 59, fully loaded with the hammer down on a round in the chamber and the safety off, may discharge if dropped muzzle-first on a hard surface from a height of four feet — between belt and aiming level. Looking back, one notes in the small print of the early Smith & Wesson literature on the Model 39, the warning that users should engage the thumb safety.

This should be academic, since nobody drops guns, right? The truth is, nobody wants to drop guns, but in the hairy confrontations guns like this were built for, dropping is a very real hazard. A friend of mine, a nationally recognized karate master and an auxiliary policeman of some experience, found himself in an altercation on a lakeside dock with a group of toughs. They muckled onto his arm, and he had the choice of dropping his gun or having it torn from his hands. He flipped the piece into the water, and then, deadly weapons now being out of the picture, did his number. By the time his service sidearm was fished out of the muddy shallows, his fists and feet had sent his attackers to the hospital.

In cold weather climes, it is not uncommon for officers to slip on icy surfaces and fall flat on their backs. If, as many officers do, they have unstrapped their sidearms, it is entirely possible that the gun will wind up bouncing on the hard ice. If that ever happens to me, the only noise I want to hear is a metallic clank, and not the sound of a cap busting a hot 9mm cartridge.

Arguments to the contrary, it appears that this is almost equally possible with a 1911 pistol carried hammer down on a live one. A 1911 type should be carried cocked and locked or not at all; if one carries a Smith 39 or 59, a secure holster is imperative.

The 9mm cartridge of the 39/59 is an excellent manstopper with proper loads!

This contention is arguable, on two counts. First, gunfights in the police sector and especially in military history in this century (the classic comparison of 9mm Parabellum vs. .45 ACP in hardball) indicate that the Nine is a poor manstopper, the .45 a fairly reliable one. Observations of combat actions in WWI and WWII reinforced the belief among gun experts that the 9mm Luger, in full-jacketed configuration, was designed to wound rather than kill, thus tying up more of the enemy's personnel in removing casualties.

In modern loads — light, high-speed projectiles designed to expand via soft or hollow noses — 9mm performance is dramatically improved. However, reports of police gunfights involving such rounds indicate that they perform

S&W's 115-grain jacketed semi-wadcutter load was an attempt to improve the notoriously poor shock effect of the FMJ bullet in the 9mmP round. It helped, but not much.

When gunwriter Dean Grennell served as a police officer in a Midwestern department that allowed patrolmen to carry the duty weapon of their choice, he usually carried this S&W Model 24 in .44 Special, alternating at times with a Model 1911 Colt .45 ACP or S&W Model 27 in .357 magnum, 3½".

much like the Super Vel genre of .38 Special and .357 magnum revolver cartridges; while they are better than round noses for stopping power, they are far from ideal in terms of manstopping finality.

Most gun buffs are under the delusion that all police who carry 9mms use high performance ammo, not the hardball loads that are notorious for poor shock but high penetration, the exact opposite on both counts of what the cop or law-abiding citizen needs in terms of defensive gunfighting performance.

Many have been told that Illinois State Police, the first major American law enforcement agency to adopt the Model 39, carries Winchester 100-grain Power Points in their service guns. Actually, round-nose full-jacketed ammo was carried in the troopers' guns, and always had been. Some had harrowing tales to tell of troopers who had been involved in gunfights where they hit their opponents several times and they kept firing back, only to collapse later from loss of blood. ISP finally began issuing the Power Points early in 1976.

The Wrentham, Massachusetts, police department, perhaps the first in the country to standardize on the Model

59 pistol in early 1973, carried hardball in the guns for some time. Last we knew, they were planning to convert to "hot loads."

The problem is that the concept of the hot load in most police calibers, including 9mm Parabellum, involves increased velocity for a lighter 90 to 100-grain bullet. Lighter means shorter, and in an auto pistol, shorter means feeding difficulties, since all 9mm pistols are built around the standard load's dimensions.

Velocity in the 124-grain bullet is more than sufficient to create good expansion and shock effect provided that the projectile has expansion capability, but we have seen no such round commercially produced that was tapered and jacketed enough toward the hollow front cavity to allow totally reliable feeding. The Winchester 100-grain Power Point (semi-jacketed soft-nose) is a reliable 9mm Parabellum combat round, the choice of most police agencies going to high-performance ammo in this caliber. Remington's 115-grain JHP is earning quite a reputation for itself.

Recent Federal tests indicate that the 9mm may be more potent than the .45 ACP, but you have to read between the

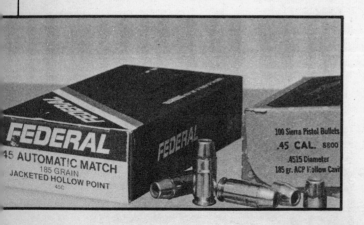

Federal's Index No. 45C match load for the .45 ACP carries the Sierra 185-grain JHC bullet and it is generally regarded as one of the most accurate .45 ACP loads available, with the added bonus of offering exceptional expansion so that it also serves well as a duty load in guns chambered to .45 ACP.

lines. Synopsis of the tests indicates that few conventional 9mm rounds out-perform the Remington 185-grain hi-speed hollow point in .45, save for the controversial Glaser Safety Slug, a super-destructive Nine. In reliable feeding hardball, though, Federal test results showing the 9mm superior to the .45 must be taken with a grain of salt. Those tests were conducted on gelatin, not human tissue; the LaGarde studies done on cadavers around the turn of the century showed the Nine a poor contender with the .45 for impact energy and destructive effect. You can scoop out gelatin with your fingers, but not human skin and muscle tissue; it's a comparison of apples and oranges.

The same comment holds true for those articles you see in gun magazines where the 9mm is rated above the .45 on the basis of relative effect on sealed cans of water. A .45 slug will knock such a can flying, with water dribbling out of its holes, while a 9mm hardball round will burst it at the seams with a spectacular splash.

"Since the human body is ninety-eight-percent water," some say, "the same effect would occur in an opponent's body."

Our tissues are not liquid, which is why we do not gurgle when we walk, and people don't blow up into mist when hit with fast bullets. In fact, if they're not hit with something that knocks them down or disconnects their nervous system, they may even reverse the experiment and shoot back. People who have been in gunfights and studied the aftermath of other such confrontations lean a lot farther toward .45s than 9mms.

A .45 ACP steel-frame 39 or 59 has been dreamt of by gun experts since the early Fifties, when Smith introduced their line of service automatics. The concept hasn't gotten beyond the walls of the factory in Springfield, where prototypes have reportedly been built. When such a caliber is introduced, it will make the 39/59 a better tool for the

purpose it is built to serve. That the gun-buying public agrees may be seen in the relatively high sales figures of .45 Colt automatics as compared to identical models in 9mm Parabellum and .38 Super.

By all accounts, the Model 39 was a major advance in handgun design in our time, and the 59, a worthy follow-up. Many of the nationally recognized experts who determine public and private trends in handguns have, at one time or another, seemed to endorse it. Yet a survey of present positions shows some surprising insights. Let's take the experts one by one.

Colonel Charles C. Askins, Jr., was one of the first supporters of the .39. A man who loves controversy, the good colonel stated in print at various times that the 9mm Parabellum was all that was needed for "social purposes." Yet in previous writings, he had accused that round of being a wounder rather than a stopper, and auto pistols in general, with the possible exception of the 1911 .45, poor choices for gunfighting. Lately, he has waxed more eloquent over the .45 than the 9mm.

Colonel Askins has survived more gunfights than any writer in the business, with the possible exception of Bill Jordan. He survived those gunfights with shotguns mostly, revolvers occasionally, and automatics never, no matter what their caliber.

During World War II, when he was perhaps America's leading handgun authority (he may still be, many feel), he eschewed the auto pistol for Colt New Service sixguns, despite the fact that he had won at least one national championship with a custom radical Walther P-38 double-action 9mm Parabellum. We respect the colonel's conclusions, but looking over his collected writings, tend to lean toward the advice he gave in earlier days, when those life-and-death confrontations were fresher in his memory.

Elmer Keith, though he generally favors Smiths over

The Index No. 3620 9mmP load from Omark/CCI-Speer carries a 125-grain JSP bullet at a muzzle velocity of 1100 fps, making it one of the most effective 9mmP loads in terms of expansion capability. The problem lies in the fact that the large area of exposed lead at the nose may pose feeding problems when used in some autoloaders.

Colts, has just about always been in favor of the .45 over the 9mm, with the 1911 vs. S&W double action argument a secondary consideration in which he favored the latter.

Contemporary gun buffs like to scoff at his theories, but he has long been the dean of American gun writers, and as such privy to reports on gunfight windups that don't reach other authorities. His opinions carry weight beyond his reputation.

Skeeter Skelton, practical and flexible in the face of change and development, once said that only revolvers would do for combat, and anyone who wanted to carry an automatic would do equally well with a Smith & Wesson 9mm or a Colt .45, so long as he bought extra life insurance the same day he purchased the gun. Today, Skeeter carries and boosts 1911 .45s and P-35s — but seldom mentions the 39 and 59. One can only assume that Skelton, a true gentleman, doesn't speak of something unless he has a good word for it.

Bill Jordan, do-or-die revolver man, doesn't have that much use for automatics, but he is more fond of the Model 59 than the 1911 .45. This is partly for its firepower, and partly for its double-action mechanism, which he likes better than a (slow) hammer-down or (dangerous) cocked-and-locked .45. He stated once that he considered the 59 an excellent backup gun for a Model 19 .357 or Model 57 .41 magnum revolver.

Jeff Cooper has been called "the high priest of the .45 cult," and his comments on the 39 and 59 are in the same vein you would expect if you asked a Chapparal driver to analyze the Lotus Elan. Quite apart from his rejection of the 9mm Parabellum as an ineffective manstopper in any loading, and his criticism of all double-action to single-action-trigger systems as awkward, he has called the 9mm Smith autoloaders fragile, clumsy to operate, and generally not winners' equipment.

The late George Nonte was perhaps the only leading firearms authority to stand foursquare behind the 39/59. He felt it the most modern and practical of service sidearms for police or military or civilian defense. He did much custom work on the instrument to improve feeding of high-performance loads (much as Cooper has with the "throated" .45).

The 39/59 makes the amateur-to-average shooter perform better, while it hampers the expert, because it combines excellent human engineering with lousy intrinsic accuracy.

In the hands of a trained man, it provides what may be a life-saving margin of volume firepower and rapid, controlled delivery. At the same time, it is more likely to malfunction than either a good service revolver or a Colt/Browning automatic of equal size and caliber. It is safer than other automatics in some respects, while certain design features create false confidence and cancel at least one purpose of the auto pistol, which is the ability to return fire if attacked while reloading.

Its applications in law enforcement are likewise ironic. I know of at least two departments where investigators carry Model 59s and uniformed officers pack revolvers, thus giving the most firepower to the men who, in many cases, may be less likely to need it.

In many departments, it has been adopted because the administrators of the agency wanted their men to have maximum gunfight capability, yet to keep the guns from jamming and therefore destroying the men's confidence, they had to issue hardball ammo that produced minimal shock effect and increased danger to bystanders due to excessive penetration and ricochet.

Because the autoloading pistol still seems radical to the conservative majority of lawmen, it has been adopted mostly by officers in small towns. This tends to mean rural areas, where the distances between combatants tend to be somewhat longer, showing up the disadvantage of the poorly-grouping 39/59. On the other hand, rural officers are more remote from backup in such cases, and the high capacity of these 9mm autos more than compensates for mediocre accuracy in such situations.

For those with the capability of reloading for the 9mmP, this 115-grain JHC bullet by Sierra can be made up to provide a high degree of feeding reliability, coupled with outstanding expansion characteristics and good accuracy.

100 Sierra Pistol Bullets

9 MM

Jacketed Hollow Cavity
115 Gr.

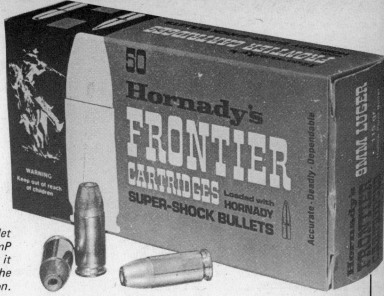

Hornady Frontier ammunition, from the well known bullet maker in Grand Island, Nebraska, can be had in 9mmP with this 115-grain JHP projectile. It is unusual in that it nearly duplicates the shape and feeding reliability of the FMJ hardball load, meanwhile retaining good expansion.

In the end, when you look at the reams that have been written about the Smith & Wesson Model 39 and 59 double action 9mm autos, you may tend to agree with the popular assessment. A unique design that has much to offer in terms of handling capability, it is flawed by mediocre accuracy and poor safety structure, and lacks the shock power that it could have. It improves the shooting ability of those with limited training, but ironically, one must have *added* training to master the mechanics of these pistols, and it is still uncertain whether those extra hours might not be spent in teaching mastery of the .38 and .357 revolvers that most lawmen (and most armed civilians) carry.

Experts would like to see a steel-frame Smith & Wesson automatic, chambered for .45 ACP and perhaps .38 Super as well as 9mm Parabellum. The gun they envision would have more accuracy, perhaps on a par with the Colt Government Model MK IV with collet barrel bushing. The double-action mechanism would be redesigned to allow safe carry with the hammer down on the live round with safety off, and the option of locking the cocked gun a la 1911 or P-35. The magazine safety would probably be eliminated.

But as it is now, the Model 39 and 59 are classic pistols, guns that are to our time what the 1911 must have been when it was introduced. And they will be popular for the rest of our lifetimes. They will sell more to amateurs and enthusiasts new to the field than they will to experts, but they will serve their owners well. Future historians who analyze the tools of the 1960 and 1970 Americans probably will put these pistols in the same category as the Ford Mustang and the Quasar television.

All those instruments will have served their purpose for the people who owned and used them. The critical knowledge of contemporary experts will be a secondary consideration, forgotten as we today have forgotten whatever Frontier gunsmiths and gunfighters may have criticized about the Peacemaker.

Ultimately, any tool will be judged not by how it worked for a handful of experts, but how many of the general populace adopted it and trusted it. So will it be with the Smith Parabellums. The contemporary specialists will never try to blacken the name of a legendary piece. They can only try to show it as it is — in this case, something good but not perfect.

An exceptionally popular .45 ACP load is Remington's No. R45AP2, with its 185-grain JHP bullet. Velocity out of five-inch M1911 barrels exceeds 1000 fps comfortably.

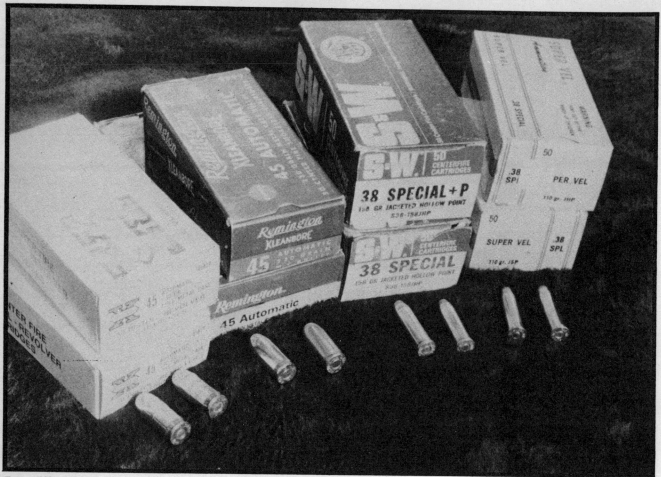

Four different sets of nominally identical ammunition, each in two lot numbers, were used for tests reported here.

Chapter 21

HOW IMPORTANT ARE AMMO LOTS?

Knowing Something Of Manufacturer's Coding Could Help Your Shooting

NLESS YOU'RE AN artilleryman — or an artilleryman emeritus — you may find the reference to "lots" puzzling. Gunpowder is interesting stuff. It's not all that complicated chemically, but the processes involved in its manufacture are such that it tends to be manufactured in separate batches rather than as a continuous process. These different batches of powder are the main reason all ammunition is made up in separately identified lots. Lord knows that artillerymen and their archfoes in the ordnance know about ammunition lots. They've been the source of many a hot argument over the years.

When you set out to make smokeless powder, the purity and concentration of the ingredients are bound to vary somewhat from batch to batch. The same is true of the steps in the manufacturing process; they're never conducted in exactly the same way. These things are controllable, of course, but like everything else in life, how well you're able to control eventually boils down to a matter of economics. And, too, there is always progress. Manufacturers are continually discovering an abbreviated way to accomplish a certain manufacturing step, or a better way to do something else. Improvements always are in order. But the end result is that while each new batch of a certain powder is very much like the last, it's still unique. Unique in how fast it burns, in how progressively, in how its energy curve develops and in how much energy it delivers per grain of weight.

Powder isn't the only element that is a variable. Cases, primers, bullets and the ways they are made and assembled — all are the subject of constant industry research and development, which means change and improvement. Practical economics enter here, too. Raw materials and subcontractor-made components are sometimes cheaper from one source, sometimes from another, with the inevitable result that components other than powder also

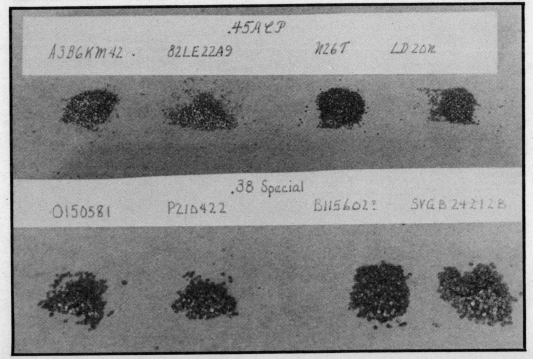

Ammunition manufacturers customarily use non-canister powders not available to the home reloader, establishing properties, performance and load data in their laboratories. Visual inspection will give relative coarseness and coloration, but little else. Weight of charge can be checked on reloading scale.

Ammunition lot tests were conducted at Marine Corps' range facilities near Quantico, Virginia, using Lee pistol rest and Medaris M500D chronograph.

are different in small ways. When one batch of powder comes together in the manufacturing process with individual batches of other components, a new lot is born. Earlier we made joking reference to the Ordnance Corps as being archfoes of artillerymen. That was, of course, untrue, but it points out the fact that gunners have brought constant pressure upon ordnance to lessen the differences in performance between different lots of artillery ammunition. Fortunately for artillerymen, accuracy against large area targets such as a piece of ground 100x100 yards is directly related to uniform velocity. In the firing tables, a variation of ten feet per second in velocity can be translated into a specific distance in yards (or meters) the round will fall short or over! Obviously, ammunition is wanted with the smallest possible velocity variation round to round, and also with different lots to be as close to each other on the average as possible.

Our ordnance friends, ever since World War II, have claimed that there is no greater velocity variation between the averages of two lots than there is between rounds within a given lot. Buffalo dung! Don't make any bets on it! This may be true under the beautifully controlled and instrumented conditions at Aberdeen Proving Ground with ammunition that — we suspect — had been carefully selected by the contractor operator of the ammunition plant, but it sure is not true on the frozen, filthy rice paddies of Korea and the steamy heat of the Vietnam lowlands. We have seen lots that shot more than one

Super Vel's .38 Special printed this group on target using Hamilton's eyeball sight method.

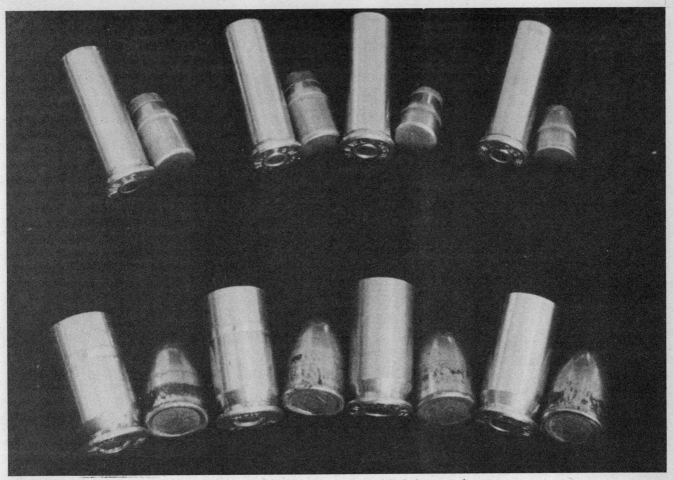
Cartridges were pulled down and the bullets were measured, together with their respective cases.

hundred yards away from the point of impact of the last one in use. That's why artillerymen still insist that each new ammunition lot brought into the unit be checked out by firing to see just where it does, in fact, shoot.

To be fair, ordnance has made heroic efforts to improve our artillery ammunition and it's true that ours is the best in the world today. The technique ordnance uses to keep lot-to-lot variations as small as possible is governed by the real world of economics. Each component, from propellant through the shell and its fuse, is quality controlled to the extent cost will permit. Then, since powder is the easiest variable to work with, rounds of the new lot are assembled and test fired varying the powder charges until the desired pressure and velocity are achieved. This, of course, is done under carefully instrumented conditions of gun, air and powder temperature, air density and elasticity, humidity, ballistic winds aloft, and other meteorological factors. We're sure that commercial handgun ammunition manufacturers use much the same approach to keeping

their lots as close as possible to each other in performance.

Last Spring, in preparation for the annual match season, the Marine Corps Marksmanship Training Unit at Quantico sent its handgun senior armorer to visit all of the major ammunition manufacturers. He went to test fire all of the target ammunition they offered for the .45 ACP and .38 Special. Based upon the results, match ammunition for the coming season was to be purchased. The sergeant discovered one lot of Federal .45 ACP FMJ wadcutters loaded to full power which stood out head and shoulders above all the rest of the brands and lots he tested. He also found some Federal .38 Special that was particularly good. It goes without saying that these were the lots the Marine Corps used that year. We saw the .45 ACP results out of some of his fine, reworked guns off a Ransom Rest and they truly were remarkable. At fifty yards you could very nearly cover some of the groups with a silver dollar, except for one flier in each case.

Standard National Rifle Association twenty-five-yard targets were used as aiming point for the group tests.

To learn more about handgun ammunition lots, we wrote to Remington, Federal, Winchester, Smith & Wesson, Speer and H&H (Super Vel's successor), asking for the standards they have established to control performance lot to lot. Interestingly, it turns out that in all but one case in which we received replies, the companies concerned consider this information confidential. Federal was the exception, and most courteously provided the following information for the .38 Special only. For each new lot, they require velocity to be within fifty feet per second, on the average, from a standard set for that particular load; average group spread for five five-shot targets must be three inches or less at fifty yards off the machine rest; pressure must not vary in excess of 6200 cup on the average. The Federal reply may have let the cat out of the bag, too, since they went on to indicate that these "are industry standards" and will soon be available as an "American National Standards Institute standard."

We must admit more than a little surprise at the pressure variation mentioned. For a cartridge which nominally operates at about 15,000 to 17,000 cup, a tolerance of 6200 cup seems enormous.

It also occurred to us to inquire of the Sporting Arms and Ammunition Manufacturers' Institute where such matters are made a matter of record. The institute, however, chose not to respond to our inquiry.

To find the answer to our own question about the relevance of ammunition lots as a handgunner consideration, we resolved to find different lots of some common loads put up by the makers, shoot them off against each other and see what the results might be. This turned out easier to think about than to accomplish. We had to cover half the state of Virginia to find four examples of loads of different lots. What we ended up with was two lots, each of Western Super X and Remington .45 ACP in

230-grain hardball. To that we added two lots each of S&W and old Super Vel .38 Special. The S&W was 158-grain JHPs and the Super Vel 110-grain JHPs.

First, we looked over the test loads carefully to see if there were any outward physical indications of differences in components. The only thing externally visible on the Western Super X .45s was a slightly deeper and more pronounced cannelure on the cases of lot 82LE 22A9 below the bullet.

Remington lots of .45 differed in headstamp; N26T was stamped REM-UMC 45 AUTO while LD20N bore the stamping R-P 45 AUTO. Both lots have plated cases but

S&W K-38 was used in testing .38 Special loads.

An Ohaus scale and 630 Ball Powder were used in checking case capacity.

those of lot N26T are distinctly less shiny and look almost like stainless steel.

The noses of the bullets of S&W lot 0150581 all show white signs of lead oxide formation. The headstamps of the two lots are the same but done in letters of different size. The primers of lot P210422 seem ever so slightly smaller than those of the other lot.

The two Super Vel lots also were different in the size

lettering and in that the primers of lot GB 212428 seemed slightly smaller.

Next, we broke down ten of each lot of cartridges for examination in greater detail. (See chart below.)

Case capacity was measured by filling the unfired, primed case to the brim with 630 ball powder, leveling, then weighing the result.

We found this comparison quite instructive. Note for

| Lot | Bullet | | | Case | | | | Powder | | Total Weight |
	Diameter	Length	Weight (grain)	Diameter	Length	Weight (grain)	Capacity (grain)	Nature	Weight (grain)	
.45 A3B6 KM42	.453	.661	229	.470	.887	84.2	28.1	Coarse, green color.	5.1	320
.45 82LE 22A9	.454	.664	231.6	.457	.890	84.8	28.0	Much finer; grey.	5.7	323.7
.45 N26T	.451	.667	229.5	.471	.890	88.1	28.4	Same	4.6	322.7
.45 LD20N	.451	.665	229.8	.469	.890	86.5	27.3	Same	4.3	321.9
.38 0150 581	.357	.675	157.7	.379	1.150	72.5	24.0	Very coarse; greenish	4.9	235.7
.38 P210 422	.357	.680	158.0	.377	1.156	77.8	24.0	Same	5.3	241.7
.38 B115 602	.355	.490	109.8	.376	1.153	68.3	24.8	Same but grey	7.2	185.8
.38 SVGB2 42128	.355	.490	109.9	.376	1.155	66.4	25.5	Same	6.3	182.9

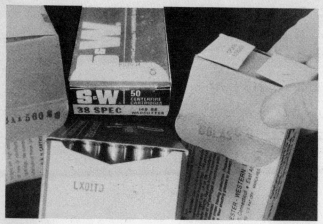

Placement of lot numbers varies from one manufacturer to another. Smith & Wesson prints the numbers on box tongue, Remington puts it on the end of the inner box while W-W and Super Vel stamp the numbers on inner surface of box tongue.

example the wide difference in average powder charge weights between all the lots. We think that while some of the same powders may have been used this makes it clear that different powder lots were involved. The closeness of the case capacities of the two Western .45 lots (A3B6 and 82LE) together with their other average dimensions makes us suspect that the same lot of brass was used for both. On the other hand, while the two Smith & Wesson .38 Special lots (0150 and P210) had identical average case capacities, we doubt that this brass is from the same batch because of the great difference in average weight. Of course, keep in mind that our rather small ten unit sampling from each lot doesn't support firm conclusions.

We could not identify the powders used. It's known that the makers often use powders not available to the handloader and to attempt to visually identify powders is a dangerous business, we think.

An interesting point noted was that all of the .45 caliber bullets examined had been sealed in the case; none of the .38 Special bullets had been. Someone at some time must have complained to Smith & Wesson about the firmness of their bullet crimp. They have certainly corrected that. We had several bullet cores come out of the jackets when we tried to pull them with the inertia puller. No way would those jackets come free without tearing up the case! Some have had that experience before with Smith & Wesson .38 Special loads.

Next came the shooting. We took the loads, and Chronograph Specialists M500D and Lee Rest down to Quantico in early November and got set up to shoot for velocity, velocity spread, groups and their points of impact using the standard NRA twenty-five-yard target over the fifty-yard range. (See chart for velocity results we measured. The manufacturers' advertised velocity shown, when available, for comparison.)

Of course in a sense it was academic to test old Super Vel ammunition, but when you're trying to assemble different lots of the same load you soon learn to take anything you can get!

For the test shoot we used two guns: a 1960 vintage Colt Government Model, which has been accurized by Haywood Nelms and has a Bar-Sto stainless barrel and bushing; a Smith & Wesson K-38 vintage of about 1951. In both cases the guns qualify as new having had less than fifty rounds fired through them before this shoot, which brings up an interesting point. The reader must take the velocities we got as relative at best; I know that two other guns identical to the two we used might well record velocities

Load Description	Lot Number	Average Velocity[2]	Extreme Spread	Factory Velocity[1]
.45 ACP Western 230-grain FMJ	A3B6KM42	719 fps	103 fps	810 fps
	82LE22A9	785	10	810
.45 ACP Remington 230-grain FMJ	N26T	801	9	850
	LD20N	748	12	850
.38 Special S & W 158-grain JHP	0150581	764	65	1000
	P210422	831	60	1000
.38 Special Super Vel 110-grain JHP	B115602	1152[3]	155	Not
	SVGB242128	1079	39	Available

NOTES:
1. Factory velocities are obtained in test barrels, some of which are ventilated to simulate revolvers.
2. Based upon ten shots.
3. This lot gave hard extraction and flattened primers.

Load Description	Lot Number	Average Group	Aiming Point Displacement
.45 ACP Western 230 grain FMJ	A3B6KM42	6.5 inches	3 inches high
.45 ACP Western 230 grain FMJ	82LE22A9	7.3	1 inch right, 1 inch low
.45 ACP Remington 230 grain FMJ	N26T	6.7	5 inches low
.45 ACP Remington 230 grain FMJ	LD20N	7.0	3 inches low, 5 inches right
.38 Special S & W 158 grain JHP (-P)	0150581	5.0	3 inches left
.38 Special S & W	P210422	5.3	4 inches high, 2 inches right
.38 Special Super Vel 110 grain JHP	B115602	6.7	3 inches low, 2 inches left
.38 Special Super Vel 110 grain JHP	SVGB242128	6.0	2 inches low, 5 inches left

differing from ours by more than one hundred fps using the same ammunition!

We weren't successful the first day at shooting for groups. It took us three tries in all before we managed to get a sufficiently solid base for the Lee Rest to operate on. Even then our groups did not resemble the three-inch

Hamilton found solid mounting of the base essential in obtaining precision results with the Lee pistol rest.

tolerance that Federal allows between their lots! We were lucky to get results twice that large.

When we did our group shooting — finally — we decided not to move the sights of the guns in any way (both were equipped with target sights) but to use the black center of the NRA twenty-five-yard target as an aiming point in each case and then estimate the center of impact of the group from that. This seemed to work quite well and the results were just what we'd hoped for: an indication of where each particular lot shoots in these guns with respect to the other.

There is no longer any doubt in our minds. Different lots of handgun factory ammunition do not perform identically, and the handgunner would be wise to check out each new lot of favorite load he buys. Different lots give different average velocities, different velocity variations, and shoot to somewhat different points of aim. Although we did not test this aspect, we would not be surprised to discover that bullets from different lots do not expand on impact in the same way either. Once again, though, there is so much individuality about bullet performance from shot to shot in differing targets it's hard to know if anything meaningful could be determined. We have seen two successive shots out of the same revolver cylinder strike only inches apart yet produce monumentally different results!

We learned a lesson, too. While velocity variations are certainly of vital concern to the artilleryman out at the far end of the trajectory, for the handgunner they are not what determines accuracy! Try as we may we have not been able to relate the velocity variations found in the various lots to how well they shoot. Some, like that first lot of Western with the worst spread of all the .45 ammunition gave the best average target! And then old N26T with its hard-to-believe 9 fps variation spread didn't print impressively at all. Obviously, at handgun ranges there are other factors which far outweigh velocity variation.

*Olin/Winchester-Western's Q4030 load
was one of that maker's earlier
efforts toward providing ammo
for police use with capability
beyond the lead round nose.*

Chapter 22

POLICE AMMUNITION TODAY

POLICE AMMUNITION, pretty much standard until the 1960s, underwent several drastic changes in the following years. Cumulative statistics had proven that standard ammunition had one or both of two shortcomings: lack of stopping power on a human adversary, and/or lack of penetrating power when the officer had to punch a bullet through a car door or other barricade to neutralize a violent offender.

In the Sixties, the big development was Lee Jurras' Super Vel ammunition, a production cartridge based on the Harvey Jugular bullets of the 1950s that never were used by police. Lee Jurras found that by using a lighter bullet at higher velocities, a much more potent result could be delivered to the target, provided that the bullet was scientifically designed. The result was a series of semi-jacketed soft-nose and hollow-point bullets in 90-grain or 112-grain weight in the 9mm instead of the standard 124, or scaling 110 to 125 grains in .38 and .357 instead of the conventional 158-grain weight. The combination of efficient expanding bullets with the increased velocity — from perhaps 700-plus feet per second (fps), out of a four-inch .38 revolver, to well over 1000 fps — instantly proved on the street that it magnified shock power. At the same time, these bullets seldom exited or ricocheted, and danger to innocents was reduced. As a result, more than half of America's police today use either soft-nose or hollow-point ammunition that derives directly from the Super Vel concept.

Several other police cartridges emerged during the period

of the mid-Sixties through the early Seventies. They are still with us, and still serve special purposes.

One will be examined only briefly. It is the MBA Shortstop cartridge out of Southern California, where it has found some popularity among sheriff departments for special purposes. It consists of a little bag full of shot crammed into a .38 cartridge case. Once out of the barrel, the bag would expand. Those Southwestern deputies used it in courthouses because almost any other type of load could ricochet almost endlessly through a marble-lined building. Penetration was poor, and a man in a leather coat might have escaped a lethal wound from it; accuracy was also terrible. The LEAA report on RII (Relative Incapacitation Index) of police ammo rated the MBA wound at absolute bottom. Still, it was claimed that at close range, on unprotected flesh, the MBA Shortstop could tear a frightful wound that *would* "stop an opponent short." It was obviously, however, a special-purpose cartridge with no place in general law enforcement.

In the early Seventies, Michigan Fire Rescue Equipment marketed the Quad-.38, a round that was kind of a .38 wadcutter with the bullet sliced into four sections. Larry Kelly of the Mag-na-port Company tested the original prototype, which had only three sections, and liked it enough to endorse it; he says that the decision to go to the four-section design was based strictly on the fact that the company thought "Quad-.38" was a catchy name.

The round would place four projectiles into the target on every pull of the service revolver's trigger. The trouble

224   LAW ENFORCEMENT HANDGUN DIGEST

Current W-W No. W38SPD load has a bullet similar to that of the Q4030 and it's loaded to the +P pressure levels for use in guns whose manufacturers sanction the use of such higher-performance cartridges.

Norma's No. 19106 load in .357 mag carries an unusual 158-grain FMJ semi-wadcutter bullet that delivers remarkably good penetration.

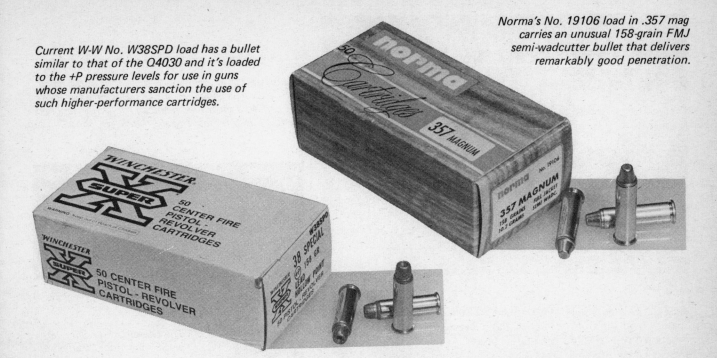

Speer's 140-grain JHP bullet has earned a fine reputation for accuracy and effectiveness. It's available as a load in both .38 and .357 mag.

A Thoughtful Look At General-Purpose And Specialized Loads Available For Obtaining Specific Results In Law Enforcement!

Current packaging of Omark/CCI-Speer Lawman Ammunition, with their 110-grain JHP bullets in both .38 Special and .357 mag.

The Shortstop load, below, was marketed in the small plastic bandoliers shown at left. As illustrated at lower left, it carried a shot-filled beanbag projectile designed to fly flat-side-foremost toward the target, shedding cap.

was, the flat discs were kind of like lead Rolaids. The more mass behind the front surface of the bullet, the greater its "sectional density" and penetrating power. Again, a man at a distance or wearing heavy clothes might not receive a penetrating and incapacitating wound. After a year or so, the Quad-.38 loads went out of production. No one in the police sector really missed them.

Some other developments of the period have survived and exist today to help police officers who face unusual circumstances where their lives are threatened in the line of

The Glaser Safety Slug, left, in .357 magnum, displays an odd looking plastic enclosure over the nose of its specially designed disintegrating bullet.

duty. Armor-piercing is one, and Jack Cannon's Glaser Safety Slug, previously known as the Deadeye Safety Slug, is another.

The Glaser round received unprecedented publicity when the aforementioned LEAA report rated it at the top of the shock power listings, right up there with the Speer .44 magnum high-speed hollow-point (the Glaser round tested had been fired from a 9mm automatic). The other Glaser calibers quickly filled in the top places.

Essentially, the Glaser round is a copper jacket that becomes a cup in which fine No. 12 birdshot is suspended in thick liquid Teflon. A substance that resembles the material seen in pencil erasers "caps" the cup. Because the total projectile is extremely light (in the vicinity of 90-grains in calibers where 158-grains were once standard) the velocity is extremely high. The 9mm is is in the vicinity of 1900 fps, which is more than some high-powered rifles, compared to perhaps 1200 fps for a "hot" 9mm load with a

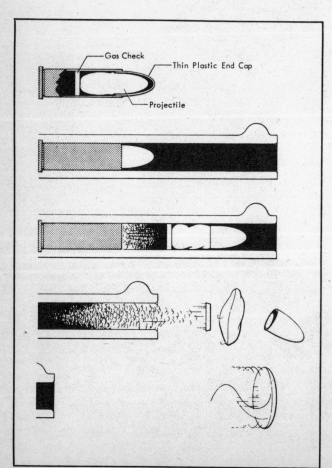

Gas Check
Thin Plastic End Cap
Projectile

This drawing shows how the Shortstop load was designed to employ centrifugal force from the rifled bore to make the unusual projectile open up after shedding its nose cone.

Speer's 200-grain JHP for the .45 ACP has an unusually large nose cavity and, not surprisingly, it expands well, even at the modest velocities attained by that cartridge. It's available as a reloading component or as loaded ammunition.

solid projectile. In .357 magnum, the velocity exceeds 2000 fps.

When you approach 2000 fps, you are getting into the level of ballistics where the projectile is traveling so fast that it sets up shock waves that radiate for several inches around the actual path of the bullet. This is not merely the so-called temporary wound channel seen with high-speed

The 115-grain load by S&W for the 9mm Parabellum carries unusual jacketed semi-wadcutter bullets.

handgun projectiles in the 1000 to 1500 fps range. When such bullets are shot into clay or Duxseal, they leave impressive cavities, but are not so destructive on flesh. Skin and muscle tissue are elastic and tend to snap back into place after those milliseconds in which they were stretched out of shape by the bullet's shock wave. When the velocity accelerates toward the 2000 mark, however, the temporary wound cavity leaves massive and permanent damage.

There have been over ninety documented shootings by police with the Glaser bullet (the projectile, incidentally, is sold only to police and shipped only to police departments). All have been instant one-shot stops.

According to inventor Jack Cannon, only one of those luckless violators survived. Tissue destruction with the Glaser is so massive that a by-product of its instant stop is almost certain instant death. There is little danger that the bullet will exit and strike innocent bystanders.

Cannon recently announced three new calibers: .44 Special (for the Charter Arms Bulldog popular among detectives and narcs), .44 magnum, and .45 automatic. Because these big-bore projectiles are heavier, there *is* a chance that they'll penetrate completely, but Cannon doesn't think that presents any more danger to bystanders.

Shortcomings? Early Glasers exhibited poor accuracy. The Arizona Highway Patrol found that, even at fifteen yards, the light, unstable projectiles hit so randomly that they couldn't be counted on to land on a human-size target reliably. Those tests were conducted in 1974. In 1976, Cook County, Illinois, Sheriff's Department ran tests using machine rests in which the Glaser Safety Slugs in .38 Special caliber actually grouped slightly *better* than conventional mid-range wadcutter ammunition, which is

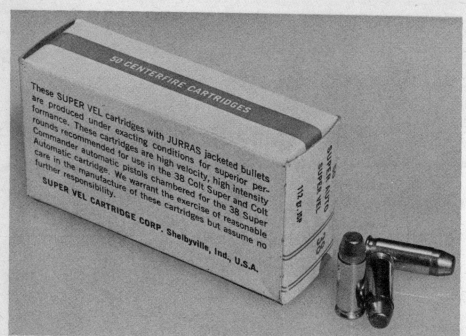

Introduced by Super Vel founder Lee Jurras not long before the Shelbyville, Indiana, production was halted, this 112-grain JSP load for the .38 Colt Super was an outstandingly accurate performer. The current maker, H&H Cartridge Corporation, no longer makes .38 Super.

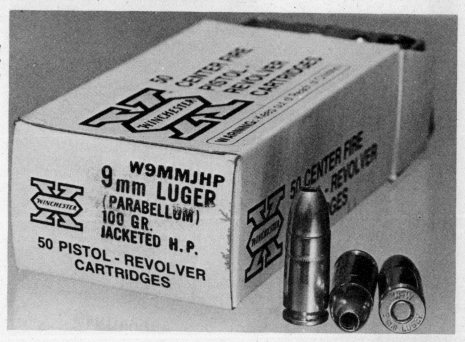

W-W No. W9MMJHP load carries a 100-grain JHP bullet offering reliable feeding and good expansion.

famous for its precision target accuracy. We have talked to the law enforcement principals who conducted both tests. Jack Cannon has made a number of subtle design changes since his Glaser rounds first came out, and it now appears that current production Safety Slugs have sufficient accuracy for a policeman not to worry about hitting the wrong target if his sights are "on" when he fires.

Cannon does point out, however, that because of the light weight and high velocity, the Glaser rounds will strike six or so inches below where a standard lead bullet, even at high speed, will hit. They also have a much louder report and a greater muzzle flash.

Penetration characteristics of the Glaser present a curious and contradictory set of results. They won't go through a windshield, and when fired at the flat side windows of an automobile, will just rain harmless, scattered bits of No. 12 birdshot onto the occupants. At the same time, the projectile in 9mm and .357 would go through steel plates that would stop copper-jacketed .45 automatic slugs cold, and they will penetrate virtually every type of soft body armor (Kevlar, ballistic nylon) now available.

The reason is that when the tip of the bullet hits a hard substance, it is designed to hold together and crash through it, and then release its payload immediately when it hits the soft stuff (or any subsequent, lesser resistance). When fired at safety glass, the release is instantaneous upon the bullet's exit through the resisting substance, hence the harmless shower of birdshot inside the suspect vehicle. When hitting the firm resistance of Kevlar, the shot capsule seems to "tighten" (for want of a better descriptive term), and go on

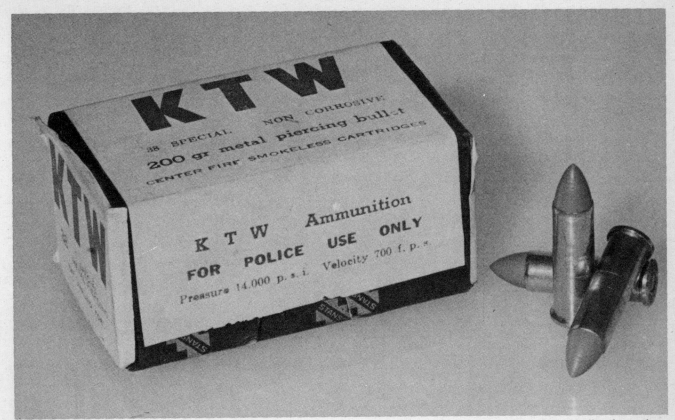

An early sample of KTW metal-piercing ammunition, from the days when they used Teflon-coated tungsten bullets instead of bronze and, later, the steel cores employed today. Tungsten is over half-again as heavy as lead, but very expensive.

through. However, it is not yet known whether the Glaser bullet that goes through a Safariland or Second Chance or Armourhide vest will do fatal damage on the other side. Indications are that it will create an ugly, bloody flesh wound, but not necessarily deliver a lethal, penetrating blow on the body behind the barricade.

This point is still ambiguous because such tests have to be done in the field with living beings, to be relevant. We should be grateful that no cops with Kevlar vests have yet been shot with Glasers to prove or disprove the point. It has generally been felt that tests on animals would be inhumane.

The manufacturer has made a point of playing down the

A more contemporary load in .38 Special by KWT lists its performance specs as determined by H.P. White Labs.

At left, below, two of the early tungsten KTW bullets with green Teflon coating in .357-inch diameter, with three .429-inch steel bullets coated with black Teflon covering.

lethal effects of the round and concentrating on the factor of safety to innocents. Even though hollow-point bullets are much less likely to ricochet than are standard loads, it is still possible that they can do so; the Glaser, with its light construction and super-high velocity, is virtually ricochet-proof. In this respect it is, indeed, a safety slug, and probably the safest of all.

It is understandable with some forces trying to ban even hollow-point bullets, that Jack Cannon should be a little hesitant about emphasizing the destructive effects of his ammunition. Yet, for special police purposes (SWAT, armed robbery stakeout, hostage scenes, and counter-ambush situations involving street cops) it is undeniable that the instant first-shot stopping capability of the Glaser is something that should be made known to police.

Unlike KTW armor-piercing, another specialized and successful type of ammo, Safety Slugs are sold only to police. KTW is available through any dealer with a Federal Firearms License, and can therefore be sold to anyone, despite the manufacturer's mandate to its dealers that they limit sales to police only.

Jack Cannon takes no such chances. You get your ammo from him, direct, and he will ship it only to police headquarters in care of the officer. While this makes its acquisition difficult for the officer whose department has strict ammo regulations, it also ensures that you aren't going to run into street people carrying this stuff to use on you. If your department frowns on its use, you may be able to get it through another officer. Some departments, including certain ones in Illinois, have adopted Glaser Safety Slugs as standard issue ammo.

Though all are high pressure rounds (the .357 hits 43,000 pounds per square inch [psi] pressure in your gun's chamber), all but the .380 are within the safety limits prescribed by the industry. The .380 is a little hotter than you should be using, according to industry specs, though Cannon says it's safe enough, and he carries it in his personal Walther PP. He has no minimum order, and will ship you one cartridge or a gunload or more, paying the shipping himself. He does have a maximum, however: no more than 2500 rounds to a customer, so he won't have to tell any cop he can't give him the ammo that may save his life 'cause he's out of stock.

The barricade penetration problems, and the massive destructive effect if the officer is shot with his own gun, makes us leery of recommending the Glaser Safety Slug as the load to carry up front in your duty handgun. There is no question that for a stakeout (where you may have to worry about innocents behind the suspect, yet can't afford to let the suspect stay upright with his own weapon for an extra second for fear that he'll shoot those innocents) the Glaser has a definite application.

This is the ammo to carry in an officer's concealed

In terms of delivered foot-pounds of energy (fpe), Norma's Index No. 19119 load with 110-grain JHP bullet may be the most powerful .38 Special cartridge commercially available today. From a six-inch barreled revolver, it averages 1371 feet per second (fps), giving the 110-grain bullet 459 fpe against typical figures of 250 to 300 fpe with most loads.

Omark/CCI-Speer's No. 3620 load for the 9mm Luger leaves the muzzle at 1100 fps for an impressive 335 fpe at that distance. One hundred yards out, it still goes 935 fps and packs 243 fpe; more than most .38 Specials at the muzzle!

backup gun because (a) that gun isn't where a surprise assailant can grab it and shoot you with it; (b) a backup gun is most likely to be used when you've been surprised and relieved of your regular sidearm, so we're probably talking about a face-to-face confrontation with no barricades between; and (c) you may already have been injured or manacled, and can't shoot straight, and the magnified shock of a Glaser capsule out of your backup gun is probably the only way you can get a one-shot stop with a non-vital hit out of your small caliber Number Two sidearm.

In a recent service pistol survey, a small but respectable percentage of the respondents stated that their first choice of ammo would be armor-piercing loads. There have always been a certain number of state troopers, highway patrolmen, and other rural police, who believed that, since their confrontations were mory likely to involve automobiles, they should have the firepower to drill through steel.

Even in standard loadings, the 9mm Parabellum (9mm Luger) cartridge used by the Illinois State Police has always had impressive capability to pierce heavy barricades. Bullet for bullet, the 9mm will often puncture body armor that defeats the vaunted .357 magnum. Doubters need only look through the bulletproof vest catalogs to see that many units rated to stop the mighty magnum make no reference to the 9mm.

As experience proved in Illinois time and again, however, sheer penetrating power is not the complete answer. A projectile designed solely to punch through metal has exactly the opposite characteristics of those required for an anti-personnel round.

Armor-piercers usually are long and narrow, with pointy noses and hard jackets. They are made expressly to hold together and not deform. By contrast, a defensive combat load has a blunt nose, preferably flat or hollowed, and mushrooms to wide diameter, while stopping within a few inches of soft fleshlike substance. As a result, most anti-personnel rounds have mediocre performance on auto bodies, body armor, and heavy glass, while armor-piercing slugs are notoriously poor manstoppers.

For many years, ISP carried a special full-jacketed, high-speed 9mm round that exhibited excellent penetration qualities and would even drill through a number of bulletproof vests that were rated to stop conventional 9mm ammunition. Analysis of gunfight results involving troopers showed that this ammunition had two undesirable side effects.

First, the penetration that was so good on hard obstacles was excessive for man-to-man confrontations, since the bullet would almost always exit the attacker's body with enough force to have killed or injured any bystander located behind the suspect. Fortunately, thanks to the good

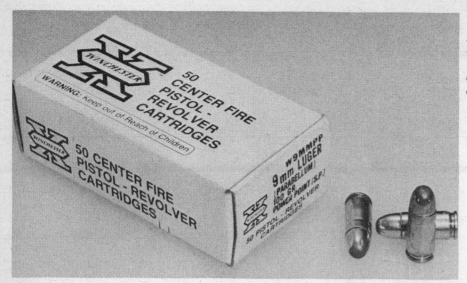

As discussed elsewhere in this book, W-W's No. W9MMPP load with its 100-grain Power Point bullet has won considerable acceptance among those departments authorizing the 9mmP.

One of the newer but very promising ammunition makers is Hornady Frontier, employing bullets from the extensive and highly regarded line made by Hornady Manufacturing Company in Grand Island, Nebraska.

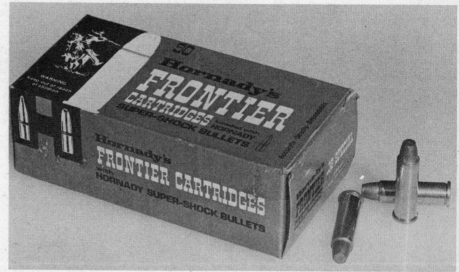

judgment and excellent training of the Illinois State Policemen, no innocents were ever hit by the overtraveling bullets, because the troopers simply didn't shoot when a bystander was in the line of fire. It was always possible, however, that an incident might crop up where an innocent might be victim number two of a trooper's bullet, because he was blocked from view by the felon's body. This is one reason the department switched to soft-nose ammunition last year.

Secondly, the load was a poor manstopper. As far as we can determine, the only instant one-shot stops with the full jacketed bullet occurred when the felon was hit in the central nervous system (brain or spine). By contrast, well-designed anti-personnel loads in medium calibers (9mm, .38 Special, .357 magnum) generally give one-shot stops at least fifty percent of the time with soft-tissue torso hits.

When Illinois State Police went to the Winchester 100-grain Power-Point soft-nose for the 9mm, the message was clear: "We no longer wish to run the dual risks of overpenetration, or of a trooper being injured or killed because his gunfire didn't stop an armed assailant quickly enough."

Former ISP superintendent Dwight Pitman, who authorized the change to the Power-Point, made it clear that the only reason ISP didn't adopt hollow points, as per recommendation, was that the agency did not wish to become embroiled with the then widely publicized drive to ban police use of high performance ammunition, on humanitarian grounds.

The Power-Point, while a definite improvement, still doesn't seem to be the whole answer. In shootouts that have gone down since its adoption, the cartridge was proven to have overpenetrative qualities (in one gunfight, three of the four bullets that hit a shotgun-armed psycho, who was trying to kill an ISP sergeant, exited the felon's body). At the same time, stopping power does not seem to have been markedly increased.

But, getting back to our opening point, how well does the current ammo stack up in terms of penetration? The answer is, very well in most instances. Ordnance found penetration quite adequate in the 1975-76 Illinois State Police tests.

The only problem might come with oblique-angle hits on sloping surfaces of hard metal or heavy glass. Designed with reliable feeding as the main consideration, the Power-Point has a round nose, and when one convex surface strikes another convex surface, you don't need a physics professor to tell you that it's likely to glance off. It will not, however, ricochet, except on extreme angle hits. This is something that cannot be said of the popular GI .45 automatic load, which is notorious for glancing off hard objects, when hitting at even the slightest oblique angle.

A majority of the troopers, who favored auto pistols, said they'd rather have .45s than 9mms. While the .45, in the full metal jacket, round-nose military load, has good auto body penetration if it hits straight on, it has been known to bounce off slanted windshields. On body armor, it's one of the easiest projectiles to stop, while the 9mm is one of the hardest.

Apart from the old, specially loaded Winchester/Western ISP round, there are not many cartridges available in 9mm expressly suited for maximum penetration. One reason for this is that munitions makers realize that the standard 9mm round already has extremely penetrative qualities.

For maximum metal-piercing potential, however, there are two rounds that are available in this caliber. One is military surplus Lapua ammunition from Finland, which is jacketed with steel instead of copper. Foreign military surplus ammo in 9mm is available from other countries as well, but like the Lapua, it tends to be old, and there is no way for the officer who buys it to determine whether it has

The new .45 and 9mm Winchester magnum cartridges, compared to .45 ACP and 9mm Luger rounds, were developed for use in the Wildey gas-operated auto pistol. Although capable performers, it's doubtful that they'll see police use.

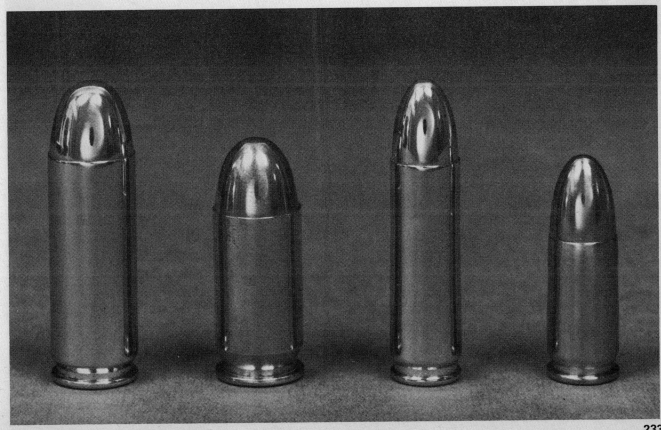

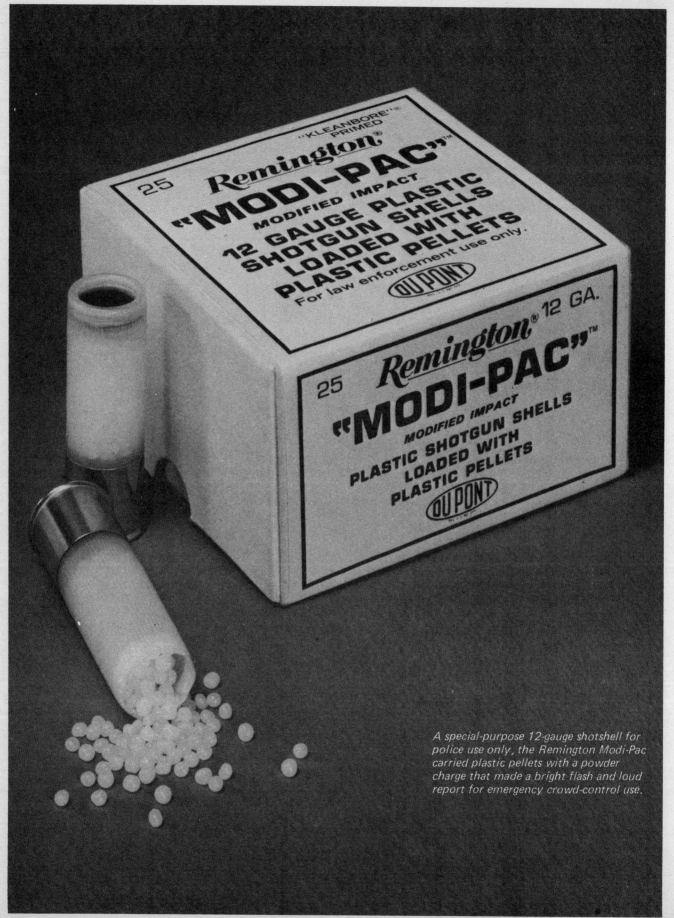

A special-purpose 12-gauge shotshell for police use only, the Remington Modi-Pac carried plastic pellets with a powder charge that made a bright flash and loud report for emergency crowd-control use.

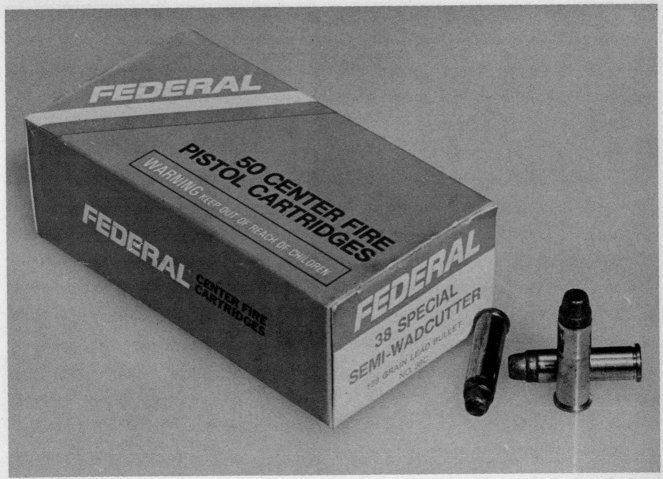

The traditional .38 Special police load carrying the 158-grain round-nosed lead bullet generally is regarded as woefully short on stopping power. Even shifting to the semi-wadcutter shape for the bullet nose produces a useful gain in performance, as in the example of Federal Cartridge Corporation's Index No. 38C load; a popular choice with police.

been stored properly. The result is an enhanced likelihood of misfires, which cannot be tolerated in a police service load.

The other alternative is KTW ammunition, expensive, special purpose loads designed purely for maximum penetration. The original KTW slugs had tungsten cores, but as that superhard metal became prohibitively expensive, the manufacturer changed to steel bullets. The projectiles are jacketed with Teflon to reduce friction drag as the slug passes through the target substance.

The performance of KTW's distinctive green bullets is truly awesome, even though the round has lost a little since the tungsten composition was dropped. These bullets drill effortlessly through auto bodies end-to-end (no, they won't shatter engine blocks, but neither will anything else short of bazookas). They'll punch through sections of railroad track and of unbelievable thicknesses of cold-rolled steel. Ayoob tells us, he has shattered boulders with them and recovered the slugs afterwards which were undeformed, except for the

slightest traces of rifling marks. They could have been reloaded into fresh casings and fired again.

In .38 and .357 revolver rounds, the KTWs have a pointed configuration, which, as we said earlier, makes for poor shock power. It creates a wedge effect in living tissue, pushing tendons and arteries out of the way, instead of chopping through them, and leaving only a puncture wound of very small diameter.

Fortunately, the KTW loads for automatic pistols are better shaped. In both 9mm and .45 auto, the projectiles have a flat nose that is rounded on the edges and tapered back toward the cartridge case.

This means that they chop a destructive wound channel in living tissue. That is good news and bad news. From a standpoint of pure stopping power, it's good, because the exit wound means more blood loss and greater likelihood of the antagonist collapsing as soon as possible. The bad news, obviously, is that the super-penetrative KTW bullet almost certainly will exit the felon's body with enough residual velocity to kill anyone standing behind him. In terms of humaneness to the felon the officer is shooting at, such bullets are more likely to result in that person's death for two reasons. First, dealing with two open wounds in the body is much more difficult, as far as first aid and surgery, than dealing with only one open wound, as would be the case with a hollow point. Second, most armor-piercing bullets lack shock effect, and the trooper will likely have to shoot the felon several times before the latter ceases hostilities. The more bullet wounds, the more hemmorrhage and vital organ damage. Victims of multiple hits are much less likely to survive, no matter how good the officer is at first aid.

As we said, however, the 9mm or .45 KTW is an exception to the poor-shock rule of armor-piercing ammo, and may well do the job with a single torso hit.

Is there, then a purpose for purely armor-piercing ammunition in the police service context? Yes, but again, it's a special purpose thing.

The barricaded felon, who may kill officers or innocents if he is not neutralized as soon as possible, may be in such a position that he is immune to conventional handgun fire. A round like the KTW can punch through the walls of a house or mobile home, even through the thick wooden support beams of a door that deadly offender may be crouching

behind. If the officer has a rough idea of where the concealed and barricaded would-be killer is situated — and if the officer is sure that no innocent bystanders or hostages are concealed behind those same walls — then a clip full of 9mm KTW, or equivalent, might well neutralize that individual, before he can emerge with his own deadly weapon and make a final desperate try to take innocent life.

Such instances are rare. More likely is the situation of a lone trooper or patrolman involved in a gunfight in a burglary-scene building, or a confrontation that has culminated in a foot pursuit into the woods or a parking lot. If the officer can be certain there are no bystanders in the line of fire, and he knows the cover position his armed opponent has taken, armor-piercing ammo gives him the capability of shooting through the lethal opponent's cover, be it an auto body, a carton in a warehouse, or a small tree.

If he can drop the assailant through the barricade, instead of waiting for him to come into the open with his own gun blazing, the trooper's safety, and that of brother officers and innocents around him, has been greatly enhanced.

Like any useful, but strictly special-purpose gear, armor-piercing police ammo should be carried in a reserve, not up front. The author, a municipal peace officer for

If the .38 Special round-nosed lead bullet must be used, Federal's No. 38D high-velocity load is available, offering 915 fps and 294 fpe at the muzzle instead of their standard velocity No. 38B load with its 755 fps and 200 fpe performance figures.

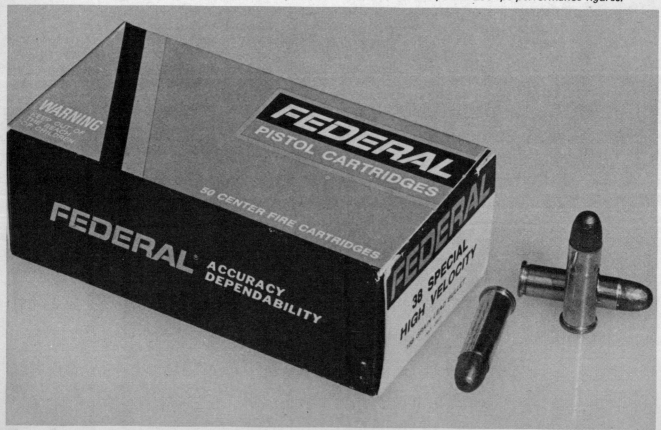

Plus-P loads in .38 Special, such as W-W No. W38WCP above and Federal No. 38D on facing page, should be used only in modern guns in top shape whose makers recommend their use for higher pressures developed.

several years, chose to carry a .45 automatic loaded with hollow points. One of the two spare magazines on the belt was filled with the same ammo. The second backup clip was loaded with KTW armor-piercing. As a spare clip of the same product in 9mm would be for an Illinois trooper, the special-purpose capability was there, in reserve. It could be put into the gun in a few seconds, yet did not jeopardize the public if a situation occurred where the officer would have no control over the surroundings.

And control over the surroundings, thankfully, is one thing the officer will have, in most situations that require use of armor-piercing loads. The need presumes a situation where the subject is barricaded and probably not, at the moment, able to shoot the officer without exposing himself to the policeman's gunfire. Under this kind of tactical conditions, the officer will likely have time to drop the magazine of soft noses out of his 9mm and shove in a clip of KTW.

The problem with KTW is, that it's not authorized for most departments. It's expensive, but so is anything that does a special job better than anything else.

The real answer for the troopers may come when, and if, hollow points are authorized. If that happens, odds are that the load will be the Remington 115-grain jacketed hollow point in 9mm. This is rapidly becoming *the* service load in other police departments that issue the 9mm, for several reasons. It expands well and gives close to the maximum shock effect that can be obtained from any conventional

9mm Parabellum cartridge. Because the projectile is copper-jacketed up to and over the hollow nose, there is no soft lead at the tip to deform and cause a jam. The load was expressly designed to feed perfectly through the 9mm Smith & Wesson police automatic. And, according to departments that have adopted the round, its auto body penetration is excellent.

Hollow-point bullets in police revolvers often shatter on impact and fail to penetrate car doors and windshields. This is because they have soft lead at the tip and upset on contact. The full jacketed Remington hollow point slices through sheet metal like a cookie-cutter and expands only on contact with soft fleshlike masses. It appears to be the ideal 9mm cartridge for law enforcement.

Even so, the armor-piercing round will have its place in certain tactical situations, including incidents which happen now and again where the policeman's opponent is likewise wearing a bulletproof vest. This latter consideration, incidentally, is important. Many police officers have bought soft vests out of their own pockets. The Power-Point won't pierce a good Second Chance, Safariland, or Armour of America vest, but one of the old ISP rounds might, and a KTW most certainly will. Remember that one in five officers shot in the line of duty is killed with his own gun. Illinois troopers have an edge, because someone who grabs their Model 39 automatic will have a hard time getting it to fire, so long as the safety is engaged, but it's still a good reason why armor-piercing ammo, if carried at all, should be strictly for backup.

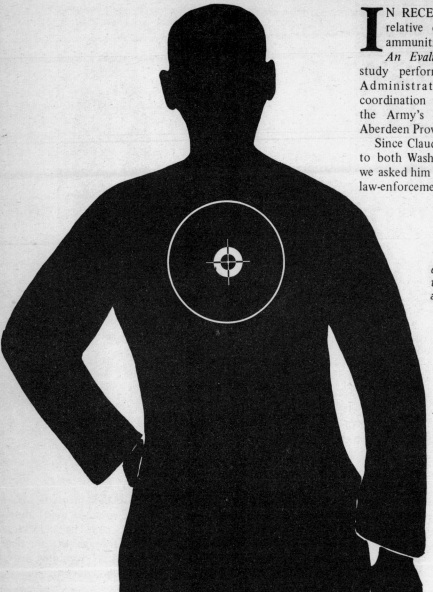

I N RECENT years much has been written about the relative effectiveness of various kinds of handgun ammunition. The most notable recent effort has been *An Evaluation of Police Handgun Ammunition*, a study performed by the Law Enforcement Assistance Administration of the Department of Justice, in coordination with the National Bureau of Standards and the Army's Ballistic Research Laboratories located at Aberdeen Proving Ground, Maryland.

Since Claud S. Hamilton is located in the East and close to both Washington, D.C., and the Maryland installation, we asked him to investigate the report and what it means to law-enforcement types.

The new high aiming point, as discussed here, is located in the center of the torso, about at armpit level.

Chapter 23

THE NEW HIGH AIMING POINT

In moments of extreme stress, the officer tends to use the aiming point emphasized in routine practice sessions.

Only the summary report of this monumental study has been published thus far, and the raw data upon which it is based are not generally available for public use.

One interesting conclusion of the study which seems thus far to have largely escaped shooter attention has to do with shooter skill and the aiming point on the human figure which should be used for defense shooting. (Defense shooting is that type of performance which stresses the need to quickly incapacitate the target, and is not a measure of lethality.)

The aiming point most commonly used today in police training is at the center-line of the trunk and between the elbows. The study task group used two groups of officers, one skilled and the other relatively unskilled as shooters. They compared the quick incapacitation results achieved by both groups when shooting at the standard aiming point with that achieved when a new, higher aiming point at arm-pit level was used. The summary report states that the higher aiming point gave higher rates of quick incapacitation.

Does Raising The Aiming Point About Ten Inches Make Rookies Score Better?

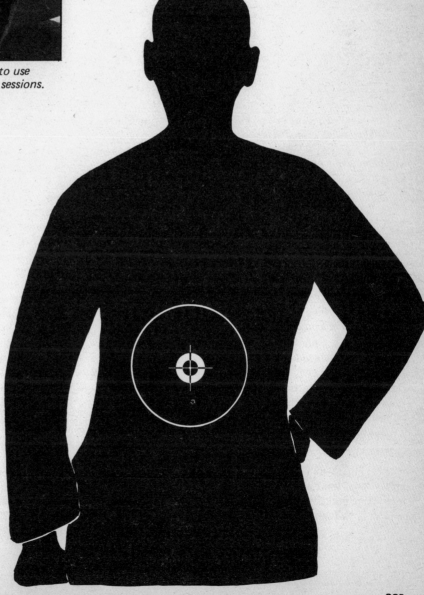

Traditional aiming point was in center of torso at about elbow level or a bit higher.

Aiming Point & Shooter	Quick Incap. Hits	Other Hits	Total Hits	Misses
Standard Aiming Point				
Skilled Shooters	34 %	56 %	90 %	10 %
Unskilled Shooters	23 %	41 %	64 %	36 %
Average	28.5%	48.5%	77 &	23 %
High Aiming Point				
Skilled Shooters	33 %	40 %	73 %	27 %
Unskilled Shooters	30 %	28 %	58 %	77 %
Average	31.5%	34 %	65.5%	34.5%

"I find this a most interesting point, and I wonder if the raw data reveal more," Hamilton reports. "Unfortunately, the only way to find out would be to resort to the Freedom of Information Act. As a long time insider in the Federal Government, I know all too well the barricades the bureaucrats can throw up to delay, confuse and thwart you when you go after information they don't care to release. I have neither the time nor the money for that. The next best thing is to use the data available in the summary report.

"I did a graphical analysis of the four representative targets reproduced in the summary report to see what might be deduced from the results. This was mostly a hit and miss count, but I attempted to divide the hits into those which would probably result in quick incapacitation and those which probably would not.

"Since I did not have the 'computer man' data used in the study, which reduce incapacitation to an exact science, I had to use my own judgment. I did my best, but certainly can make no claim that my figures are more than generally valid. I feel sure that the eventual full report when published will provide a much better basis."

Hamilton's results are shown in the accompanying charts:

Keeping in mind the fact that Hamilton's data have a pretty large built-in error probability, they do present some interesting indications:

The new, higher aiming point does seem to give a higher rate of quickly incapacitating hits, as the study summary report states.

The reason for this seems to be that both head and heart areas are brought into the dispersion pattern of the shots. Logically, Hamilton feels, hits in either area are likely to be quickly (if not permanently) incapacitating. With the standard aiming point, the dispersion pattern of shots is centered more on the heart and lower organs and fewer head hits result.

For the good shooters, the higher aiming point offers no advantage in quick incapacitation hits scored. But it does improve the performance of the poorer shooters notably.

A matter of some concern, however, is the fact that with the high aiming point the percentage of misses increased dramatically...more even than the number of quickly incapacitating hits increased for the poorer shooters.

"I hardly need mention that marksmanship pays; the experienced shooters got appreciably more hits no matter which aiming point was used. What is surprising to me, though, is the comparatively small advantage they seemed to enjoy in quickly incapacitating hits. Once again, this conclusion is based upon my admittedly iffy data.

"From my analysis, it would seem that while both groups may benefit from the use of the higher aiming point, the unskilled shooters get by far the most good out of it. On the other hand there is that matter of the increased number of misses to consider. Makes you stop and think, doesn't it?"

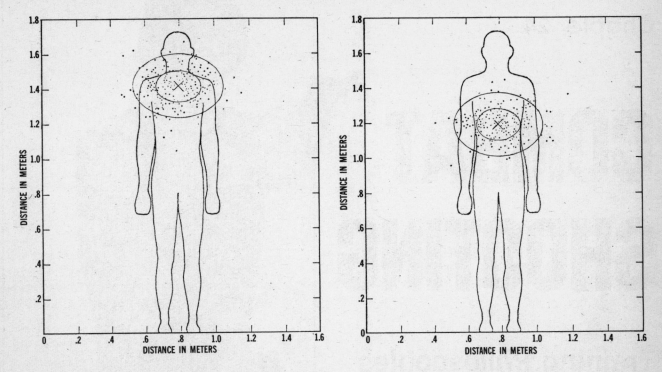

Hit distribution for skilled shooters at six meters, using
the high aiming point, as distributed on computer image.

Hit distribution for skilled shooters at six meters, using
the customary lower aiming point under test conditions.

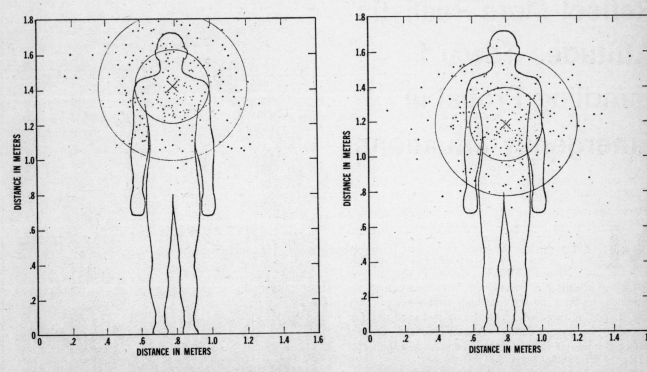

With shooters of lesser skill, use of the higher aiming
point produced this distribution on computer man image.

Lower aiming point for unskilled test group resulted in
this distribution of hits and misses, as discussed in text.

Chapter 24

COMBAT SHOOTING

Training Philosophies Have Changed To Reflect More Realistic Attitudes Toward Handling Probable Emergency Situations

MOST POLICEMEN who have had firearms training believe that they know all they need to know about combat-firing positions and techniques. More often than not, they're deluding themselves. Even the best instructors are sometimes teaching outdated methods, simply because they were trained by those who went strictly by the book. The "book" is, of course, decades old and is seldom updated despite the lessons learned on the range and in the street during the intervening years.

The standard program is the Practical Pistol Course (PPC), which involves shooting from the hip; at eye level; from behind barricades; and in standing, crouching, kneeling, sitting, and prone positions. Some instructors

The general theory behind the combat crouch, opposite page, is that, if hit, the shooter is apt to fall forward and be able to continue firing. However, as shown in the photo at upper right, the prone position can be very awkward if the target is close enough to involve much elevation of the muzzle.

In many instances, the supine position, right, affords more efficient aiming capabilities.

eliminate the hip-shooting stage, and permit the trainee to bring the gun up to eye-aiming level at all times.

We asked Massad Ayoob to examine all of these positions, to see why they were standardized, and how, perhaps, they can be improved.

Like most American police pistol training, indeed the PPC itself, the crouch position was developed by the FBI in the 1930s. It was a great course in an era when standard police revolver training was at bull's-eye targets with the arm extended like a target-shooter's, the gun cocked for each shot.

The FBI course is still the basis for most police weapons practice. However, many years of experimentation and gunfighting indicate to top police gun experts that some aspects of the FBI-style training are obsolete. The crouch position is one disputed aspect.

The purpose of the crouch position — knees deeply flexed, body bent forward at the waist — is twofold: a crouching figure is a smaller target, and if the crouching officer takes a bullet, he supposedly will fall forward, and thus be able to keep on firing. The "smaller target" idea is valid, but the second theory is open to question.

Stand in a combat crouch, and have another officer poke you sharply in the chest. It will throw you off balance. If you are standing erect, you will find that one leg involuntarily moves back in a quick short step, catching you and keeping you upright. If you're crouching, however,

you're more likely to topple over backward, because in that position, your flexed legs don't move quickly enough to instinctively retain balance. The deeper you crouch, the more off-balance you'll be.

Also, if a gunman's bullet slams you to the ground, you may have a better chance to keep shooting and get him before he hits you again, if you land on your back.

Consider that the average gunfight occurs at about seven paces. If you've fallen face down, you'll have to raise your entire upper body from the ground to get a good view of both your sights and you opponent. You may not be able to do so if you've been hit solidly above the waist.

On your back you have only to cast your eyes downward and lift the revolver slightly. Try it both ways on a close-range silhouette and see the difference for yourself.

(Another theory, that of famed gunfighting expert Bill Jordan, is that dropping into the crouch is just one more distracting thing to remember at a moment when time is of the essence. A big-city detective team has killed eleven men between the two of them, in some sixteen gunfights. Neither has ever bothered to flex his knees before he fired.)

The crouch has one advantage when you're shooting "from the hip." Instinctively, the crouch makes you naturally thrust the weapon out in front of you, putting it in line with your opponent's belly or midsection. When hip-shooting from a straight-up position, most officers fire as soon as the gun clears leather, meaning that the gunhand

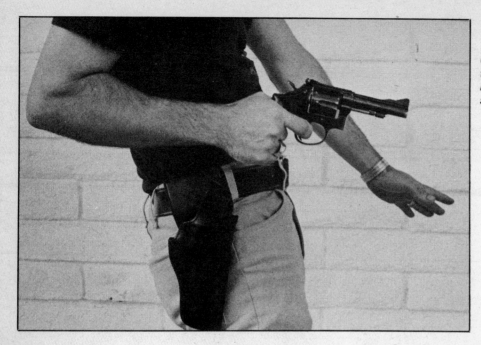

On a hasty panic draw, with the gun fired as soon as its muzzle clears leather, the shot is apt to strike very low.

is almost adjacent to the hip. Because forearm and wrist are pointed sharply downward in this position, the shots tend to go *very* low, into the leg or foot area of anything beyond a short distance.

The rationale of hip-shooting is that confrontations can break so fast a swift surprise assault or ambush that the officer has barely enough time to clear the gun and pull the trigger, with not a second to spare to bring it to eye level.

This, again, is traditional FBI-type training. In gunfight situations, it has been found that hip-shooting produces few stopping hits. One Boston officer, surprised by a gunman and already hit once in the chest, drew and fired three shots from the hip. All three missed. The range was 3½ feet, and the policeman was an excellent marksman. In New York, a hip-shooting detective emptied his .38 at a gunman who stood within arm's length. He hit him once. He, too, held an expert's badge.

Unless the department has plenty of training time, it is best to teach the rookie to bring the gun to "point-shoulder," at arm's length in both hands. The gun need not be at eye level for precise sighting; held straight out from the chest, the length of the barrel is visible in the officer's lower peripheral vision as he focuses on his target, and it "points itself." A rookie who drops all his shots low from the hip, will find it hard to miss the chest from point-shoulder at close range. The difference between the two styles in draw-and-fire speed, can be measured in milliseconds.

There are, however, rare conflicts where even that fraction of a second will determine the outcome. These are almost invariably at point-blank range — touching distance. The officer should be trained to cope with these instant-fire situations. The best method we have seen is that used by the New Hampshire State Police. The rookie stands six feet from the silhouette target, and on command, he draws, fires the instant the gun clears leather, and empties his weapon

In the point-shoulder position, the sights need not be lined up with shooter's eyes, as discussed in the text above.

Seated position, with arms braced on upraised knees, offers remarkable steadiness and comfortable aiming.

as fast as he can pull the trigger. The exercise simulates the situation of an officer who has flung open a door, to find himself looking down a gun barrel. It's the only kind of situation where hip-shooting has a place.

Many police weapons instructors and veteran gunfighters question the use of the sitting position, which is usually employed on the fifty-yard line. We know of no recorded shootout where an officer sat down to shoot someone. It's an awkward position to get into, and a harder one to get out of. A man involved in a shootout needs to be able to move instantly.

The prone position does have advantages. It makes the smallest possible target of the officer, and is very steady. It is practical for long-range gunfights, or when the officer is caught in the open by multiple, barricaded felons. The one change would be to have it used at close range as well as the traditional fifty yards. To simulate a "fallen officer" position, such an exercise should be performed with the officer alternately bellydown and on his back.

In some police combat tournaments, the sitting position is eliminated in favor of the "auto-hood" stance, in which the officer kneels or crouches behind the shooting bench, resting his gun arm on it as he would if firing from behind the protective bulk of his police cruiser.

Kneeling position, with elbows atop bench, simulates situation in which the trooper may fire across the hood of his patrol unit for better protection. On distant targets, the prone position, below, is steady, too.

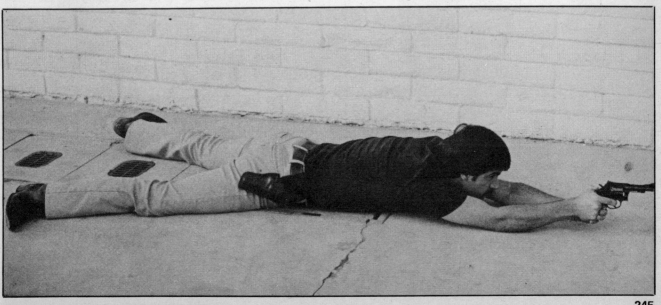

This is one of the most practical and effective police gun-fighting positions: the man who drops to one knee has as much stability as in the sitting position, and much more mobility. If he has time to squeeze his shot off carefully, he should brace the elbow of his supporting arm on his knee. The gun should be in the solid double-fisted grip we'll describe shortly. The left foot (of a right-handed officer) should face the target; his right knee should be splayed out at a thirty-five-degree angle, the knee touching the ground firmly for added solidity. He sits on his right heel. Because he is balanced on the ball of his right foot, he can spring to his feet or jump aside quickly.

In a situation where he must shoot fast, the kneeling officer should not take time to settle his elbow on his knee, but rather, extend both arms into a point-shoulder position. Some officers will find this version of the kneeling position more comfortable under all circumstances, especially if they're a bit overweight.

At close range, the kneeling position momentarily pulls the officer down out of the line of fire of a gun that is aimed at his head. However, a bullet that would have hit his stomach now will get him in the chest, and what would have been a chest shot will take him in the head. Never drop to your knee with the idea of ducking a bullet; you'll

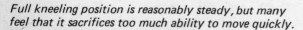

Full kneeling position is reasonably steady, but many feel that it sacrifices too much ability to move quickly.

Dropping to one knee, as discussed, is even steadier and the officer retains a greater degree of mobility.

get your deciding hit in faster if you just stand up and shoot. (In a situation where you know you're going to be hit before you can draw, go all the way down and hit the deck.)

A change some would like to see in the PPC would be a kneeling stage at the seven-yard line, with both knees on the ground. This would approximate the situation of a man who has "stopped one" and fallen to his knees.

This excellent stage of the PPC training also derives from the old FBI course. The officer fires from behind a wooden post with both left hand and right, preparing him to shoot from behind the protective cover of the corner of a building, a door frame, etc.

The majority of police pistol instructors, however, don't take full advantage of this stage of the course, because they don't teach the proper grip and hand position.

Most officers are trained to put one hand flat against the post (or wall), with the thumb extended at a right angle; the thumb goes under the wrist of the gunhand, supporting it. Unfortunately, this is not conducive to good control of the gun in fast combat fire, as only one hand is controlling the weapon (we'll consider the importance of grip variations in a moment).

The only advantage of such a hand position in barricade shooting is that if a bullet strikes the officer in his shooting hand, he will have one good hand left to shoot back with. This is only true if the criminal's bullet doesn't penetrate the pistol grip as well as the holder's fingers, and smash the mainspring there. In any case, it's unlikely that this small area of the officer's exposed body will be hit. It's much more likely that he'll lose the gun battle by missing a target he could have hit, using an improved barricade position.

That better position is to hold the gun firmly in both hands, the knuckles of the supporting hand pressed firmly against the wall or barricade. The thumb of the supporting hand is put against the surface of the barricade, steadying the weapon to reduce vertical slipping of the gun hands. This gives much better control of the weapon than does the traditional "supporting hand flat against the wall" stance.

Twenty years ago, the officer who held his gun in both hands often was considered a bit of a sissy. Today, the man who shoots with one hand becomes the butt of jokes about cowboy fantasies. The pros use the double-fisted grip exclusively, because of the enormous increase in control over the handgun.

Unfortunately, many do not use the two-hand grip to full advantage. The officer is commonly taught to cup his supporting hand under the gunhand. It's better than doing it one-handed, but it has two shortcomings. One is that the

recoil of a hot .38 load or a .357 magnum will lift the gunhand right out of the supporting palm, necessitating that the officer re-grip his weapon every round or two. The second is that the supporting hand, in this position, does not aid the officer in double-action trigger control.

For everything but long range sniping, the officer is taught to fire his revolver double-action, with one long, heavy, straight-through trigger stroke rather than thumb-cocking the weapon. We're talking about twelve pounds of pressure, through a finger movement of half an inch, exerted on a two-pound gun. That pressure jerks the muzzle this way and that, which is why it's so hard for most men to keep the sights lined up during double-action shooting.

A proper two-fisted hold eliminates this problem. The supporting hand should be wrapped around the gun hand, with the fingertips interlocked in between the knuckles of the shooting hand, and the thumb wrapped over the shooting hand to a point just behind the hammer of the gun.

The gun now is held between ten fingers instead of five. It is therefore twice as easy to hold on target during that long, firm trigger stroke. Moreover, the gun doesn't jump nearly as much in recoil, and there is no need to re-grip the gun midway through a burst of rapid fire.

This is the grip that should be used in any position, with

A closer look at the braced two-hand hold for firing from barricade shows support designed to cope with recoil.

the exception of "instinct" shooting from the hip. Curiously, some instructors permit trainees to use both hands in hip-shooting, but this is meaningless: if they have time to grab with the one hand, they have enough time to bring the gun up to the more effective point shoulder position. The officer should learn to make himself less of a target in *any* combat shooting position. From the barricades, he should be reminded that only shoulder, gun hands, and enough of his head to let him see the sights, should protrude. From prone, he should be instructed to keep his feet close together, and to face his target straight on, making that much less of his body visible over his opponent's gunsights.

An officer always should take an extra second to get behind cover before calling out his challenge, if circumstances permit.

An increasing number of departments are putting shotguns into the cruisers as standard equipment. Thus, an officer going into a potential shooting situation is increasingly more likely to have a riot gun in his hands when combat breaks out.

The shotgun is designed to be fired from the shoulder. Shooting from the hip, the buttstock is held against the side at gunbelt level by the forearm of the trigger arm; the forward hand is well out in front of the body, and therefore somewhat higher. Consequently, a shotgun blast from the hip will almost invariably go 'way high.

Moreover, the left hand, which controls the direction of the muzzle, tends to pull the weapon to the left when facing a suspect, unless the officer makes a constant, conscious effort to keep the gun pointing straight ahead. The tendency of almost all right-handed officers, therefore, is to shoot high left from the hip to such a degree that they can easily miss a target beyond point-blank range.

Hip-shooting with a revolver can be rationalized in speed situations where the officer can't take the extra split second to raise the gun to eye level. This isn't true with the shotgun, since the officer carrying it into a danger situation usually holds it sort of at port arms, muzzle high and butt low. It takes no more time to bring the stock to the shoulder than it does to bring the muzzle down to waist level, and accuracy and control are much greater when fired from the shoulder. It is also easier to pump the action for repeat shots when the gun is held at the shoulder: when shot from the hip, the gun recoils straight back, making the back-and-forth movement of the slide awkward (and causing the muzzle to climb as the gun is pumped).

The proper combat shotgun position, for a right-handed

Firing the pump-action police shotgun from the barricade takes thoughtful practice to avoid mashed fingers.

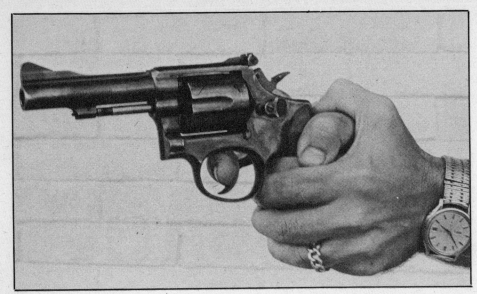

The two-hand hold puts the weak hand wrapped around the shooting hand, as shown, with weak thumb over the top, out of way of hammer.

Note position of trigger finger in double-action pull, with the first joint of the finger over the trigger.

officer, is: left leg about eighteen inches in front of the right, and slightly flexed so that the officer is leaning into the gun to better absorb its heavy recoil; butt pulled tightly into the shoulder, again to minimize kick; and cheek firmly down on the stock for a good sight picture, and to prevent the stock from slapping his face upon recoil. The forward hand should be firmly on the slide for fast follow-up shots (indeed, any gun should be held as tightly as possible, for maximum control). The trigger hand should not be held against the shooter's face, so the base of his thumb won't give him a bloody nose when the shotgun recoils.

These variations of combat-shooting position have been developed by professionals: police who have survived gunfights against otherwise hopeless odds because of their mastery of the service revolver, and police who have fired hundreds of thousands of rounds in combat competition.

To the man who has only limited experience and proficiency with his revolver, these considerations may sound trivial, but if he only takes time to try them, he will find that they give him vastly greater control of his weapon in the superfast, only-hits-count kind of shooting the police service sidearm was designed to do.

He will find that these techniques will improve his scores on the qualification range. But more important, they will better prepare him to preserve his life, and the lives he is paid to protect, if he ever is involved in a gunfight — an encounter where there are no rules at all, and where the man who takes every subtle edge is the man who comes out alive.

A New Course For The Illinois
Numerous Practical

Chapter 25

QUALIFICATION

AS IS TRUE with many law enforcement agencies, members of the Illinois State Police felt they needed more emphasis on combat shooting than on paper-punching of the type that comes with the Practical Pistol Course.

"There has always been great concern — it has been a constant thing — about the realism of the training," according to Lynn Baird, superintendent of the Illinois State Police. "The guys always wanted to change it: 'More combat! More combat!' So now they have more combat."

At the time of the updating in training techniques, Illinois Department of Investigation agents were being equipped with snub-nose stainless steel Smith & Wesson Model 66 Combat Magnum revolvers. An added challenge was to develop a course of fire compatable for both these revolvers and the 9mm Smith & Wesson Model 39 auto, which the state police troopers carry.

Demonstrating the pros and cons of the new course for Massad Ayoob was Jerry Cavanaugh, one of only two men on the Illinois force to hold the coveted Distinguished Pistol Shot badge.

The twenty-five-yard bull's-eye target is the one concession to the purely marksmanship aspects of the old course that was retained in the new, and then only for five shots. In this first stage, the officer has five minutes to fire five shots offhand, and five kneeling, at a "timed- and rapid-fire size" bull's-eye target.

The first sequence is fired in the conventional marksman's position, using only one hand. Cavanaugh likes to distribute his weight evenly, in a boxer's stance, and hold his head erect, as he concentrates on the sights. Two and a

Firing from the barricade stresses maximum concealment of the shooter from hazards of opposing fire, with the added benefit of aiding usefully in steadiness of aiming.

State Police Incorporates Innovations

COURSES

half minutes is plenty of time for this phase, and the trooper still should take his time to lay the gun down and rest between shots, taking a few deep breaths.

The kneeling phase is fired in what some police departments call "the auto-hood position." In other words, the shooting bench is used as if it were the hood of a squad car the trooper was crouching behind. This makes for an extremely stable support, and with the remaining half of the five-minute time limit, the trooper can take a rock-steady position and squeeze each round carefully into the black.

Cavanaugh likes to lay his forearms flat atop the bench for maximum stability, taking care that the actual gun butt doesn't touch the wood (such a contact would cause vibrations that would throw the shot awry). Others may find that, so long as the gun doesn't touch the table, using the bottom of the fist for support would be better. Kneeling is perhaps the most difficult of the combat shooting positions, and, certainly, the hardest one to tailor for individual physique and comfort.

In the twenty-five-yard barricade segment, the trooper switches to the B-27 silhouette target, the same difficult mark used in registered police combat revolver competition. As applied to the new course, this stage is, in effect, a highly "practicalized" version of the old timed-fire course, with twenty seconds per five-shot string. Here, though, the trooper or investigator uses the barricade for support and fires with both hands. There is a five-in-twenty string for left hand and right hand each.

Cavanaugh makes a point of positioning himself so that, from a target's-eye view, almost all of his body would be

---

The classic, picturesque, and incredibly impractical offhand stance is held to just five rounds in the Illinois State Police qualification course, as discussed in text.

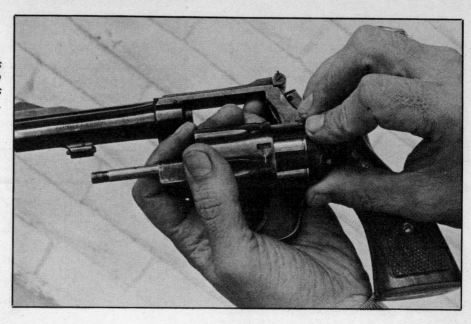

Event at fifteen yards stresses rapid reloading ability with employment of speedloaders for the shooters using revolver.

hidden behind the barricade. This makes sense, since the barricade phase of the course is to simulate an officer who has taken cover behind a building or similar obstacle and is shooting back at his opponents. In real life, it would be suicidal to step out of cover for a clearer shot, and this principle is therefore carried into the new Illinois State Police course.

When shooting with both hands against the barricade, the gun should be held in a good double-fisted grip, with either the back of the support hand touching the side of the barricade, or the knuckles of that hand against the rear face of the barricade. This latter is the position favored by combat champions.

For the fifteen-yard point shoulder event, the qualifying officer now faces multiple targets, a pair of silhouettes a reasonable distance apart. He will have twenty-five seconds to fire ten shots (emptying all eight in the loaded automatic and reloading with a magazine containing two rounds, or firing six from the revolver and reloading with four). This simultaneously encourages optimum use of the loaded gun's capacity, while teaching rapid reloading. Some veteran automatic users will want to fire seven, leave the eighth in the chamber, and then reload the magazine and fire three, but Corporal Homer Clark, head of ordnance, won't allow that.

In theory, the practice makes good tactical sense. With the live round left in the chamber, even though a Model 39 can't be fired until a magazine is inserted again, the shooter has only to swap clips and saves the time taken by releasing the locked-back slide into firing position again. In real life, however, police studies show that the heat of a deadly shootout causes the officer to lose count of his rounds, and he is likely to fire back so swiftly and desperately that he has emptied the gun before he realizes it. Therefore, Clark

and the other ordnance specialists want the trooper to know how to reload a completely empty gun, instinctively, under stress.

To add to the practical realism, this stage is fired in bursts, alternating two shots at a time on each. Questions of 9mm stopping power aside, the first shot may miss or be badly placed, or a violent suspect, high on adrenalin or narcotics, may not be fully neutralized by a single, well placed hit.

At fifteen yards, you can use the sights and would be well advised to do so. A two-hand hold, of course, is mandatory. In this stage, the shooters with automatics fire the first shot double action, while the investigators fire their revolvers double action every shot.

In seven-yard pointshooting we have truly fast combat shooting. The officer faces a single target, and on the signal, draws his gun and empties it into the target, then reloads and shoots again, until he has pumped in a total of ten bullets. Time is ten seconds for troopers with automatics, twenty seconds for investigators with revolvers. That's fast shooting action. A recent IPSC course in Litchfield (IPS is a shooting discipline famed for super-high speed shooting) allowed more time than that for automatics. For the revolver shooters, the time is ten to twenty seconds less than is allowed in FBI or NRA-style combat shooting in the fastest stages of the course at the same distance. Those revolver-men using six-at-once speed-loaders will have to compete within the same ten-second time frame as the automatic-users.

As is the case at the fifteen-yard line, the time starts with the gun in the holster, with the safety strap fastened, if you're a uniformed trooper, and reloading time is included.

Where to carry the spare magazine? Cavanaugh likes to

put his in his left sidepocket, floorplate up. Some place it in their trouser belt loops, and others shove it down inside their belt, again with the floorplate up and preferably with the bullet noses facing front. An issue magazine pouch is still being looked at by ordnance.

At the seven-yard stage, you are not allowed to line up the sights. You can shoot from the hip or point the gun at chest level. This is to simulate a darkness situation, where you can't see the sights, or an encounter where the danger is approaching so swiftly there is no time to take a sight picture, before you fire.

Both hands may be used at this stage and should be. Some shooters drop into the FBI-style gunfighters' crouch, but Cavanaugh prefers to stand upright for better balance. That way also gives a little more speed, since the fewer parts of your body you have to move, the quicker your gun is going to come up shooting.

FBI statistics show that most police gunfights occur within seven yards, but when you read the fine print, you notice that most of those are within more like ten feet. Therefore, ISP has added a close-combat phase at the four-yard line, where the trooper or DOI agent again faces multiple targets.

Again, the sights are not to be used; neither is the spare hand. The assumption is that you may be shooting at night, with a flashlight in your other hand, or that you may be fending off an assault with knife or club at this point-blank range. In any case, it's strictly one-hand shooting.

You face two targets, and if you thought the shooting was getting fast and furious at seven yards, you really feel the heat in this final, close-in phase of the course. On signal, you draw and fire a shot into each of two silhouettes, in only two seconds. When you include reaction time and drawing time, that leaves you with little space in which to hold and squeeze, even if you could use the sights.

In this phase, Cavanaugh is the epitome of economy of movement. He is moving only his gun arm, and then only enough to rock the gun out of the holster and fire from belt level into the paper opponent's midriff. It is noteworthy that, while demonstrating the course, Cavanaugh shot a sizzling 480 out of a possible 500, amply validating his claim to his Master's badge, despite the fact that it was his first time over the new course.

How will the others do? Corporal Clark told us, "It looks as if the shooters will stay in roughly the same categories they were in before. A man who shot low expert on the old course will probably shoot low expert on the new one. The ones who were low shooters previously are, however, going up more than the ones who were high before."

This, Clark explains, is due to several factors. On the old course, the qualification levels were as follows out of 500 possible points: Master, 450-500; Expert, 400-449; Sharpshooter, 350-399; and Marksman, 300-349. The new course, also with 500 points possible, has been numerically

Personnel using autoloading pistols are taught to fire the gun until the slide locks open on an empty chamber on the theory that this approach is less apt to result in confusion when firing under the stress of emergency conditions.

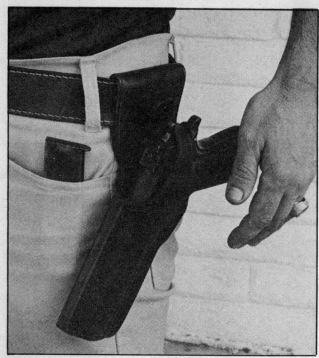

Spare magazines for autos can be carried in pocket of trousers. Holster is the Model 55 made by Safariland.

Massad F. Ayoob demonstrates the two-hand Wesson hold.

upgraded: Master, 470-500; Expert, 430-469; Sharpshooter, 390-429; and Marksman, 350-389.

The course isn't quite as much tougher as it sounds. True, the shooting is a lot more wild and woolly with a lot more time-stress and pressure as it should be if it is to simulate real-life gunfighting, but the increased use of solid, supported two-hand holds at twenty-five yards improves scores. So, even more, does the fact that in the point-blank shooting, *any* hit on the silhouette counts as a full ten points.

That latter aspect may eventually come in for criticism, though there is much to say for it. Such prestigious combat shooting schools as the Jeff Cooper program and the Smith & Wesson Academy have stages where any hit on the silhouette counts the same as another, the theory being that, when you engage in fast combat shooting, you should make it clear that a fast hit anyplace on a body is much more desirable than a slow center-X bullet placement.

On the other hand, there is no arguing that, if they can be delivered in the same time frame, the hit in the center X means more than the peripheral bullet hole. The day may come when you shoot for scoring-ring points on the four-yard qualification, but it is going to be a while.

The Illinois rangemasters fear, and rightly, that such scoring would encourage the qualifying officers to take extra time for a precision shot, thus destroying a learning experience that is supposed to teach them fast area-pointing, instead of pinpoint-aim combat shooting. While using the scoring rings might be the way to go in a

At seven yards, firing is done with one hand on assumption that the other may be holding flashlight.

Even when placidly engaged in the most routine types of police duties, the officer must remember that his uniform makes him a potential target; he must be ready to react.

"safe," but now carries it ready-to-shoot, since the new qualification course came in.

How are the detectives' revolvers making out against the troopers' automatics? Only a handful of investigators failed to qualify with their Combat Magnums. However, due to supply problems, they had to fire with mild mid-range wadcutter practice ammunition. In future qualifications, they, like the troopers, will shoot with full-power ammo equivalent to the duty load.

In their case, that will be the Federal Plus-P .38 Special cartridge with 125-grain semi-jacketed hollow point bullet. These rounds have noticeably more recoil and muzzle blast, factors that will make fast, straight shooting more difficult. The extra ten seconds in the seven-yard stage will help scores. But, as one veteran trooper notes, "The division gives them extra time, so they can qualify. But nobody on the street is going to give them a ten-second handicap."

All things considered, the new qualification course is one of the most challenging — and most realistic — police firearms training programs in the country. It is an experience many other state policemen would envy and one that may eventually keep many Illinois State Policemen alive.

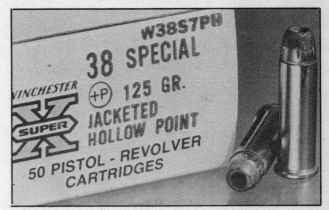

Plus-P loads for the .38 Special generate considerably more noise and recoil and are used in qualification to maintain realistic correlation between duty and practice.

combat tournament, the way the course is scored now is probably better in most ways for combat training.

As before, those officers carrying the autoloading pistol will be on their honor to carry it in the qualification shoots the way they do on duty: with the safety on, if that's the way they wear it to work. Thumbing off the safety before you unleash the first quick shot is something that needs practice to do positively, when the chips are down, and qualifying with the gun ready to go, but carrying it locked, is only cheating oneself, says Clark.

Still, thumbing the safety up into the fire position can slow one down considerably in those fast stages. It doesn't hurt in the second part of the four-yard sequence, where the two rounds left in the revolver or four left in the automatic, the shooter has to draw and put a shot into each target again and again, until he has fired six rounds in ten seconds, including reloading time. But in that first, "two shots at two targets in two seconds" part, a fumble with the safety could blank you out. Some troopers say it could do the same on the street. Still, ISP has at least three cases on record where troopers were saved wherein someone grabbed the gun from them and couldn't make it go off, because they couldn't figure out how to work the safety.

It is the individual trooper's decision. We do know of one officer, a master shooter, who used to carry his gun on

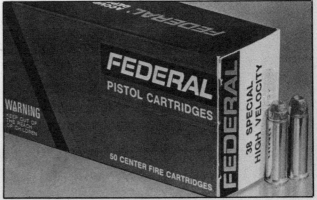

The official duty load in .38 Special for the Illinois State Police is Federal's No. 38E with 125-grain JHP bullets.

Chapter 26

BODY ARMOR

These are not cops and the body armor is far from concealed, but Marines in Vietnam learned the value of their flak jackets during tank-infantry operations. The learned value of body armor has led directly to acceptance by law enforcement officers.

NOT EVERY LAW ENFORCEMENT officer is convinced that wearing a concealable, lightweight armor vest or other garment all the time is to his or her benefit. But it would be hard to convince a couple hundred officers whose lives have been unequivocably saved because they were wearing some sort of protection that body armor is not at least as essential as a gun and a badge. Add to this group an unknown several hundred who have been saved from varying degrees of injury because they were wearing armor and you have a strong group of armor proponents who are difficult to ignore.

There are some old-timers and some new-timers who do not believe that wearing armor vests will effectively promote their health and prolong their lives. There are others who find the vests simply too cumbersome or too hot or too restrictive to be bothered with the garment. Yes, and there are officers who either don't have the money or won't budget the nominal amount to buy body armor. Some of these cops will never be convinced of the benefits of armor, no matter what. One of the hurdles which the body armor industry must try to overcome is the emotional opposition from the street cops as well as the chiefs of police and purchasing officers of the department. Is it worth it? Is the stuff any good? Will the officers wear it once we buy it?

Not Every Cop Wears One — But Armor Vests Are Saving Lives

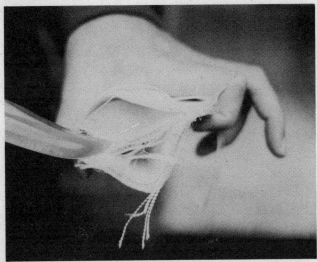

The development of Kevlar, its weaves, and how the layers of material are put together, has led the revolution of concealable body armor, above. At right, Tom Ferguson of the San Antonio Police Department, shows the virtual invisibility of Kevlar body armor on plainclothes personnel.

Generally, modern concealable body armor was introduced to the police consumer in about 1972 and early 1973. Bringing the product to the street cop's attention and convincing him that body armor will help him is a major effort on the part of the nine or ten firms in the business. The education process must be directed to all levels of the department, from top to bottom; from the chief, the director of the police protective association, the civilian advisory board, the purchasing department and especially through the cop on the beat.

And the education is not a one-way street. Too often the beat officer is not consulted in the development of some new product for law enforcement, be it shoes, belts, sidearms, holsters, vehicles or body armor. Departments have been known to make a decision on one brand of armor over another without any consideration of who will wear the device, where and when it may be worn, the practicality of the garment or potential acceptance among the troops on the line. Result: The protective armor remains hanging in the locker or in the car trunk, ready to be donned when the officer is about to be shot. The selected piece of equipment may turn out to be a solution without a problem if it is never worn.

Since the Middle Ages and the introduction of firearms to the battlefield, body armor was thought to be a thing of the past. The warrior of the time did not take long to become aware that the most primitive musket could penetrate the heaviest and finely crafted armor plate with which a man could be fitted and lifted onto a horse. It

Police departments often conduct their own ballistics tests on body armor, though not always scientifically controlled. Typical loads failed to penetrate this early vest, convincing officers of the value of body armor.

wasn't until the advent of World War II and development of new synthetic materials such as lightweight nylon, plastics and metal alloys that armorers began to get a leg up on the projectiles of war.

True, some of the personal armor worn by some fighters persisted until more recent times and before the turn of the present century. The gorget, which looks like a medallion and often is mistaken for same in American Revolution illustrations, was seen draped around the throat. The gorget was for protection against sword thrusts, but was not known to be very successful. Another device was the leather collar worn by Colonial Marines of the time,

intended to ward off sword and saber swings. How many heads it saved is unknown, but the band left the Marines a nickname which has stayed with the fighting organization ever since: Leathernecks.

Those hundreds of thousands who became familiar with the people and terrain of Vietnam, as recently as a decade ago, will attest to the weight and bulk of the flak jacket or armored vest. Weight and bulk, yes, but it saved a lot of hides. In the steaming jungles, the vest was hot and uncomfortable but it did work. The flak jacket gave many an infantryman riding in a helicopter, heading into a hot landing zone, a definite sense of security while sitting on the vest. But a soldier could get careless if the bullets weren't flying every day. At first, you wore the vest every hour of every day. After a few weeks, you tended to leave it off during certain activities or certain parts of the day or night. You might travel through somewhat quieter areas without the vest and nothing happened. One does not need to read the rest of the scenerio to guess what could and often did happen. Bullets and shrapnel would be stopped by a flak jacket laying on top of the bunker but that did you little good unless you had it on at the time.

About the time of the events just described, the Du Pont company was developing and producing a new miracle synthetic material called Kevlar Aramid. Kevlar is a thread, or filament, material, the early application of which was for strengthening cord in automobile tires. Kevlar continues to be used in tires, also finding uses in aircraft spars and in boats, especially those of the speed variety. It is strong, wear-resistant and has greater flexibility than its predecessors. The most popular body armor vests on the market today are produced from several layers — how many is a matter of debate among the producers — of woven material produced from the Kevlar Aramid. Du Pont produces the Kevlar thread while firms including Burlington Industrial Fabrics and J.P. Stevens Company weave the tough fabric. The weave of the Kevlar fabric affects its ballistic qualities. If the weave is too tight, it tends to become too stiff, making the armor itself uncomfortable to wear. Weave it too loosely, making it more flexible and the

Safariland Ballistics body armor is specifically designed for a woman's body. Vest will protect wearer against knives as well as bullets.

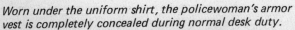

Worn under the uniform shirt, the policewoman's armor vest is completely concealed during normal desk duty.

armor quality is reduced; bullets may penetrate. The compromise results in the toughest fabric possible which is flexible enough for comfort.

San Antonio, Texas, police officer Tom Ferguson's experience with ballistic vests occurred recently during tests conducted by the San Antonio Police Department on its underground range. Test results left him thoroughly impressed with the stopping potential of Kevlar. The department bought and issued a large number of lightweight vests. Both the test and purchase were prompted by a shooting incident involving a patrolman in a neighboring city the previous October.

While on routine night patrol, the officer discovered an open door at the rear of a high school and went inside alone to investigate. This was common practice in his department, and his failure to call for a backup man doesn't necessarily reflect bad judgment. Midway through the darkened corridors, he was shot in the back at close range by an unknown assailant armed with a .380 automatic. Fortunately, he was wearing an early model body armor vest under his shirt which stopped the slug. He never saw his would-be killer, and had no chance to return the fire.

In describing the incident, he stated he at first thought he had been struck with a club, then noticed a stinging sensation. He was taken to a hospital for examination where doctors found a serious bruise under the left shoulder blade. The 95-grain round-nose projectile was recovered, having penetrated only two layers of the vest. Without it, the slug would have gone directly through his heart from the rear.

The SAPD tests began almost immediately afterward and involved products from half a dozen firms. Since haste was paramount, they wasted no time putting the vests against such puny performers as the .22s, various .32s and even the .380. "We wanted to know primarily if the vests would take a close range hit from a major caliber combat weapon, fully realizing that many officers are shot with their own revolvers," according to Ferguson.

SAPD regulations allow officers to carry revolvers of .38 Special caliber or larger, with barrel length not to exceed six inches. Plainclothes personnel are allowed to use a wide variety of weapons provided the .38 caliber floor is observed; therefore a comprehensive list of major calibers was readily available. Ammunition used in the tests was mostly commercial loads of virtually every type and description from FMJs to JHPs. To simulate the resistance offered by a human body and to prevent excessive give, each vest was draped over a large cardboard box filled with sand.

Firing began at fifteen feet after the following list of handguns had been assembled:

Handgun	Ammunition
1. Browning 9mm Hi-Power	FMJ, JSP, JHP
2. Colt .38 Super	FMJ only
3. S&W .38 Spl., M10, 4"	JSP, JHP, FMJ, (mil.), SWC, WC
4. S&W .357 mag, M19, 4"	JSP, JHP, SWC, W-W Lubaloy
5. S&W .357 mag, M28, 6"	JSP, JHP, SWC, W-W Lubaloy
6. S&W .41 mag, M58, 4"	lead SWC, JSP
7. S&W .44 mag, M29, 4"	lead SWC, JSP

When the lengthy shooting session terminated, four of the six entries had been eliminated, having been penetrated by both the six-inch .357 magnum and the .38 Super.

Few shooters appreciate the penetrating capability of the .38 Super, and may be surprised to learn that it was originally designed to blast through the primitive bulletproof glass and body armor of the Prohibition Era. Before the advent of the .357 magnum, it was favored

For tactical work, such as SWAT operations, the Safariland model M3 vest is definite improvement over military flak jacket. Side closures are Velcro fastened, as are accessory pocket flaps.

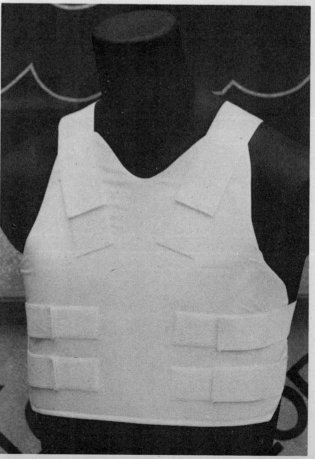

Velcro closures are used on shoulder straps as well as in front of Safariland S soft type flexible body armor.

among FBI agents whose task was to confront various Al Capone types.

"I was unable to drive any sort of handgun projectile through either vest. In attempting to do so, I laid each vest directly on the sand trap on the underground range and fired into each with the issue service revolver, the S&W .41 magnum. The ammo was Remington's 210-grain JSP which chronographs at 1250 feet per second from the four-inch barrel. The gun muzzle was approximately 2½ feet away. After firing I found each bullet balled up very nicely in a classic mushroom shape about halfway through each vest," Ferguson reports.

Realizing that police officers face other deadly weapons, Ferguson utilized a favorite Buck hunting knife with a six-inch Bowie-type blade to prove another point.

"Each garment was placed on a sturdy wooden table with me leering over in a Jack-the-Ripper fashion; the ominous-looking blade clutched in my right hand. Arm muscles bulging, I gave each an overhand stroke which would have eviscerated a crocodile. Neither vest was punctured, and the outside cover was only slightly cut. Unsatisfied, I tried again using two hands, but the result was the same: no penetration."

Ballistic testing of today's body armor is considerably more sophisticated and scientific. Testing and certifying is carried out by independent test firms who have no stake in the outcome. The companies conducting the tests are reluctant to release specific data about their testing procedures and results except to the client who requests and pays for the testing. Generally speaking, any body armor producer is able to have its armor tested by standard methods.

Human simulators have been used extensively in tests conducted by the Department of Transportation (DOT), intended to evaluate the trauma effect of automobile accidents upon the human body. Under controlled conditions, the simulators are subjected to the stresses of a collision and integral transducers measure and record the stresses involved. By this means, safety devices and different types of auto construction can be evaluated quite realistically without needless human suffering.

Sierra Engineering Company, 123 East Montecito Avenue, Sierra Madre, California 91024, has utilized a series of the human simulators, as developed for the DOT auto

Construction of this type body armor provides for removable Kevlar armor to be carried in deep pockets. Ballistic package is sealed, allowing laundering of carrier when necessary. Extended coverage protects sides of wearer. Vest is lightweight and flexible.

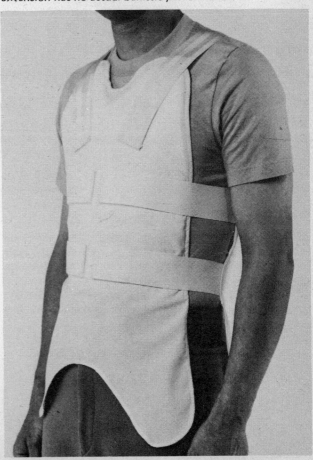

Standard M series by Safariland offers shirttail feature for better concealability, although lower extension has no actual ballistic performance.

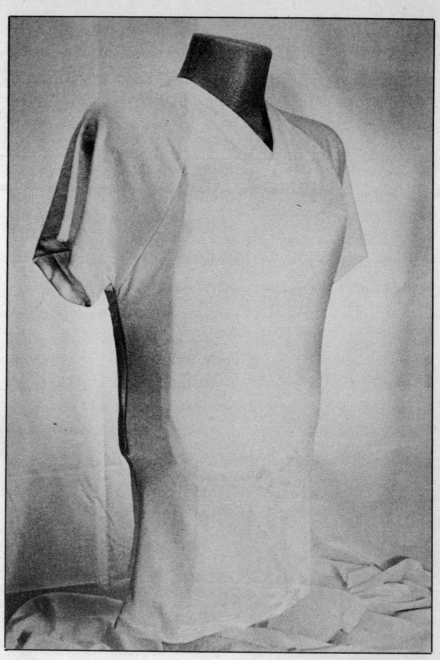

The lightest and latest innovation from Second Chance is the Deep Cover model concealable body armor. The ballistic panels are carried in a T-shirt design rather than the more familiar vest. Ballistic panels of varying strengths may be ordered and inserted in shirt.

accident tests, in the evaluation of body armor. SEC has extensive experience in producing and testing prosthetic and protective devices and, in the course of a previous program, had occasion to set up a ballistic test range.

The simulator used in testing body armor has the same compression ratio in the thorax area as does the human body. It comprises all the components present in the human body, each being identical in dimensions, weight, center of gravity and location. The simulator is scaled to the ninety-fifth percentile dimensions — six feet two inches in height and weighing 210 pounds — which is to say that ninety-five out of every one hundred adult males will be no larger than the test unit.

Under impact, the simulator's thorax deflects in exact proportion — both in distance and time span — to that of the human body. Integral sensing units transmit the

deflection forces to measuring and recording instruments. The usual procedure is to feed the readout to an oscilloscope or cathode ray tube. The cathode ray tube trace then is photographed for future reference, showing the exact amount of deflection as a graph line in relation to the time of duration.

The test simulator can be subjected to several typical forms of physical violence, such as blows with the human fist or clubs, kicks or similar stresses. The force thus involved is measured and recorded for comparison to the readings obtained when bullets are impacted against the thorax of the simulator. A bullet striking the protective body armor can transmit three hundred foot-pounds of kinetic energy or more and that sounds impressive. However, a lusty roundhouse clout from the human fist can transmit a great force, over a somewhat longer duration, as can a well-swung length of a two-by-four or, for that matter, a cue stick.

There is not complete agreement among manufacturers of body armor as to the compromise between light weight and wearability and out-and-out stopping power. Second Chance Body Armor, Inc., Box 578, Central Lake, Michigan 49622, operates under the philosophy that the concealable vest must be light enough in weight and comfortable enough to be worn at all times by the on-duty officer. Second Chance's literature tends to discount the effects of the blunt trauma which may occur when a bullet is stopped by the Kevlar armor. Blunt trauma is the serious bruise caused to the body when the bullet is stopped by armor. Some of the force is bluntly transferred through to the body. It might be similar to hitting a billiard ball or something like pounding croquet balls across the turf. The hit ball still contains plenty of energy. Such blunt trauma is capable of causing major injury to the outer surface or even to the inner organs of the body. The question is, of course, just how much injury is present and can the officer continue to function after receiving the injury?

The Army's Edgewood Arsenal Biomedical Laboratory, Biophysics Division, conducted extensive tests into the blunt trauma effect on laboratory animals. Some of the findings have proven interesting to the user or potential user of body armor. Projectile velocity as well as bullet shape and type, plus angle of impact, seem to be major factors in producing serious blunt trauma. Reports say that the estimated mortality rate of one to five percent might be expected if the wearer of a Kevlar vest were hit over a vital area with a really powerful handgun projectile, though the need for surgery would be reduced from eighty to one hundred percent. For the street cop, these figures would seem to be eminently acceptable.

Kevlar body armor stops a bullet by slowing it down — albeit rapidly and forcing it to deform as it does so. As the bullet deforms, the kinetic energy of the bullet is lost to the Kevlar and the bullet continues to slow. The bullet deforms further, and is caught in the Kevlar material, slowing still further until it comes to a stop. The deformation causes the loss of force. The slowing to stop process may take but two thousandths of a second.

There is no material, Kevlar or anything else, that will stop all bullets all the time. Each vest, concealable or visible, is tested and rated to stop various bullets and loads, which may or may not include .357 and .44 magnums.

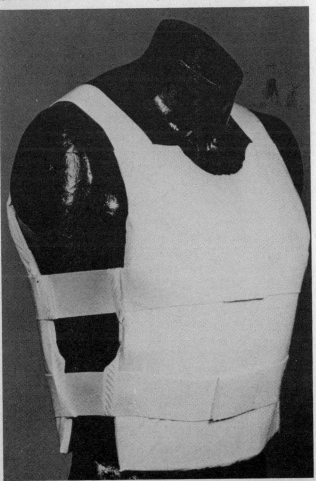

Four sizes of Second Chance standard vest are designed to fit officers 5'6" to 6'5". Ballistic panels may be removed from carrier for separate laundering.

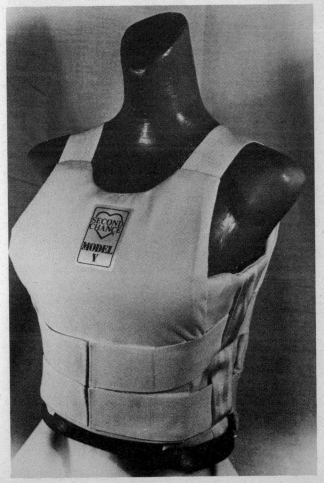

Side protection and back coverage are features of this Second Chance female model. Vest will be produced to fit individual height, weight, body contours.

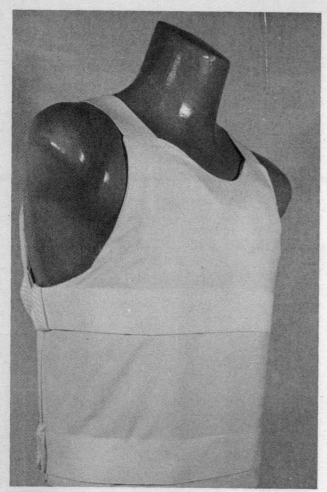

Broad coverage of front and sides enhance protection of this Second Chance model; design tends to retain body heat.

something more than 600 police officers killed in the line of duty in the United States. There has been a trend during those same years which indicates that the number per year killed has steadily decreased. Of course, one per year is too many, but the downward trend, if it continues, is encouraging. Statistics can be made to show almost anything, but it should be noted that the sale and acceptance of lightweight body armor seems to coincide with these figures. Second Chance has no doubts of the lives saved. They claim 163 officers' lives saved as of October 1979; officers who were wearing their body armor.

Another danger peculiar to certain wearers of body

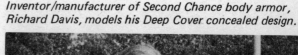

Inventor/manufacturer of Second Chance body armor, Richard Davis, models his Deep Cover concealed design.

There was a time when most police felt that the risk of a criminal carrying and using anything more powerful than a .38 was minimal. However, of late there is a definite trend among the criminal element to use heavier calibers. Witness the Son of Sam killings in New York City not so long ago. Part of the trend noted may be due to the publicity of cops wearing body armor. The adviseability of every law enforcement type being equipped with and wearing body armor is great but the bad guys know about it too. Heavier guns and bullets would seem to dictate heavier armor.

Safariland Ballistics, Inc., 1946 South Myrtle, Monrovia, California 91016, subscribes more to the theory that the armor must stop the bullet and prevent serious blunt trauma injury at the same time. To effect that, it is worth some discomfort to the wearer. The problem is actually one of education of the officer. Cops want the impossible: Maximum protection against any and all loads, minimum bulk and visibility and maximum comfort. There has to be some compromise among these elements and perhaps it should not weigh against the side of stopability. The individual officer is the only one who can make that decision.

From 1974 through the middle of 1979, there have been

Officer Tom Ferguson models an early armored vest dating from Prohibition days, popular with law enforcement personnel of the day. The vest weighs 35 pounds.

armor is the "invincible Superman" syndrome. There is some evidence that some cops will put on the armor and believe that "nothing can hurt me, now." Such an attitude is dangerous at any time but particularly in these times with the criminals using heavier guns and themselves wearing body armor. Incidents of criminals being detected wearing body armor are cropping up with unpleasant frequency. At present, there is no legal prohibition against civilians wearing armor. But most manufacturers try to restrict the sale of their products to law enforcement, certain couriers, threatened judicial personnel and the like. Some localities and dealers try to handle the sale of body armor much as

most law enforcement agencies handle the licensing of persons to carry a concealed weapon, although there are few if any statutes governing this. It would behoove each officer and agency having anything to do with possession and security of body armor to maintain tight control of each piece of armor. There may come a time when we all wear body armor when driving our automobiles but the time is not yet.

Even the finest, most expensive body armor is worthless unless it is worn. It does not make the wearer indestructible, either. The best it can do is improve survivability odds.

TODAY'S HANDGUNS

TARGET AUTOLOADERS

COLT GOLD CUP NAT'L MATCH MK IV Series 70
Caliber: 45 ACP, 7-shot magazine.
Barrel: 5", with new design bushing.
Length: 8⅜". **Weight:** 38½ oz.
Stocks: Checkered walnut, gold plated medallion.
Sights: Ramp-style front, Colt-Elliason rear adj. for w. and e., sight radius 6¾".
Features: Arched or flat housing; wide, grooved trigger with adj. stop; ribbed-top slide, hand fitted, with improved ejection port.
Price: Colt Royal Blue **$370.95**

SMITH & WESSON 38 MASTER Model 52 AUTO
Caliber: 38 Special (for Mid-range W.C. with flush-seated bullet only). 5-shot magazine.
Barrel: 5".
Length: 8⅝". **Weight:** 41 oz. with empty magazine.
Stocks: Checkered walnut.
Sights: ⅛" Partidge front, S&W micro click rear adj. for w. and e.
Features: Top sighting surfaces matte finished. Locked breech, moving barrel system; checked for 10-ring groups at 50 yards. Coin-adj. sight screws. Dry firing permissible if manual safety on.
Price: S&W Bright Blue **$411.50**

TARGET REVOLVERS

COLT PYTHON REVOLVER
Caliber: 357 Magnum (handles all 38 Spec.), 6 shot.
Barrel: 2½", 4" or 6", with ventilated rib.
Length: 9¼"(4" bbl.). **Weight:** 38 oz. (4" bbl.).
Stocks: Checkered walnut, target type.
Sights: ⅛" ramp front, adj. notch rear.
Features: Ventilated rib; grooved, crisp trigger; swing-out cylinder; target hammer.
Price: Colt Blue .... **$422.95**   Nickeled **$435.95**

SMITH & WESSON MASTERPIECE TARGET MODELS

Model: K-22 (M17). K-22 (M48).
Caliber: 22 LR, 6 shot. 22 RF Magnum, 6 shot.
Barrel: 6", 8⅜". 4", 6" or 8⅜"
Length: 11⅛" (6" bbl.). 11⅛" (6" bbl.).
Weight: 38½ oz. (6" bbl.). 39 oz.(6" bbl.).
Model: K-32 (M16). (Illus.) K-38 (M14).
Caliber: 32 S&W Long, 6 shot. 38 S&W Special, 6 shot.
Barrel: 6". 6", 8⅜".
Length: 11⅛". 11⅛". (6" bbl.)
Weight: 38½ oz. (loaded). 38½ oz. (6", loaded).
Features: All Masterpiece models have: checkered walnut, Magna stocks; grooved tang and trigger; ⅛" Patridge front sight, micro. adj. rear sights. Swing out cylinder revolver. For 8⅜" barrel add **$9.00**.
Price: Blued, all calibers M-17, 6" bbl. **$181.00**
Price: Blued, all calibers M-48, 4", 6" bbl. **$209.00**

Smith & Wesson Accessories

Target hammers with low, broad, deeply-checkered spur, and wide-swaged, grooved target trigger. For all frame sizes, **$7.42** (target hammers not available for small frames). Target stocks: for large-frame guns, **$14.25** to **$16.00**; for med.-frame guns, **$12.00** to **$14.50**; for small-frame guns, **$10.75** to **$14.00**. These prices applicable only when specified on original order.

As separately-ordered parts: target hammers (**$15.75**) and triggers, **$13.55**; stocks, **$15.13-$26.40**.

Consult our Directory pages for the location of firms mentioned.

SMITH & WESSON COMBAT MASTERPIECE

Caliber: 38 Special (M15) or 22 LR (M18), 6 shot.
Barrel: 2" (M15) 4" (M18)
Length: 9⅛" (4" bbl.). **Weight:** Loaded, 22 36½ oz, 38 30 oz.
Stocks: Checkered walnut, Magna. Grooved tangs and trigger.
Sights: Front, ⅛" Baugham Quick Draw on ramp, micro click rear, adjustable for w. and e.
Price: Blued, M-15 . . . . **$149.50**
Price: Nickel M-15 . . . . **$161.00**
Price: Blued, M-18 . . . . **$181.00**

SMITH & WESSON 1955 Model 25, 45 TARGET

Caliber: 45 ACP and 45 AR, 6 shot.
Barrel: 6½" (heavy target type).
Length: 11⅞". **Weight:** 45 oz.
Stocks: Checkered walnut target.
Sights: ⅛" Patridge front, micro click rear, adjustable for w. and e.
Features: Tangs and trigger grooved; target trigger and hammer standard, checkered target hammer. Swing-out cylinder revolver. Price includes presentation case.
Price: Blued **$331.50**

TAURUS MODEL 86 TARGET MASTER REVOLVER

Caliber: 38 Spec., 6-shot.
Barrel: 6" only.
Weight: 41 oz. **Length:** 11¼" over-all.
Stocks: Over size target-type, checkered Brazilian walnut.
Sights: Patridge front, micro. click rear adj. for w. and e.
Features: Blue finish with non-reflective finish on barrel. Imported from Brazil by International Distributors.
Price: About **$149.00**
Price: Model 96 Scout Master, same except in 22 cal, about **$149.00**

———— AUTOLOADERS, SERVICE & SPORT ————

AMT COMBAT GOVERNMENT

Caliber: 45 ACP.
Barrel: 5".
Weight: 38 oz. **Length:** 8½" over-all.
Stocks: Checkered walnut, diamond pattern.
Sights: Combat-style, fixed.
Features: All stainless steel; extended combat safety, loaded chamber indicator, beveled magazine well, adjustable target-type trigger, custom-fitted barrel bushing, flat mainspring housing. From AMT.
Price: **$395.00**

AMT 45 ACP HARDBALLER
Caliber: 45 ACP.
Barrel: 5″.
Weight: 39 oz. **Length:** 8½″ over-all.
Stocks: Checkered walnut.
Sights: Adjustable combat-type.
Features: Extended combat safety, serrated matte slide rib, loaded chamber indicator, long grip safety, beveled magazine well, grooved front and back straps, adjustable target trigger, custom-fitted barrel bushing. All stainless steel. From AMT.
Price: $450.00
Price: 45 Skipper (as above except 1″ shorter) $450.00

AMT 45 ACP HARDBALLER LONG SLIDE
Caliber: 45 ACP.
Barrel: 7″
Length: 10½″ over-all.
Stocks: Checkered walnut.
Sights: Fully adjustable Micro rear sight.
Features: Slide and barrel are 2″ longer than the standard 45, giving less recoil, added velocity, longer sight radius. Has extended combat safety, serrated matte rib, loaded chamber indicator, wide adjustable trigger, custom fitted barrel bushing. From AMT.
Price: About $595.00

ASTRA CONSTABLE AUTO PISTOL
Caliber: 22 LR, 10-shot; 32 ACP, 8-shot; and 380 ACP, 7-shot.
Barrel: 3½″.
Weight: 26 oz.
Stocks: Moulded plastic.
Sights: Adj. rear.
Features: Double action, quick no-tool takedown, non-glare rib on slide. 380 available in blue or chrome finish. Imported from Spain by Interarms.
Price: Blue $205.00
Price: Chrome $220.00

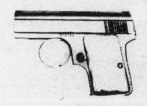

BAUER AUTOMATIC PISTOL
Caliber: 25 ACP, 6-shot.
Barrel: 2⅛″
Weight: 10 oz. **Length:** 4″.
Stocks: Plastic pearl or checkered walnut.
Sights: Recessed, fixed.
Features: Stainless steel construction, positive manual safety, magazine safety.
Price: Satin stainless steel, 25ACP $104.85

BERETTA MODEL 70S PISTOL
Caliber: 22 LR, 380 ACP.
Barrel: 3.5″
Weight: 23 ozs. (Steel) **Length:** 6.5″ over-all.
Stocks: Checkered black plastic.
Sights: Fixed front and rear.
Features: Steel frame in 32 and 380, light alloy in 22 (wgt. 18 ozs.). Safety lever blocks hammer. Side lever indicates empty magazine. Magazine capacity is 8 rounds (22), 7 rounds in 380. Introduced 1977. Imported by Beretta Arms Co.
Price: $198.00

BERETTA MODEL 92 DA PISTOL
Caliber: 9mm Parabellum (15-shot magazine).
Barrel: 4.92″.
Weight: 33½ ozs. **Length:** 8.54″ over-all.
Stocks: Smooth black plastic.
Sights: Blade front, rear adj. for w.
Features: Double-action. Extractor acts as chamber loaded indicator, inertia firing pin. Finished in blue-black. Introduced 1977. Imported by Beretta Arms Co.
Price: $398.00
Price: With wood grips $425.00

BERETTA MODEL 81/84 DA PISTOLS
Caliber: 32 ACP (12-shot magazine), 380 ACP (13-shot magazine)
Barrel: 3¾″.
Weight: About 23 oz. **Length:** 6½″ over-all.
Stocks: Smooth black plastic (wood optional at extra cost).
Sights: Fixed front and rear.
Features: Double action, quick take-down, convenient magazine release. Introduced 1977. Imported by Beretta Arms. Co.
Price: M-81 (32 ACP) $285.00
Price: M-84 (380 ACP) $285.00
Price: Either model with wood grips $305.00

BERNARDELLI MODEL 80 AUTO PISTOL
Caliber: 22 LR (10-shot); 32 ACP (8-shot); 380 ACP (7-shot).
Barrel: 3½".
Weight: 26½ oz. **Length:** 6½" over-all.
Stocks: Checkered plastic with thumbrest.
Sights: Ramp front, white outline rear adj. for w. & e.
Features: Hammer block slide safety; loaded chamber indicator; dual recoil buffer springs; serrated trigger; inertia type firing pin. Imported from Italy by Interarms.
Price: Model 80 .... $163.00

Bernardelli Model 100 Target Pistol
Similar to Model 80 except has 5.9" barrel and barrel weight; heavy sighting rib; checkered walnut thumbrest grips; 22 LR only (10-shot). Comes with case, cleaning equipment and tools. $285.00

BROWNING HI-POWER 9mm AUTOMATIC PISTOL
Caliber: 9mm Parabellum (Luger), 13-shot magazine.
Barrel: 4²¹/₃₂ inches.
Length: 7¾" over-all. **Weight:** 32 oz.
Stocks: Walnut, hand checkered.
Sights: ⅛" blade front; rear screw-adj. for w. and e. Also available with fixed rear (drift-adj. for w.).
Features: External hammer with half-cock and thumb safeties. A blow on the hammer cannot discharge a cartridge; cannot be fired with magazine removed. Fixed rear sight model available.
Price: Fixed sight model $359.95
Price: 9mm with rear sight adj. for w. and e. $389.95

Browning Renaissance Hi-Power 9mm Auto
Same as Browning Hi-Power 9mm Auto except: fully engraved, chrome plated, Narcolac pearl grips, with deluxe walnut case.
Price: With adj. sights $1,400.00
Price: With fixed sights $1,450.00

BROWNING BDA-380 D/A AUTO PISTOL
Caliber: 380 ACP, 12-shot magazine.
Barrel: 3¹³/₁₆".
Weight: 23 ozs. **Length:** 6¾" over-all.
Stocks: Smooth walnut with inset Browning medallion.
Sights: Blade front, rear drift-adj. for w.
Features: Combination safety and de-cocking lever will automatically lower a cocked hammer to half-cock and can be operated by right or left-hand shooters. Inertia firing pin. Introduced 1978.
Price: $262.50

BROWNING BDA AUTO PISTOL
Caliber: 45 ACP only (7-shot).
Barrel: 4¹³/₃₂".
Weight: 29 ozs. (9mm) **Length:** 7²⁵/₃₂." over-all.
Stocks: Checkered black plastic
Sights: Blade front, drift adj. rear of w.
Features: Double action. De-cocking lever permits lowering hammer onto locked firing pin. Squared combat-type trigger guard. Slide stays open after last shot. Introduced 1977. Imported by Browning.
Price: 45 ACP $349.95

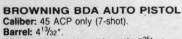

Consult our Directory pages for
the location of firms mentioned.

COLT COMMANDER AUTO PISTOL
Caliber: 45 ACP, 7 shot; 38 Super Auto, 9 shot; 9mm Luger, 9 shot.
Barrel: 4¼".
Length: 8". **Weight:** 36 oz.
Stocks: Sandblasted walnut.
Sights: Fixed, glare-proofed blade front, square notch rear.
Features: Grooved trigger and hammer spur; arched housing; grip and thumb safeties.
Price: Blued $276.95

Colt Lightweight Combat Commander
Same as Commander except high strength aluminum alloy frame, wood panel grips, weight 27 oz. 45 ACP only.
Price: Blue $268.95

COLT GOV'T MODEL MK IV/SERIES 70
Caliber: 9mm, 38 Super, 45 ACP, 7-shot.
Barrel: 5".
Weight: 40 oz. **Length:** 8⅜" over-all.
Stocks: Sandblasted walnut panels.
Sights: Ramp front, fixed square notch rear.
Features: Grip and thumb safeties, grooved trigger. Accurizor barrel and bushing. Blue finish or nickel in 45 only.
Price: Blue $276.95
Price: Nickel $292.95

Colt Conversion Unit
Permits the 45 and 38 Super Automatic pistols to use the economical 22 LR cartridge. No tools needed. Adjustable rear sight; 10-shot magazine. Designed to give recoil effect of the larger calibers. Not adaptable to Commander models. Blue finish $143.95

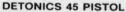

COLT SERVICE MODEL ACE
Caliber: 22 LR, 10-shot magazine.
Barrel: 5".
Weight: 42 ozs. **Length:** 8⅜" over-all.
Stocks: Checkered walnut.
Sights: Blade front, fully adjustable rear.
Features: The 22-cal. version of the Government Model auto. Based on the Service Model Ace last produced in 1945. Patented floating chamber. Original Ace Markings rolled on left side of slide. Introduced 1978.
Price: Blue only $292.95

DETONICS 45 PISTOL
Caliber: 45 ACP, 6-shot clip.
Barrel: 3¼" (2½" of which is rifled).
Weight: 29 ozs. (empty). **Length:** 6¾" over-all, 4½" high.
Stocks: Checkered walnut.
Sights: Combat type, fixed; adj. sights avail.
Features: Has a self-adjusting cone barrel centering system, beveled magazine inlet, "full clip" indicator in base of magazine; standard 7-shot (or more) clip can be used. Throated barrel and polished feed ramp. Introduced 1977. From Detonics.
Price: Blue $444.47
Price: Nickel $473.48
Price: Hardchrome $487.04
Price: Polished blue with adj. sights $493.60

ERMA KGP22 AUTO PISTOL
Caliber: 22 LR, 8-shot magazine.
Barrel: 4".
Weight: 29 ozs. **Length:** 7¾" over-all.
Stocks: Checkered plastic.
Sights: Fixed.
Features: Has toggle action similar to original "Luger" pistol. Slide stays open after last shot. Imported from West Germany by Excam. Introduced 1978.
Price: $178.00

ERMA KGP32, KGP38 AUTO PISTOLS
Caliber: 32 ACP (6-shot), 380 ACP (5-shot).
Barrel: 4".
Weight: 22½ ozs. **Length:** 7⅜" over-all.
Stocks: Checkered plastic. Wood optional.
Sights: Fixed.
Features: Toggle action similar to original "Luger" pistol. Slide stays open after last shot. Has magazine and sear disconnect safety systems. Imported from West Germany by Excam. Introduced 1978.
Price: Plastic grips $183.00

FTL 22 AUTO NINE PISTOL
Caliber: 22 LR, 8-shot magazine.
Barrel: 2¼", 6-groove rifling.
Weight: 8¼ oz. **Length:** 4⅜" over-all.
Stocks: Checkered plastic.
Sights: U-notch in slide.
Features: Alloy frame, rest is ordnance steel. Has barrel support sleeve bushing for better accuracy. Finish is matte hard chrome. Introduced 1978. From FTL Marketing.
Price: **$159.95**

F.I.E. TITAN 25 PISTOL
Caliber: 25 ACP, 6-shot magazine.
Barrel: 2⁷/₁₆".
Length: 4⅝" over-all. **Weight:** 12 oz.
Stocks: Checkered nylon.
Sights: Fixed.
Features: External hammer; fast simple takedown. Made in U.S.A. by F.I.E. Corp.
Price: Blued . . . . **$49.95**   Chromed **$59.95**

F.I.E. TITAN II E32, E380 PISTOLS
Caliber: 32 ACP, 380 ACP, 6-shot magazine.
Barrel: 3⅞".
Weight: 25¾ ozs. **Length:** 4" over-all.
Stocks: Checkered nylon, thumbrest-type.
Sights: Fixed.
Features: Magazine disconnector, firing pin block. Standard slide safety, available in blue or chrome. Introduced 1978. From F.I.E. Corp.
Price: 32, blue **$95.95**
Price: 32, chrome **$99.95**
Price: 380, blue **$109.95**
Price: 380, chrome **$114.95**

F.I.E. "THE BEST" A27B PISTOL
Caliber: 25 ACP, 6-shot magazine.
Barrel: 2½".
Weight: 13 ozs. **Length:** 4⅜" over-all.
Stocks: Checkered walnut.
Sights: Fixed.
Features: All steel construction. Has thumb and magazine safeties, exposed hammer. Blue finish only. Introduced 1978. From F.I.E. Corp.
Price: **$109.95**

HAWES/SIG-SAUER D.A AUTO PISTOL
Caliber: 9mm, 38 Super or 45 ACP, (9-shot in 9mm, 7 in 45).
Barrel: 4⅜".
Weight: 28¼ oz. (9mm). **Length:** 7¾" over-all.
Stocks: Checkered walnut.
Sights: Blade front, drift adj. rear for w.
Features: Double action. De-cocking lever permits lowering hammer onto locked firing pin. Squared combat-type trigger guard. Slide stays open after last shot. Imported by Hawes Firearms.
Price: **$349.95**

HAWES/SIG-SAUER P-230 D.A. PISTOL
Caliber: 32 ACP (8-shot), 380 ACP, 9mm Police (7 shot).
Barrel: 3¾".
Weight: 16¼ oz. (32), 16 oz. (380), 18¾ oz. (9mm Police) **Length:** 6½" over-all.
Stocks: One piece black plastic.
Sights: Blade front, rear adj. for w.
Features: Double action. Same basic design as P-220. (9mm, 38 Super, 45 ACP). Blowback operation, stationary barrel. Introduced 1977. Imported by Hawes.
Price: 32 or 380 . . . . **$299.95**
Price: 9mm Police **$349.95**

HECKLER & KOCH HK-4 DOUBLE ACTION PISTOL
Caliber: 22 LR, 25 ACP, 32 ACP, 380 ACP, 8-shot magazine (7 in 380).
Barrel: 3¹¹/₃₂″.
Weight: 16½ oz. **Length:** 6³/₁₆″ over-all.
Stocks: Black checkered plastic.
Sights: Fixed blade front, rear notched drift-adj. for w.
Features: Gun comes with all parts to shoot above four calibers; polygonal (hexagon) rifling; matte black finish. Imported by Heckler & Koch, Inc.
Price: HK-4 380 with 22 conversion kit **$285.00**
Price: HK-4 in 380 only **$265.00**
Price: HK-4 in four cals. **$340.00**
Price: Conversion units 22, 25 or 32 cal., each **$68.00**

HECKLER & KOCH VP '7OZ DOUBLE ACTION AUTO
Caliber: 9mm Para., 18-shot magazine
Barrel: 4½″.
Weight: 32½ oz. **Length:** 8″ over-all.
Stocks: Black stippled plastic.
Sights: Ramp front, channeled slide rear.
Features: Recoil operated, double action. Only 4 moving parts. Double column magazine. Imported by Heckler & Koch, Inc.
Price: **$268.00**

HK P9S DOUBLE ACTION AUTO PISTOL
Caliber: 9mm Para., 9-shot magazine.
Barrel: 4″.
Weight: 33½ oz. **Length:** 5½″ over-all.
Stocks: Checkered black plastic.
Sights: Open combat type.
Features: Double action; polygonal rifling; sliding roller lock action with stationary barrel. Loaded chamber and cocking indicators; un-cocking lever relaxes springs. Imported from Germany by Heckler & Koch, Inc.
Price: P-9S Combat Model **$384.00**

HECKLER & KOCH P9S DOUBLE ACTION 45
Caliber: 45 ACP, 7-shot magazine.
Barrel: 4¹/₃₂″.
Weight: 32½ oz. **Length:** 7½″ over-all.
Stocks: Checkered black plastic.
Sights: Open, combat type.
Features: Double action; polygonal rifling; delayed roller-locked bolt system. Imported by Heckler & Koch, Inc.
Price: **$384.00**
Price: With adj. trigger, trigger stop, adj. rear sight **$436.00**
Price: 8″ hunting barrel **$87.00**

IVER JOHNSON MODEL X300 PONY
Caliber: 380 ACP, 6-shot magazine.
Barrel: 3″.
Weight: 20 oz. **Length:** 6″ over-all.
Stocks: Checkered walnut.
Sights: Blade front, rear adj. for w.
Features: Loaded chamber indicator, all steel construction. Inertia firing pin. Thumb safety locks hammer. No magazine safety. Lanyard ring. From Iver Johnson's.
Price: Blue **$170.00**
Price: Nickel **$180.25**
Price: Military (matte finish) **$170.00**

L.E.S P-18 AUTO PISTOL
Caliber: 9mm Parabellum, 18-shot magazine.
Barrel: 5½″, stationary; polygonal rifling.
Weight: About 36 oz.
Stocks: Checkered resin.
Sights: Post front, V-notch rear drift adj. for w.
Features: Gas-assisted action; all stainless steel; inertia firing pin Made in U.S.A. Both single and double action models offered, in two finish grades. From L.E.S.
Price: Std. D.A. (matte finish) **$299.95**
Price: Deluxe D.A. (polished) **$389.95**
Price: Combat D.A. **$309.95**
Price: Std. S.A. (matte finish) **$279.95**
Price: Deluxe S.A. (polished) **$369.95**
Price: Combat S.A. **$289.95**

HK P9S

Price: P-9S Target Model **$436.00**
Price: P-9/P-9S Competition Model (similar to Target except comes with wrap around match grips, bbl. weight, 4″ & 5½″ bbl. **$599.00**

HI-STANDARD SHARPSHOOTER AUTO PISTOL
Caliber: 22 LR, 10-shot magazine.
Barrel: 5½″.
Length: 9″ over-all. **Weight:** 45 oz.
Stocks: Checkered walnut.
Sights: Fixed, ramp front, square notch rear adj. for w. & e.
Features: Military frame. Wide, scored trigger; new hammer-sear design. Slide lock, push-button take down.
Price: Blued **$179.50**

LLAMA XI AUTO PISTOL
Caliber: 9mm Para.
Barrel: 5″.
Weight: 38 oz. **Length:** 8½″.
Stocks: Moulded plastic.
Sights: Fixed front, adj. rear.
Features: Also available with engraved, chrome engraved or gold damascened finish at extra cost. Imported from Spain by Stoeger Industries.
Price: **$249.95**

LLAMA MODELS VIII, IXA AUTO PISTOLS
Caliber: Super 38 (M. VIII), 45 ACP (M. IXA).
Barrel: 5".
Weight: 30 oz. **Length:** 8½"
Stocks: Checkered walnut.
Sights: Fixed.
Features: Grip and manual safeties, ventilated rib. Engraved, chrome engraved or gold damascened finish available at extra cost. Imported from Spain by Stoeger Industries.
Price: **$249.95**

MKE MODEL TPK AUTO PISTOL
Caliber: 32 ACP, 8-shot; 380, 7-shot.
Barrel: 4"
Weight: 23 oz. **Length:** 6½".
Stocks: Checkered black plastic.
Sights: Fixed front, adj. notch rear.
Features: Double action with exposed hammer; safety blocks firing pin and drops hammer. Chamber loaded indicator pin. Imported from Turkey by Firearms Center.
Price: **$259.95**

MAUSER PARABELLUM SWISS MODEL PISTOL
Caliber: 30 Luger, 9mm Para., 8-shot.
Barrel: 4" (9mm), 6" (30 Luger).
Weight: 32 oz. **Length:** 8.66" (4" bbl.).
Stocks: Checkered walnut.
Sights: Fixed.
Features: Manual and grip safeties, American eagle over chamber and Mauser banner on toggle. Final production—guns offered until supply exhausted. Imported from Germany by Interarms.
Price: **$625.00**

MAUSER HSc "ONE OF FIVE THOUSAND" PISTOL
Caliber: 32 ACP, 380 ACP, 7-shot.
Barrel: 3¾".
Weight: 23 oz. **Length:** 6.05".
Stocks: Checkered walnut.
Sights: Fixed.
Features: Double action, manual and magazine safeties. Matted non-glare sight channel. Inertia firing pin. Comes in fitted case with extra magazine, bore brush, test target. Final HSc production. Imported from Germany by Interarms.
Price: Bright blue only **$275.00**

RG 26 AUTO PISTOL
Caliber: 25 ACP, 6-shot magazine.
Barrel: 2½".
Weight: 12 ozs. **Length:** 4¾" over-all.
Stocks: Checkered plastic.
Sights: Fixed.
Features: Blue finish. Thumb safety. Imported by RG Industries.
Price: **$45.00**

RAVEN P-25 AUTO PISTOL
Caliber: 25 ACP.
Barrel: 3".
Weight: 12 oz.
Stocks: Smooth walnut or Pearl-O-Lite.
Sights: Ramped front, fixed rear.
Features: Available in blue, nickel or satin nickel finish. From EMF Co.
Price: **$55.95**

LLAMA MODELS XV, XA, IIIA AUTO PISTOLS
Caliber: 22 LR, 32 ACP and 380.
Barrel: 3¹¹/₁₆".
Weight: 23 oz. **Length:** 6½".
Stocks: Checkered plastic, thumb rest.
Sights: Fixed front, adj. notch rear.
Features: Ventilated rib, manual and grip safeties. Model XV is 22 LR, Model XA is 32 ACP, and Model IIIA is 380. Models XA and IIIA have loaded indicator; IIIA is locked breech. Imported from Spain by Stoeger Industries.
Price: **$182.95**

SILE-BENELLI B76 DA AUTO PISTOL
Caliber: 9mm Para., 8-shot magazine.
Barrel: 4¼", 6-groove. Chrome-lined bore.
Weight: 34 oz. (empty). **Length:** 8¹/₁₆" over-all.
Stocks: Walnut with cut checkering and high gloss finish.
Sights: Blade front with white face, rear adjustable for windage with white bars for increased visibility.
Features: Fixed barrel, locked breech. Exposed hammer can be locked in non-firing mode in either single or double action. Stainless steel inertia firing pin and loaded chamber indicator. All external parts blued, internal parts hard-chrome plated. All steel construction. Introduced 1979. From Sile Dist.
Price: $290.50

SMITH & WESSON 9mm MODEL 39 AUTO PISTOL
Caliber: 9mm Luger, 8-shot clip.
Barrel: 4".
Length: 7⁷/₁₆". **Weight:** 26½ oz., without magazine.
Stocks: Checkered walnut.
Sights: ⅛" serrated ramp front, adjustable rear.
Features: Magazine disconnector, positive firing pin lock and hammer-release safety; alloy frame with lanyard loop; locked-breech, short-recoil double action; slide locks open on last shot.
Price: Blued . . . . $210.50   Nickeled $232.00

SMITH & WESSON MODEL 59 DOUBLE ACTION
Caliber: 9mm Luger, 14-shot clip.
Barrel: 4".
Length: 7⁷/₁₆" over-all. **Weight:** 27½ oz., without clip.
Stocks: Checkered high impact moulded nylon.
Sights: ⅛" serrated ramp front, square notch rear adj. for w.
Features: Double action automatic. Furnished with two magazines. Blue finish.
Price: Blued $252.00
Price: Nickel $275.00

STAR MODEL PD AUTO PISTOL
Caliber: 45 ACP, 7-shot magazine.
Barrel: 3.94".
Weight: 25 oz. **Length:** 7" over-all.
Stocks: Checkered walnut.
Sights: Ramp front, fully adjustable rear.
Features: Rear sight milled into slide; thumb safety; grooved non-slip front strap; nylon recoil buffer; inertia firing pin; no grip or magazine safeties. From Interarms.
Price: Blue $255.00

STAR BM, BKM AUTO PISTOLS
Caliber: 9mm Para., 8-shot magazine.
Barrel: 3.9".
Weight: 25 oz.
Stocks: Checkered walnut.
Sights: Fixed.
Features: Blue or chrome finish. Magazine and manual safeties, external hammer. Imported from Spain by Interarms.
Price: Blue, BM and BKM $215.00
Price: Chrome, BM only $230.00

STERLING MODEL 300
Caliber: 25 ACP, 6-shot.
Barrel: 2½".
Length: 4½" over-all. **Weight:** 13 oz.
Stocks: Cycolac, black or white.
Sights: Fixed.
Features: All steel construction.
Price: Blued $89.95
Price: Stainless steel $108.95

STERLING MODEL 450 D.A. AUTO
Caliber: 45 ACP, 8-shot magazine.
Barrel: 4¼".
Weight: 35 ozs. **Length:** 7½" over-all.
Stocks: Checkered walnut.
Sights: Blade front, rear adj. for w. & e.
Features: All steel, reversible safety, inertia firing pin. Introduced 1977.
Price: Blue only $269.95

STERLING MODEL 302
Caliber: 22 LR, 6-shot.
Barrel: 2½".
Length: 4½" over-all. **Weight:** 13 oz.
Stocks: Cycolac, black or white.
Sights: Fixed.
Features: All steel construction.
Price: Blue $89.95
Price: Stainless steel $108.95

STERLING MODEL 400 MK II DOUBLE ACTION
Caliber: 380 ACP, 7-shot.
Barrel: 3¾".
Length: 6½" over-all. **Weight:** 18 oz.
Stocks: Checkered walnut.
Features: All steel construction. Double action.
Price: Blued $199.95
Price: Stainless steel $249.95

TDE "BACKUP" AUTO PISTOL
Caliber: 380 ACP, 5-shot magazine
Barrel: 2½".
Weight: 17 oz. **Length:** 5" over-all.
Stocks: Smooth wood.
Sights: Fixed, open, recessed.
Features: Concealed hammer, blowback operation; manual and grip safeties. All stainless steel construction. Smallest domestically-produced pistol in 380. From AMT.
Price: About $235.00

TARGA MODELS GT32, GT380 AUTO PISTOLS
Caliber: 32 ACP or 380 ACP, 7-shot magazine
Barrel: 4⅛".
Weight: 26 oz. **Length:** 7⅜" over-all.
Stocks: Checkered nylon with thumb rest. Walnut optional.
Sights: Fixed blade front; rear drift-adj. for w.
Features: Chrome or blue finish; magazine, thumb, and firing pin safeties; external hammer; safety lever take-down. Imported from Italy by Excam, Inc.
Price: 32 cal., blue $95.00
Price: 32 cal., chrome $99.00
Price: 380 cal., blue $109.00
Price: 380 cal., chrome $116.00
Price: 380 cal., chrome, engraved, wooden grips $152.00
Price: 380 cal., blue, engraved, wooden grips $147.00

TARGA MODEL GT27 AUTO PISTOL
Caliber: 25 ACP, 6-shot magazine
Barrel: 2⁷/16".
Weight: 12 oz. **Length:** 4⅝" over-all.
Stocks: Checkered nylon.
Sights: Fixed.
Features: Safety lever take-down; external hammer with half-cock. Made in U.S. by Excam, Inc.
Price: Blue $48.50
Price: Chrome $53.00

WALTHER P-38 AUTO PISTOL
Caliber: 22 LR, 30 Luger or 9mm Luger, 8-shot.
Barrel: 4¹⁵/16" (9mm and 30), 5¹/16" (22 LR).
Weight: 28 oz. **Length:** 8½".
Stock: Checkered plastic.
Sights: Fixed.
Features: Double action, safety blocks firing pin and drops hammer, chamber loaded indicator. Matte finish standard, polished blue, engraving and/or plating available. Imported from Germany by Interarms.
Price: 22 LR $690.00
Price: 9mm or 30 Luger $600.00
Price: Engraved models .... On Request

Walther P-38K Auto Pistol

Streamlined version of the P-38; 2¾" barrel, 6⅜" over-all, weight 26 ozs. Strengthened slide (no dust cover), recoil bearing cross-bolt. Rear sight adj. for windage, both front and rear sights have white accents. Hammer decocking lever. Non-reflective matte finish. Imported from Germany by Interarms. Introduced 1977.

Price: **$650.00**

Walther P-38IV Auto Pistol

Same as P-38K except has longer barrel (4½"); over-all length is 8", weight is 29 ozs. Sights are non-adjustable. Introduced 1977. Imported by Interarms.

Price: **$650.00**

WALTHER PP AUTO PISTOL

Caliber: 22 LR, 8-shot; 32 ACP, 380 ACP, 7-shot.
Barrel: 3.86".
Weight: 23½ oz. **Length:** 6.7"
Stocks: Checkered plastic.
Sights: Fixed, white markings.
Features: Double action, manual safety blocks firing pin and drops hammer, chamber loaded indicator on 32 and 380, extra finger rest magazine provided. Imported from Germany by Interarms.
Price: (22 LR) **$425.00**
Price: (32 and 380) **$405.00**
Price: Engraved models .... **On Request**

Walther PPK/S Auto Pistol

Same as PP except bbl. 3.27", length 6.1" o.a.
Price: 22 LR **$415.00**
Price: 32 or 380 ACP **$395.00**
Price: Engraved models .... **On Request**

──────── REVOLVERS, SERVICE & SPORT ────────

ARMINIUS REVOLVERS

Caliber: 38 Special, 357 Mag., 32 S&W (6-shot); 22 Magnum, 22 LR (8-shot).
Barrel: 4" (38 Spec., 357 Mag., 32 S&W, 22 LR); 6" (38 Spec., 22 LR/22 Mag., 357 Mag.); 8⅜" (357 Mag.).
Weight: 35 oz. (6" bbl.). **Length:** 11" (6" bbl. 38).
Stocks: Checkered plastic; walnut optional for $14.95.
Sights: Ramp front, fixed rear on standard models, w. & e. adj. on target models.
Features: Ventilated rib, solid frame, swing-out cylinder. Interchangeable 22 Mag. cylinder available with 22 cal. versions. Also available in 357 Mag. 3" 4", 6" barrel, adj. sights. Imported from West Germany by F.I.E. Corp.
Price: .... **$89.95 to $170.95**

ASTRA 357 MAGNUM REVOLVER

Caliber: 357 Magnum, 6-shot.
Barrel: 3", 4", 6", 8½".
Weight: 40 oz. (6" bbl.). **Length:** 11¼" (6" bbl.).
Stocks: Checkered walnut.
Sights: Fixed front, rear adj. for w. and e.
Features: Swing-out cylinder with countersunk chambers, floating firing pin. Target-type hammer and trigger. Imported from Spain by Interarms.
Price: 3", 4", 6" **$235.00**
Price: 8½" **$245.00**

CHARTER ARMS UNDERCOVER REVOLVER

Caliber: 38 Special, 5 shot; 32 S & W Long, 6 shot.
Barrel: 2", 3".
Weight: 16 oz. (2"). **Length:** 6¼" (2").
Stocks: Smooth walnut or checkered square butt.
Sights: Patridge-type ramp front, notched rear.
Features: Wide trigger and hammer spur. Steel frame.
Price: Polished Blue .... **$130.00** Nickel **$142.00**
Price: With checkered square butt grips, blue, 3" **$139.00**
Price: 32 S & W Long, blue, 2" **$130.00**

Charter Arms Pathfinder

Same as Undercover but in 22 LR caliber, and has 3" or 6" bbl. Fitted with adjustable rear sight, ramp front. Weight 18½ oz.
Price: 22 LR, blue, 3" **$144.00**
Price: 22 LR, square butt, 6" **$153.00**
Price: 22 Mag., square butt, 3" **$158.00**
Price: 22 Mag, square butt, 6" **$158.00**

CHARTER ARMS BULLDOG

Caliber: 357 Mag., 44 Special, 5-shot.
Barrel: 3", 6".
Weight: 19 oz. **Length:** 7½" over-all.
Stocks: Hand checkered walnut; Square butt.
Sights: Patridge type 9/64" front, square notch rear.
Features: Wide trigger and hammer, chrome-moly steel frame, unbreakable firing pin, transfer bar ignition.
Price: 44 Spec., 3" **$150.00**
Price: 357 Mag., 6" **$150.00**

CHARTER ARMS POLICE BULLDOG

Caliber: 38 Special, 6-shot.
Barrel: 4".
Weight: 20½ oz. **Length:** 8½" over-all.
Stocks: Hand checkered American walnut; square butt.
Sights: Full length ramp front; fully adj. combat rear.
Features: Accepts both regular and high velocity ammunition; enclosed ejector rod; full length ejection of fired cases.
Price: Blue only, approx. **$149.00**

CHARTER TARGET BULLDOG

Caliber: 357 Mag., 44 Spec., 5-shot.
Barrel: 4" or 6".
Weight: 20½ oz. **Length:** 8½" over-all.
Stocks: Checkered American walnut, square butt.
Sights: Full-length ramp front, fully adj., milled channel, square notch rear.
Features: Blue finish only. Enclosed ejector rod, full length ejection of fired cases.
Price: **$165.00**

COLT DIAMONDBACK REVOLVER

Caliber: 22 LR or 38 Special, 6 shot.
Barrel: 4" or 6" with ventilated rib.
Length: 9" (4" bbl.). **Weight:** 24 oz. (2½" bbl.), 28½ oz. (4" bbl.).
Stocks: Checkered walnut, target type, square butt.
Sights: Ramp front, adj. notch rear.
Features: Ventilated rib; grooved, crisp trigger; swing-out cylinder; wide hammer spur.
Price: Blue, 4" bbl., 38 Spec. **$261.00**
Price: Blue, 22-cal., 6" bbl. **$265.00**

COLT LAWMAN MK III REVOLVER

Caliber: 357 Mag., 6 shot.
Barrel: 2" or 4", heavy.
Weight: 33 oz.
Length: 9⅜".
Stocks: Checkered walnut, service style.
Sights: Fixed, glare-proofed ramp front, square notch rear.
Price: Blued **$215.95**
Price: Nickel **$229.95**

COLT TROOPER MK III REVOLVER

Caliber: 22 LR, 22 WMR, 357 Magnum, 6-shot.
Barrel: 4" 6".
Length: 9½" (4" bbl.). **Weight:** 39 oz. (4" bbl.), 42 oz. (6" bbl.).
Stocks: Checkered walnut, square butt. Grooved trigger.
Sights: Fixed ramp front with ⅛" blade, adj. notch rear.
Price: Blued with target hammer and target stocks **$264.95**
Price: Nickeled (357 Mag. only) **$286.50**

COLT DETECTIVE SPECIAL

Caliber: 38 Special, 6 shot.
Barrel: 2".
Length: 6⅝" over-all. **Weight:** 22 oz.
Stocks: Full, checkered walnut, round butt.
Sights: Fixed, ramp front, square notch rear.
Features: Glare-proofed sights, smooth trigger. Nickel finish, hammer shroud available as options.
Price: Blue **$225.00**

F.I.E. MODEL F38 "Titan Tiger" REVOLVER

Caliber: 38 Special.
Barrel: 2" or 4".
Length: 6¼" over-all. (2" bbl.). **Weight:** 27 oz.
Stocks: Checkered plastic, Bulldog style. Walnut optional ($10.95).
Sights: Fixed.
Features: Swing-out cylinder, one stroke ejection. Made in U.S.A. by F.I.E. Corp.
Price: Blued 2" or 4" ..... **$87.95**   Nickel, 2" or 4" bbl. **$109.95**
Price: Blue/Gold combo **$114.95**

HIGH STANDARD CRUSADER COMMEMORATIVE REVOLVER
Caliber: 357 Mag., 44 Mag., 45 Long Colt.
Barrel: 4¼", 6½", 8⅜".
Weight: 48 oz. (4⅛").
Stocks: Smooth Zebrawood.
Sights: Blade front on ramp, fully adj. rear.
Features: Unique gear-segment mechanism. Smooth, light double-action trigger pull. First production devoted to the commemorative; later guns will be of plain, standard configuration.
Price: 4¼", 357, 44, 45 . . . . $335.50
Price: 6½", 357, 44, 45 . . . . $340.00
Price: 8⅜", 357, 44 only $345.50

LLAMA COMANCHE REVOLVERS
Caliber: 22 LR, 38 Special, 357 Mag., 44 Mag.
Barrel: 6", 4" (except 22 LR, 6" only).
Weight: 22 LR 24 oz. 38 Special 31 oz. **Length:** 9¼" (4" bbl.).
Stocks: Checkered walnut.
Sights: Fixed blade front, rear adj. for w. & e.
Features: Ventilated rib, wide spur hammer. Chrome plating, engraved finishes available. Imported from Spain by Stoeger Industries.
Price: 22 LR, 38 Spec. $199.95
Price: Comanche 357 Mag. $209.95
Price: Satin chrome, 357 only $266.95
Price: Super Comanche, 44 Mag. (illus.) $349.95

RG 31 REVOLVER
Caliber: 32 S & W (6-shot), 38 Spec. (5-shot).
Barrel: 2".
Weight: 24 ozs. **Length:** 6¾" over-all.
Stocks: Checkered plastic.
Sights: Fixed.
Features: Cylinder swings out when pin is removed. Blue finish. Imported by RG Industries.
Price: 32 cal. $58.95
Price: 38 cal. $58.95

RG 38S REVOLVER
Caliber: 38 Special, 6-shot.
Barrel: 3" and 4".
Weight: 3", 31 oz.; 4", 34 oz. **Length:** 3", 8½"; 4", 9¼".
Stocks: Checkered plastic.
Sights: Fixed front, rear adj. for w.
Features: Swing out cylinder with spring ejector. Imported from Germany by RG Industries.
Price: Blue $77.95

RG 57 REVOLVER
Caliber: 357 Magnum, 41 Mag., 44 Mag., 45 Colt.
Barrel: 4", 6".
Weight: 44 oz. **Length:** 9½".
Stocks: Checkered plastic.
Sights: Fixed rear.
Features: Swing out cylinder, spring ejector, steel frame. Imported from Germany by RG Industries.
Price: . . . . $197.00 to $242.00

RG 40 REVOLVER
Caliber: 38 Spec., 6-shot.
Barrel: 2".
Weight: 29 ozs. **Length:** 7¼" over-all.
Stocks: Checkered plastic.
Sights: Fixed.
Features: Swing-out cylinder with spring ejector. Imported by RG Industries.
Price: $76.00

RG MODEL 88 REVOLVER
Caliber: 38 Spec., 357 Mag.
Barrel: 4".
Weight: 33 oz. **Length:** 9" over-all.
Stocks: Checkered walnut.
Sights: Fixed.
Features: Swing out cylinder, spring ejector. Wide spur hammer and trigger. Imported by RG Industries.
Price: $199.50

ROSSI MODELS 68, 69 & 70 DA REVOLVERS
Caliber: 22 LR (M 70), 32 S & W. (M 69), 38 Spec. (M 68).
Barrel: 3".
Weight: 22 oz.
Stocks: Checkered wood.
Sights: Ramp front, low profile adj. rear.
Features: All-steel frame. Thumb latch operated swing-out cylinder. Introduced 1978. Imported by Interarms.
Price: 22, 32 or 38, blue or nickel $105.00
Price: As above, 38 Spec. only with 4" bbl. as M 31 . . . . $110.00

RUGER STAINLESS SECURITY-SIX Model 717
Caliber: 357 Mag. (also fires 38 Spec.), 6-shot.
Barrel: 2¾", 4" or 6".
Weight: 33 oz. (4 bbl.). **Length:** 9¼" (4" bbl.) over-all.
Stocks: Hand checkered American walnut.
Sights: Patridge-type front, fully adj. rear.
Features: All metal parts except sights made of stainless steel. Sights are black alloy for maximum visibility. Same mechanism and features found in regular Security-Six.
Price: 2¾", 4", 6" and 4" HB $192.00
Price: 4" HB, 6" with Big Grip stocks. $207.50

RUGER POLICE SERVICE-SIX Models 107, 108

Caliber: 357 (Model 107), 38 Spec. (Model 108), 9mm (Model 109), 6-shot.
Barrel: 2¾" or 4" and 4" heavy barrel.
Weight: 33½ oz (4" bbl.). **Length:** 9¼" (4" bbl.) over-all.
Stocks: Checkered American walnut, semi-target style.
Sights: Patridge-type front, square notch rear.
Features: Solid frame with barrel, rib and ejector rod housing combined in one unit. All steel construction. Field strips without tools.
Price: Model 107 (357) **$140.00**
Price: Model 108 (38) **$140.00**
Price: Mod. 707 (357), Stainless, 4" & 4" HB **$154.00**
Price: Mod. 708 (38), Stainless, 4" & 4" HB **$154.00**

RUGER SPEED-SIX Models 207, 208

Caliber: 357 (Model 207), 38 Spec. (Model 208), 6-shot.
Barrel: 2¾" or 4".
Weight: 31 oz. (2¾" bbl.). **Length:** 7¾" over-all (2¾" bbl.).
Stocks: Round butt design, diamond pattern checkered American walnut.
Sights: Patridge-type front, square-notch rear.
Features: Same basic mechanism as Security-Six. Hammer without spur available on special order. All steel construction. Music wire coil springs used throughout.
Price: Model 207 (357 Mag.) **$140.00**
Price: Model 208 (38 Spec. only) **$140.00**
Price: Mod. 737 (357), Stainless **$154.00**
Price: Mod. 738 (38), Stainless **$154.00**

RUGER SECURITY-SIX Model 117

Caliber: 357 Mag. (also fires 38 Spec.), 6-shot.
Barrel: 2¾", 4" or 6", or 4" heavy barrel.
Weight: 33½ oz. (4" bbl.). **Length:** 9¼" (4" bbl.) over-all.
Stocks: Hand checkered American walnut, semi-target style.
Sights: Patridge-type front on ramp, rear adj. for w. and e.
Features: Music wire coil springs throughout. Hardened steel construction. Integral ejector rod shroud and sighting rib. Can be disassembled using only a coin.
Price: 2¾", 4", 6" and 4" heavy barrel **$177.50**
Price: 4" HB, 6" with Big Grip stocks **$193.00**

SMITH & WESSON M&P Model 10 REVOLVER

Caliber: 38 Special, 6 shot.
Barrel: 2", 4", 5" or 6".
Length: 9¼" (4" bbl.). **Weight:** 30½ oz. (4" bbl.).
Stocks: Checkered walnut, Magna. Round or square butt.
Sights: Fixed, ⅛" ramp front, square notch rear.
Price: Blued . . . . **$125.50**   Nickeled **$137.00**

Smith & Wesson 38 M&P Heavy Barrel Model 10

Same as regular M&P except: 4" ribbed bbl. with ⅛" ramp front sight, square rear, square butt, wgt. 34 oz.
Price: Blued . . . . **$125.50**   Nickeled **$137.00**

SMITH & WESSON 38 M&P AIRWEIGHT Model 12

Caliber: 38 Special, 6 shot.
Barrel: 2 or 4 inches.
Length: 6⅞" over-all. **Weight:** 18 oz. (2" bbl.)
Stocks: Checkered walnut, Magna. Round or square butt.
Sights: Fixed, ⅛" serrated ramp front, square notch rear.
Price: Blued . . . . **$166.00**   Nickeled **$188.50**

SMITH & WESSON Model 13 H.B. M&P

Caliber: 357 and 38 Special, 6 shot.
Barrel: 4".
Weight: 34 oz. **Length:** 9¼" over-all.
Stocks: Checkered walnut, service.
Sights: ⅛" serrated ramp front, fixed square notch rear.
Features: Heavy barrel, K-frame, square butt.
Price: Blue only, M-13 . . . . **$139.00**
Price: Nickel **$152.00**
Price: Model 65, as above in stainless steel **$154.00**

SMITH & WESSON Model 14 K-38 MASTERPIECE
Caliber: 38 Spec., 6-shot.
Barrel: 6″, 8⅜″.
Weight: 38½ oz. (6″ bbl.). **Length:** 11⅛″ over-all (6″ bbl.)
Stock: Checkered walnut, service.
Sights: ⅛″ Patridge front, micro click rear adj. for w. and e.
Price: 6″ bbl. **$195.50**
Price: 8⅜″ bbl. **$205.00**

SMITH & WESSON 357 COMBAT MAGNUM Model 19
Caliber: 357 Magnum and 38 Special, 6 shot.
Barrel: 2½″, 4″, 6″.
Length: 9½″ (4″ bbl.). **Weight:** 35 oz.
Stocks: Checkered Goncala Alves, target. Grooved tangs and trigger.
Sights: Front, ⅛″ Baughman Quick Draw on 2½″ or 4″ bbl., Patridge on 6″ bbl., micro click rear adjustable for w. and e.
Price: S&W Bright Blue or Nickel **$202.00**

SMITH & WESSON 357 MAGNUM M-27 REVOLVER
Caliber: 357 Magnum and 38 Special, 6 shot.
Barrel: 3½″, 5″, 6″, 8⅜″.
Length: 11¼″ (6″ bbl.). **Weight:** 44 oz. (6″ bbl.).
Stocks: Checkered walnut, Magna. Grooved tangs and trigger.
Sights: Any S&W target front, micro click rear, adjustable for w. and e.
Price: S&W Bright Blue or Nickel, 3½″, 5″, 6″ **$303.00**
Price: 8⅜″ bbl. **$314.50**

SMITH & WESSON HIGHWAY PATROLMAN Model 28
Caliber: 357 Magnum and 38 Special, 6 shot.
Barrel: 4″, 6″.
Length: 11¼″ (6″ bbl.). **Weight:** 44 oz. (6″ bbl.).
Stocks: Checkered walnut, Magna. Grooved tangs and trigger.
Sights: Front, ⅛″ Baughman Quick Draw, on plain ramp. micro click rear, adjustable for w. and e.
Price: S&W Satin Blue, sandblasted frame edging and barrel top . **$190.50**
Price: With target stocks **$205.50**

SMITH & WESSON 44 MAGNUM Model 29 REVOLVER
Caliber: 44 Magnum, 44 Special or 44 Russian, 6 shot.
Barrel: 4″, 6½″, 8⅜″.
Length: 11⅞″ (6½″ bbl.). **Weight:** 47 oz. (6½″ bbl.), 43 oz. (4″ bbl.).
Stocks: Oversize target type, checkered Goncala Alves. Tangs and target trigger grooved, checkered target hammer.
Sights: ⅛″ red ramp-front, micro. click rear, adjustable for w. and e.
Features: Includes presentation case.
Price: S&W Bright Blue or Nickel 4″, 6½″ **$331.50**
Price: 8⅜″ bbl. **$342.00**
Price: Model 629 (stainless steel) . . . . **N.A.**

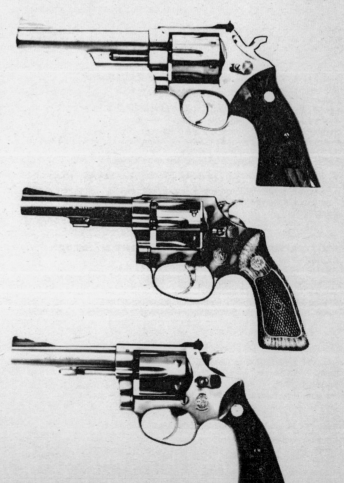

SMITH & WESSON 32 REGULATION POLICE Model 31
Caliber: 32 S&W Long, 6 shot.
Barrel: 2″, 3″, 4″.
Length: 8½″ (4″ bbl.). **Weight:** 18¾ oz. (4″ bbl.).
Stocks: Checkered walnut, Magna.
Sights: Fixed, 1/10″ serrated ramp front, square notch rear.
Price: Blued . . . . **$156.00**   Nickeled **$170.00**

SMITH & WESSON 1953 Model 34, 22/32 KIT GUN
Caliber: 22 LR, 6 shot.
Barrel: 2″, 4″.
Length: 8″ (4″ bbl. and round butt). **Weight:** 22½ oz. (4″ bbl.).
Stocks: Checkered walnut, round or square butt.
Sights: Front, 1/10″ serrated ramp, micro. click rear, adjustable for w. & e.
Price: Blued . . . . **$159.00**   Nickeled **$172.50**
Price: Model 63, as above in stainless, 4″ **$187.00**

SMITH & WESSON 38 CHIEFS SPECIAL & AIRWEIGHT

Caliber: 38 Special, 5 shot.
Barrel: 2", 3".
Length: 6½" (2" bbl. and round butt). **Weight:** 19 oz. (2" bbl.); 14 oz. (AIRWEIGHT).
Stocks: Checkered walnut, Magna. Round or square butt.
Sights: Fixed, ¹⁄₁₀" serrated ramp front, square notch rear.
Price: Blued std. M-36 ... **$147.50**   Standard weight Nickel ... **$160.00**
Price: Blued AIR'W M-37 . **$164.00**   AIRWEIGHT Nickel **$185.50**

Smith & Wesson 60 Chiefs Special Stainless

Same as Model 36 except: 2" bbl. and round butt only.
Price: Stainless steel **$181.50**

SMITH & WESSON BODYGUARD MODEL 38

Caliber: 38 Special; 5 shot, double action revolver.
Barrel: 2".
Length: 6⅜". **Weight:** 14½ oz.
Features: Alloy frame; integral hammer shroud.
Stocks: Checkered walnut, Magna.
Sights: Fixed ¹⁄₁₀" serrated ramp front, square notch rear.
Price: Blued .... **$171.00**   Nickeled **$193.00**

Smith & Wesson Bodyguard Model 49 Revolver

Same as Model 38 except steel
construction.   Weight 20½ oz.
Price: Blued .... **$159.00**   Nickeled **$172.00**

SMITH & WESSON 41 MAGNUM Model 57 REVOLVER

Caliber: 41 Magnum, 6 shot.
Barrel: 4", 6" or 8⅜".
Length: 11⅜" (6" bbl.). **Weight:** 48 oz. (6" bbl.).
Stocks: Oversize target type checkered Goncala Alves wood and target hammer. Tang and target trigger grooved.
Sights: ⅛" red ramp front, micro. click rear, adj. for w. and e.
Price: S&W Bright Blue or Nickel 4", 6" **$331.50**
Price: 8⅜" bbl. **$342.00**

SMITH & WESSON MODEL 64 STAINLESS M&P

Caliber: 38 Special, 6-shot.
Barrel: 4".
Length: 9½" over-all. **Weight:** 30½ oz.
Stocks: Checkered walnut, service style.
Sights: Fixed, ⅛" serrated ramp front, square notch rear.
Features: Satin finished stainless steel, square butt.
Price: **$145.00**

SMITH & WESSON MODEL 66 STAINLESS COMBAT MAGNUM

Caliber: 357 Magnum and 38 Special, 6-shot.
Barrel: 2½", 4", 6".
Length: 9½" over-all. **Weight:** 35 oz.
Stocks: Checkered Goncala Alves target.
Sights: Front, ⅛" Baughman Quick Draw on plain ramp, micro click rear adj. for w. and e.
Features: Satin finish stainless steel, grooved trigger with adj. stop.
Price: **$208.00**

SMITH & WESSON MODEL 67 K-38 STAINLESS COMBAT MASTERPIECE

Caliber: 38 special, 6-shot.
Barrel: 4".
Length: 9⅛" over-all. **Weight:** 34 oz. (loaded).
Stocks: Checkered walnut, service style.
Sights: Front, ⅛" Baughman Quick Draw on ramp, micro click rear adj. for w. and e.
Features: Stainless steel. Square butt frame with grooved tangs, grooved trigger with adj. stop.
Price: **$187.50**

Consult our Directory pages for
the location of firms mentioned.

TAURUS MODEL 82 HEAVY BARREL REVOLVER
Caliber: 38 Spec., 6-shot.
Barrel: 3" or 4", heavy.
Weight: 33 oz. (4" bbl.). **Length:** 9¼" over-all (4" bbl.).
Stocks: Checkered Brazilian walnut.
Sights: Serrated ramp front, square notch rear.
Features: Imported from Brazil by International Distributors.
Price: Blue, about $113.00
Price: Nickel, about $127.00

TAURUS MODEL 83 REVOLVER
Caliber: 38 Spec., 6-shot.
Barrel: 4" only, heavy.
Weight: 34½ ozs.
Stocks: Over-size checkered walnut.
Sights: Ramp front, micro. click rear adj. for w. & e.
Features: Blue or nickel finish. Introduced 1977. From International Distributors.
Price: Blue, about $115.00
Price: Nickel, about $130.00

TAURUS MODEL 84 SPORT REVOLVER
Caliber: 38 Spec., 6-shot.
Barrel: 4".
Weight: 30 oz. **Length:** 9¼" over-all.
Stocks: Checkered Brazilian walnut.
Sights: Serrated ramp front, rear adj. for w. and e.
Features: Imported from Brazil by International Distributors.
Price: Blue, about $115.00
Price: Nickel, about $130.00

TAURUS MODEL 66 REVOLVER
Caliber: 357 Magnum, 6-shot.
Barrel: 3", 4", 6".
Weight: 35 ozs.
Stocks: Checkered walnut, target-type.
Sights: Serrated ramp front, micro click rear adjustable for w. and e.
Features: Wide target-type hammer spur, floating firing pin, heavy barrel with shrouded ejector rod. Introduced 1978. From International Distributors.
Price: Blue only, about $175.00
Price: Model 65 (similar to M66 except has a fixed rear sight and ramp front) about $161.00

TAURUS MODEL 74 SPORT REVOLVER
Caliber: 32 S&W Long, 6-shot.
Barrel: 3".
Weight: 22 oz. **Length:** 8¼" over-all.
Stocks: Oversize target-type, checkered Brazilian walnut.
Sights: Serrated ramp front, rear adj. for w. and e.
Features: Imported from Brazil by International Distributers.
Price: Blue, about $113.00
Price: Nickel, about $127.00

TAURUS MODEL 80 STANDARD REVOLVER
Caliber: 38 Spec., 6-shot.
Barrel: 3" or 4".
Weight: 31 oz. (4" bbl.). **Length:** 9¼" over-all (4" bbl.).
Stocks: Checkered Brazilian walnut.
Sights: Serrated ramp front, square notch rear.
Features: Imported from Brazil by International Distributors.
Price: Blue, about $108.00
Price: Nickel, about $125.00

DAN WESSON MODEL 9-2, MODEL 15-2 & MODEL 22
Caliber: 38 Special (Model 9-2); 357 (Model 15-2), both 6 shot.
Barrel: 2", 4", 6", 8", 10", 12", 15". "Quickshift" interchangeable barrels.
Weight: 36 oz. (4" bbl.). **Length:** 9¼" over-all (4" bbl.).
Stocks: "Quickshift" checkered walnut. Interchangeable with three other styles.
Sights: ⅛" serrated blade front with red insert (Std.), white or yellow insert optional, as is Patridge. White outline, rear adj. for w. & e.
Features: Interchangeable barrels; four interchangeable grips; few moving parts, easy disassembly; Bright Blue finish only. Contact Dan Wesson for additional models not listed here. 10", 12" and 15" barrels also available with vent. rib. Rimfire specs. not available at press time.
Price: 9-2H, 15-2H (bull barrel shroud) 2" $230.90
Price: 9-2H, 15-2H, 6" bbl. $248.25
Price: 9-2V, 15-2V (vent. rib) 8" $260.45
Price: 9-2V, 15-2V, 10" $286.90
Price: 9-2VH, 15-2VH (heavy vent. shroud) 12" $334.60
Price: Pistol Pac, VH $620.05
Price: 9-2, 15-2 (Std. shroud) 2" $211.75
Price: 9-2, 15-2, 6" $227.45
Price: 9-2, 15-2, 8" $235.35
Price: 9-2, 15-2, 15" $308.25
Price: 9-2, 15-2, Pistol Pac $449.95
Price: 22-cal. same as 357 models.

DAN WESSON MODEL 8-2 & MODEL 14-2
Caliber: 38 Special (Model 8-2); 357 (Model 14-2), both 6 shot.
Barrel: 2", 4", 6", 8". "Quickshift" interchangeable barrels.
Weight: 34 oz. (4" bbl.) **Length:** 9¼" over-all (4" bbl.).
Stocks: "Quickshift" checkered walnut. Interchangeable with three other styles.
Sights: ⅛" serrated ramp front, rear fixed.
Features: Interchangeable barrels; 4 interchangeable grips; few moving parts, easy disassembly.
Price: 2" barrel $164.50
Price: 4" barrel $170.55
Price: 6" barrel $176.55
Price: 8" barrel $182.75
Price: Pistol Pac (cased with all above bbls.) $383.80

F.I.E. MODEL D-38 DERRINGER
Caliber: 38 Special or 38 S&W.
Barrel: 3".
Weight: 14 oz.
Stocks: Checkered white nylon.
Sights: Fixed.
Features: Chrome finish. Spur trigger. Tip-up barrel, extractors. Made in U.S-
  .A.
Price: **$64.95**

HI-STANDARD 9194 AND 9306 DERRINGER
Caliber: 22 Rimfire Magnum. 2 shot.
Barrel: 3½", over and under, rifled.
Length: 5" over-all. **Weight:** 11 oz.
Stocks: Smooth plastic.
Sights: Fixed, open.
Features: Hammerless, integral safety hammerblock, all steel unit is encased
  in a black, anodized alloy housing. Recessed chamber. Dual extraction. Top
  break, double action.
Price: Blued (M9194) ..... **$94.50**   Nickel (M9306) **$109.50**

SEMMERLING LM-4 PISTOL
Caliber: 45 ACP.
Barrel: 3½".
Weight: 24 ozs. **Length:** 5.2" over-all.
Stocks: Checkered black plastic.
Sights: Ramp front, fixed rear.
Features: Manually operated repeater. Over-all dimensions are 5.2" x 3.7" x
  1". Has a four-shot magazine capacity. Comes with manual, leather carrying
  case, spare stock screw and wrench. From Semmerling Corp.
Price: Complete **$645.00**
Price: Thin Version (blue sideplate instead of grips) **$645.00**

TANARMI O/U DERRINGER
Caliber: 38 Special.
Barrel: 3".
Weight: 14 oz. **Length:** 4¾" over-all.
Stocks: Checkered white nylon.
Sights: Fixed.
Features: Blue finish; tip-up barrel. Made in U.S. by Excam, Inc.
Price: **$59.50**

FIREARMS DIRECTORY

While many of the manufacturers included in the listings below are not engaged primarily in supplying equipment to law enforcement agencies, their addresses are included inasmuch as some of the products they produce or market may find use in police firearms training programs or by the individual officers in pursuit of their duties.

AMMUNITION (Commercial)

Alcan Shells, (See: Smith & Wesson Ammunition Co.)
Bingham Ltd., 1775-C Wilwat Dr., Norcross, GA 30093
Cascade Cartridge Inc., (See Omark)
DWM (see RWS)
Eastern Sports Intl., Inc., Savage Rd., Milford, NH 03055
Federal Cartridge Co., 2700 Foshay Tower, Minneapolis, MN 55402
Frontier Cartridge Co., Inc., Box 1848, Grand Island, NB 68801
H&H Cartridge Corp., P.O. Box 104, Greensburg, IN 47240 (Super Vel)
Omark-CCI, Inc., Box 856, Lewiston, Ida. 83501
Precision Prods. of Wash., Inc., N. 311 Walnut Rd., Spokane, WA 99206 (Exammo)
RWS (see Eastern Sports)
Remington Arms Co., Bridgeport, Conn. 06602
Service Armament, 689 Bergen Blvd., Ridgefield, N.J. 07657
Smith & Wesson Ammunition Co., 2399 Forman Rd., Rock Creek, OH 44084
Super Vel (see H&H Cartridge Corp.)
Velet Cartridge Co., N. 6809 Lincoln, Spokane, WA 99208
Weatherby's, 2781 E. Firestone Blvd., South Gate, Calif. 90280
Winchester-Western, East Alton, Ill. 62024

AMMUNITION (Custom)

Bill Ballard, 830 Miles Ave., Billings, MT 59101 (ctlg. 50¢)
Ballistek, Weapons Systems Div., Box 11537, Tucson, AZ 85734/602-294-1991
Beal's Bullets, 170 W. Marshall Rd., Lansdowne, PA 19050 (Auto Mag Specialists)
Bell's Gun & Sport Shop, 3309-19 Mannheim Rd., Franklin Park, IL 60131
Brass Extrusion Labs. Ltd., 800 W. Maple Lane, Bensenville, IL 60106
C. W. Cartridge Co., 71 Hackensack St., Wood-Ridge, NJ 07075
Russell Campbell, 219 Leisure Dr., San Antonio, Tex. 78201
Collectors Shotshell Arsenal, E. Tichy, 365 So. Moore, Lakewood, CO 80226
Crown City Arms, P.O. Box 1126, Cortland, NY 13045
Cumberland Arms, Rt. 1, Shafer Rd., Blantons Chapel, Manchester, TN 37355
E. W. Ellis Sport Shop, RFD 1, Box 315, Corinth, NY 12822
Ellwood Epps (Orillia) Ltd., R.R. 3, Hwy. 11 North, Orillia, Ont., Canada L3V 6H3/705-689-5333
Ramon B. Gonzalez, P.O. Box 370, Monticello, NY 12701
Gussert Bullet & Cartridge Co., Inc., P.O. Box 3945, Green Bay, WI 54303
Hi-Per Cartridge Corp., 133 Blue Bell Rd., Greensboro, NC 27406
J-4, Inc., 1700 Via Burton, Anaheim, CA 92806 (custom bullets)
Jensen's Custom Ammunition, 5146 E. Pima, Tucson, AZ 85716
R. H. Keeler, P.O. Box 536, Port Angeles, WA 98362/206-457-4702
KTW Inc., 710 Foster Park Rd., Lorain, OH 44053 (bullets)
Dean Lincoln, P.O. Box 1886, Farmington, NM 87401
Lomont Precision Bullets, 4421 S. Wayne Ave., Ft. Wayne, IN 46807 (custom bullets)
Mansfield Gunshop, Box 83, New Boston, N.H. 03070
Numrich Arms Corp., 203 Broadway, W. Hurley, N.Y. 12491
Robert Pomeroy, Morison Ave., Corinth, ME 04427 (custom shells)
Precision Ammunition & Reloading, 122 Hildenboro Square, Agincourt, Ont. M1W 1Y3, Canada
Precision Prods. of Wash., Inc., N. 311 Walnut Rd., Spokane, WA 99206 (Exammo)
Anthony F. Sailer-Ammunition, 707 W. Third St., P.O. Box L, Owen, WI 54460
Sanders Cust. Gun Serv., 2358 Tyler Lane, Louisville, Ky. 40205
Geo. Spence, 115 Locust St., Steele, MO 63877 (box-primed cartridges)
The 3-D Company, Box 142, Doniphan, NB 68832 (reloaded police ammo)
WAHIB Reloading, 2444-G Fender Ave., Fullerton, CA 92631

AMMUNITION (Foreign)

K. J. David & Company, P.O. Box 12595, Lake Park, FL 33043
Eastern Sports International Inc., Savage Rd., Milford, NH 03055 (RWS; Geco)
Guilio Fiocchi S.p.A., 22053 Lecco-Belledo, Italy
Hirtenberger Patronen-, Zündhütchen- & Metallwarenfabrik, A.G., Leobersdorfer Str. 33, A2552 Hirtenberg, Austria
Hy-Score Arms Co., 200 Tillary, Brooklyn, N.Y. 11201
Paul Jaeger Inc., 211 Leedom St., Jenkintown, Pa. 19046
S. E. Laszlo, 200 Tillary, Brooklyn, N.Y. 11201
NORMA-Precision, Lansing, NY 14882
RWS (Rheinische-Westfälische Sprengstoff) see: Eastern

AMMUNITION COMPONENTS—BULLETS, POWDER, PRIMERS

Alcan, (see: Smith & Wesson Ammunition Co.)
Ammo-O-Mart, P.O. Box 543, Renfrew, Ont., Canada K7V-4B1 (Curry bullets)
Austin Powder Co. (see Red Diamond Dist. Co.)
Ballistic Prods., Inc. 17510 19th Ave. No., Wayzata, MN 55391
Ballistic Research Inc., 935 E. Meadow Dr., Palo Alto, CA 94303 (BRI slug)
Barnes Bullets, P.O. Box 215, American Fork, UT 84003
B.E.L.L., Bell's Gun & Sport Shop, 3309-19 Mannheim Rd., Franklin Pk., IL 60131
Bitterroot Bullet Co., Box 412, Lewiston, Id. 83501. 35¢ (coin or stamps) and #10 SASE for lit.
Brass Extrusion Laboratories, Ltd., 800 W. Maple Lane, Bensenville, IL 60106
Centrix, 2116 N. 10th Ave., Tucson, Ariz. 85705
Kenneth E. Clark, 18738 Highway 99, Madera, CA 93637 (Bullets)
Curry Bullets Canada, P.O. Box 66, Hawkesbury, Ont., Canada
Division Lead, 7742 W. 61 Pl., Summit, Ill. 60502
DuPont, Explosives Dept., Wilmington, Del. 19898
Eastern Sports International, Inc., Savage Rd., Milford, NH 03055 (RWS percussion caps)
Elk Mountain Shooters Supply Inc., 1719 Marie, Pasco, WA 99301 (Alaskan bullets)
Farmer Bros., 1102 Washington St., Eldora, IA 50627 (Lage wad)
Federal Cartridge Co., 2700 Foshay Tower, Minneapolis, MN 55402 (nickel cases)
Forty Five Ranch Enterprises, 119 S. Main, Miami, Okla. 74354
Godfrey Reloading Supply, Hi-Way 67-111, Brighton, IL 62012 (cast bullets)
Lynn Godfrey, see: Elk Mtn. Shooters Supply
Gussert Bullet & Cartridge Co., Inc., P.O. Box 3945, Green Bay, WI 54303
Hardin Specialty Distr., P.O. Box 338, Radcliff, KY 40160 (empty, primed cases)
Hercules Powder Co., 910 Market St., Wilmington, Del. 19899
Herter's Inc., Waseca, Minn. 56093
Hodgdon Powder Co. Inc., 7710 W. 50th Hwy., Shawnee Mission, KS 66202
Hornady Mfg. Co., Box 1848, Grand Island, Neb. 68801
N. E. House Co., 195 West High St., E. Hampton, CT 06424/203-267-2133 (zinc bases only)
J-4, Inc., 1700 Via Burton, Anaheim, CA 92806 (custom bullets)
Keel Co., Bullet Metal Div., 327 East "B" St., Wilmington, CA 90744/213-834-2555 (bullet lead)
L. L. F. Die Shop, 1281 Highway 99 North, Eugene, Ore. 97402
Lage Uniwad Co., 1102 Washington St., Eldora, IA 50627
Ljutic Ind., Inc., Box 2117, Yakima, WA 98902 (Mono-wads)
Lomont Precision Bullets, 4421 S. Wayne Ave., Ft. Wayne, IN 46807 (custom bullets)
Lyman Products Corp., Rte. 147, Middlefield, CT 06455
Michael's Antiques, Box 233, Copiague, L.I., NY 11726 (Balle Blondeau)
Miller Trading Co., 20 S. Front St., Wilmington, N.C. 28401
Norma-Precision, Lansing, NY 14882
Nosler Bullets, P.O. Box 688, Beaverton, OR 97005
Robert Pomeroy, Morison Ave., East Corinth, ME 04427
Red Diamond Distributing Co., 1304 Snowdon Dr., Knoxville, TN 37912 (black powder)
Remington-Peters, Bridgeport, Conn. 06602
Sanderson's, 724 W. Edgewater, Portage, Wis. 53901 (cork wad)
Sierra Bullets Inc., 10532 Painter Ave., Santa Fe Springs, CA 90670
Smith & Wesson Ammunition Co., 2399 Forman Rd., Rock Creek, OH 44084
Speer Products Inc., Box 896, Lewiston, Ida. 83501
C. H. Stocking, Rte. 3, Box 195, Hutchinson, Minn. 55350 (17 cal. bullet jackets)
Taylor Bullets, P.O. Box 21254, San Antonio, TX 78221 (cast)
Vitt & Boos, 8 Overlook Dr., Weston, CT 06880 (shotgun slugs)
Winchester-Western, 275 Winchester Ave., New Haven, CT 06504
Wood Die Shop, Box 386, Florence, OR 97439 (17 cal.)
Xelex Ltd., P.O. Box 543, Renfrow, Ont. K7V 4B1, Canada (powder, Curry bullets)
Zero Bullet Co., P.O. Box 1188, Cullman, AL 35055
Wood Die Shop, Box 386, Florence, OR 97439 (17-cal. bullets)

CASES, CABINETS AND RACKS—GUN

Action Co., P.O. Box 528, McKinney, TX 75069

Alco Carrying Cases, 601 W. 26th St., New York, N.Y. 10001
Allen Co., Inc., 640 Compton St., Broomfield, CO 80020/303-469-1857
Art Jewel Enterprises, Box 819, Berkeley, IL 60163
Morton Booth Co., Box 123, Joplin, Mo. 64801
Boyt Co., Div. of Welsh Sportg. Gds., Box 1108, Iowa Falls, Ia. 50126
Brenik, Inc., 925 W. Chicago Ave., Chicago, IL 60622
Browning, Rt. 4, Box 624-B, Arnold, MO 63010
Cap-Lex Gun Cases, Capitol Plastics of Ohio, Inc., 333 Van Camp Rd., Bowling Green, OH 43402
Dara-Nes Inc., P.O. Box 119, East Hampton, CT 06424/203-267-4175 (firearms security chests)
East-Tenn Mills, Inc., 2300 Buffalo Rd., Johnson City, TN 37601 (gun socks)
Ellwood Epps (Orillia) Ltd., R.R. 3, Hwy. 11 North, Orillia, Ont. L3V 6H3, Canada/705-689-5333 (custom gun cases)
Norbert Ertel, Box 1150, Des Plaines, IL 60018 (cust. gun cases)
Flambeau Plastics Corp., 801 Lynn, Baraboo, Wis. 53913
Gun-Ho Case Mfg. Co., 110 East 10th St., St. Paul, Minn. 55101
Harbor House Gun Cabinets, 12508 Center St., South Gate, CA 90280
B. E. Hodgdon, Inc., 7710 W. 50 Hiway, Shawnee-Mission, Kans. 66202
Marvin Huey Gun Cases, Box 98, Reed's Spring, MO 65737/417-538-4233 (handbuilt leath. cases)
Ithaca Gun Co., Terrace Hill, Ithaca, N.Y. 14850
Jumbo Sports Prods., P.O. Box 280-Airport Rd., Frederick, MD 21701
Kalispel Metal Prods. (KMP), Box 267, Cusick, WA 99119 (aluminum boxes)
Kolpin Mfg., Inc., Box 231, Berlin, WI 54923
Marble Arms Corp., 420 Industrial Park, Gladstone, Mich. 49837
Bill McGuire, 1600 No. Eastmont Ave., East Wenatchee, WA 98801 (custom cases)
W. A. Miller Co., Inc. (Wamco), Mingo Loop, Oguossoc, ME 04964 (wooden handgun cases)
National Sports Div., Medalist Ind., 19 E. McWilliams St., Fond du Lac, WI 54935
Nortex Co., 2821 Main St., Dallas, Tex. 75226 (automobile gun rack)
North American Case, Inc., Industrial Park Rd., Johnstown, PA 15904/814-266-8941
North Star Devices, Inc., P.O. Box 2095, North St., Paul, MN 55109 (Gun-Slinger portable rack)
Paul-Reed, Inc., P.O. Box 227, Charlevoix, Mich. 49720
Penguin Industries, Inc., Airport Industrial Mall, Coatesville, PA 19320/215-384-6000
Pistolsafe, Dr. L., N. Chili, NY 14514 (handgun safe)
Precise, 3 Chestnut, Suffern, NY 10901
Protecto Plastics, Inc., 201 Alpha Rd., Wind Gap, Pa. 18091 (carrying cases)
Provo Steel & Supply Co., P.O. Box 977, Provo, UT 84601 (steel gun cases)
Richland Arms Co., 321 W. Adrian, Blissfield, Mich. 49228
Saf-T-Case Mfg. Co., Inc., P.O. Box 5472, Irving, TX 75062
San Angelo Co. Inc., Box 984, San Angelo, TX 76901
Buddy Schoellkopf, 4949 Joseph Hardin Dr., Dallas, TX 75236
Se-Cur-All Cabinet Co., K-Prods., P.O. Box 2052, Michigan City, IN 46360/219-872-7957
Security Gun Chest, Div. of Tread Corp., P.O. Box 13202, 1734 Granby St. N.E., Roanoke, VA 24012
Sile Distr., 7 Centre Market Pl., New York, N.Y. 10013 (leg o'mutton case)
Stearns Mfg. Co., P.O. Box 1498, St. Cloud, MN 56301
Straight Shooter Gun Cases, P.O. Box 10, Teaneck, NJ 07666
Tread Corp., P.O. Box 13207, 1734 Granby St. N.E., Roanoke, VA 24012 (security gun chest)
Trik Truk, P.O. Box 3760, Kent, WA 98301 (P.U. truck cases)
Vanguard Prods. Corp., 545 Cedar Lane, Box #10, Teaneck, NJ 07666 (Straight Shooter gun cases)
Weather Shield Sports Equipm. Inc., Rte. #3, Petoskey Rd., Charlevoix, MI 49720
Woodstream Corp., Box 327, Lititz, Pa. 17543
Yield House, Inc., RFD, No, Conway, N.H. 03860

GUN PARTS, U. S. AND FOREIGN

Badger Shooter's Supply, Box 397, Owen, WI 54460
Behlert Custom Guns, Inc., 725 Lehigh Ave., Union, NJ 07083 (handgun parts)
Philip R. Crouthamel, 513 E. Baltimore, E. Lansdowne, Pa. 19050
Charles E. Duffy, Williams Lane, West Hurley, N.Y. 12491
Federal Ordnance Inc., 9649 Alpaca St., So. El Monte, CA 91733/213-283-3880
Fenwick's Gun Annex, P.O. Box 38, Weisberg Rd., Whitehall, MD 21161
Jack First, The Gunshop, Inc., 44633 Sierra Highway, Lancaster, CA 93534
Greg's Winchester Parts, P.O. Box 8125, W. Palm Beach, FL 33407
Hunter's Haven, Zero Prince St., Alexandria, Va. 22314
Walter H. Lodewick, 2816 N.E. Halsey, Portland, OR 97232
Marsh Al's, Rte. #3, Box 729, Preston, ID 83263 (Contender rifle)
Numrich Arms Co., West Hurley, N.Y. 12491
Pacific Intl. Merch. Corp., 2215 "J" St., Sacramento, CA 95816 (Vega 45 Colt mag.)
Potomac Arms Corp. (see Hunter's Haven)
Martin B. Retting, Inc., 11029 Washington, Culver City, Cal. 90230
Sarco, Inc., 323 Union St., Stirling, NJ 07980
Sherwood Distr. Inc., 18714 Parthenia St., Northridge, CA 91324
Simms, 2801 J St., Sacramento, CA 95816
Clifford L. Smires, R.D., Box 39, Columbus, NJ 08022 (Mauser rifles)
N. F. Strebe Gunworks, 4926 Marlboro Pike, S.E., Washington, D.C. 20027
Triple-K Mfg. Co., 568-6th Ave., San Diego, CA 92101 (magazines, gun parts)

GUNS (Foreign)

American Research & Development Co., P.O. Box 11717, Salt Lake City, UT 84147/531-0180
Atlanta Outfitters, Ltd., 3648 Oakcliff Rd. N.E., Atlanta, GA 30340 (Auguste Francotte)
AYA (Aguirre y Aranzabal) see: IGI Domino or Wm. L. Moore (Spanish shotguns)
Pedro Arrizabalaga, Eibar, Spain
Armoury Inc., Rte. 202, New Preston, CT 06777
Armsport, Inc., 3590 N.W. 49th St., Miami, FL 33142/305-592-7850
Beretta Arms Co., Inc., P.O. Box 697, Ridgefield, CT 06877
Blaser/Vinzenz Huber GmbH, P.O. Box 2245, D-7900 Ulm, W. Germany
Bretton, 21 Rue Clement Forissier, 42-St. Etienne, France
Browning, Rt. 4, Box 624-B, Arnold, Mo. 63010
Carlo Casartelli, 25062 Concesio (Brescia), Italy
Century Arms Co., 3-5 Federal St., St. Albans, Vt. 05478
Champlin Firearms, Inc., Box 3191, Enid, OK 73701 (Gebruder Merkel)
Ets. Chapuis, 42380 St. Bonnet-le-Chateau, France (see R. Painter)
Commercial Trading Imports, Inc., Marketing Serv of Control Data, P.O. Box O, Minneapolis, MN 55402/612-853-5648 (Russian shotguns)
Connecticut Valley Arms Co., Saybrook Rd., Haddam, CT 06438 (CVA)
Walter Craig, Inc., Box 927-A Selma, AL 36701
Creighton & Warren, P.O. Box 15723, Nashville, TN 37215 (Krieghoff combination guns)
Morton Cundy & Son, Ltd., P.O. Box 315, Lakeside, MT 59922
Davis Gun Shop, 7213 Lee Highway, Falls Church, VA 22046 (Fanzoj, Ferlach; Spanish guns)
Dixie Gun Works, Inc., Hwy 51, South, Union City, TN 38261/901-885-0561 ("Kentucky" rifles)
Ernest Dumoulin-Deleye, 8 rue Florent Boclinville, 4410 Herstal (Vottem), Belgium
Peter Dyson Ltd., 29-31 Church St., Honley, Huddersfield, Yorkshire HD7 2AH, England (accessories f. antique gun collectors)
Eastern Sports International, Inc., Savage Rd., Milford, NH 03055 (Rottweil; Geco)
Excam Inc., 4480 E. 11 Ave., P.O. Box 3483, Hialeah, FL 33013
Armi Fabbri, Casella 206, Brescia, Italy 25100
Armi Famars, Via Cinelli 33, Gardone V.T. (Brescia) Italy 25063
J. Fanzoj, P.O. Box 25, Ferlach, Austria 9170
F.E.T.E. Corp., 2867 W. 7th St., Los Angeles, CA 90005 (A. Zoli guns)
Armi FERLIB, 46 Via Costa, 25063 Gardone V.T. (Brescia), Italy
Ferlach (Austria) of North America, P.O. Box 430435, S. Miami, FL 33143
Firearms Center Inc. (FCI), 308 Leisure Lane, Victoria, TX 77901
Firearms Imp. & Exp. Corp., 4530 NW 135th St., Opa-Locka, FL 33054/305-685-5966
Flaig's Lodge, Millvale, Pa. 15209
Auguste Francotte (see: Atlanta Outfitters)
Freeland's Scope Stands, Inc., 3737 14th Ave., Rock Island, Ill. 61201
J. L. Galef & Son, Inc., 85 Chambers, New York, N.Y. 10007
Renato Gamba, Fabbrica d'Armi, via Petrarca, 25060 Ponte Zanano di Sarezzo (Brescia), Italy
Armas Garbi, Urki #12, Eibar (Guipuzcoa) Spain (shotguns, see W. L. Moore)
Gastinne Renette, 39 Ave. F.D. Roosevelt, 75008 Paris, France
Golden Eagle Firearms, 5803 Sovereign, Suite 206, Houston, TX 77036
Georges Granger, 66 Cours Fauriel, 42 St. Etienne, France
Hawes National Corp., 15424 Cabrito Rd., Van Nuys, CA 91406
Healthways, Box 45055, Los Angeles, Calif. 90061
Gil Hebard Guns, Box 1, Knoxville, IL 61448 (Hammerli)
Heckler & Koch Inc., 933 N. Kenmore St., Suite 218, Arlington, VA 22201
A. D. Heller, Inc., Box 56, 2322 Grand Ave., Baldwin, NY 11510
Herter's, Waseca, Minn. 56093
Heym, Friedr. Wilh., Box 861, Bolton, Ont. L0P 1A0, Canada
IGI Domino Corp., 200 Madison Ave., New York, NY 10016/212-889-4889 (AYA, Breda)
Interarmco, see: Interarms (Walther)
Interarms Ltd., 10 Prince St., Alexandria, Va. 22313 (Mauser, Valmet M-62/S)
International Distr., Inc., 7290 S.W. 42nd St., Miami, FL 33155 (Taurus rev.)
Ithaca Gun Co., Terrace Hill, Ithaca, N.Y. 14850 (Perazzi)
Italguns, Via Leonardo da Vinci 169, 20090 Trezzano, (Milano), Italy
Paul Jaeger Inc., 211 Leedom St., Jenkintown, Pa. 19046
Jana Intl. Co., Box 1107, Denver, Colo. 80201 (Parker-Hale)
J. J. Jenkins, 375 Pine Ave. No. 25, Goleta, CA 93017
Kassnar Imports, 5480 Linglestown Rd., Harrisburg, PA 17110
Kerr's Sport Shop, Inc., 9584 Wilshire Blvd., Beverly Hills, CA 90212
Kimel Industries, P.O. Box 335, Matthews, NC 28105
Kleinguenther's, P.O. Box 1261, Seguin, TX 78155
Knight & Knight, 5930 S.W. 48 St., Miami, FL 33155 (made-to-order only)
Dr. Kortz Elko, 28 rue Ecole Moderne, 7400 Soignes, Belgium
L. A. Distributors, 4 Centre Market Pl., New York, N.Y. 10013
S. E. Laszlo, 200 Tillary St., Brooklyn, N.Y. 11201
Lever Arms Serv. Ltd., 771 Dunsmuir, Vancouver, B.C., Canada V6C 1M9
Liberty Arms Organization, Box 306, Montrose, Calif. 91020
McQueen Sales Co. Ltd., 1760 W. 3rd Ave., Vancouver, B.C., Canada V6J 1K5
Mandall Shtg. Suppl. Corp., 3616 N. Scottsdale Rd., Scottsdale, AZ 85251/602-945-2553
Mannlicher Div., Steyr Daimler Puch of Amer., 85 Metro Way, Secaucus, NJ 07094
Manu-Arm, St. Etienne, France
Manufrance, 100-Cours Fauriel, 42 St. Etienne, France
Mendi s. coop., P.O. Box 48, Eibar, Spain
Merkuria, P.O. Box 18, 17005 Prague, Czechoslovakia (BRNO)
Wm. Larkin Moore, 31360 Via Colinas, Suite 109, Westlake Village, CA 91360/213-889-4160 (AYA, Garbi, Ferlib, Piotte, Lightwood)

Navy Arms Co., 689 Bergen Blvd., Ridgefield, N.J. 07657
P.M. Air Services, Ltd., P.O. Box 1573, Costa Mesa, CA 92626
Pachmayr Gun Works, 1220 S. Grand Ave., Los Angeles, CA 90015
Pacific Intl. Merch. Corp., 2215 "J" St., Sacramento, CA 95816
Rob. Painter, 2901 Oakhurst Ave., Austin, TX 78703 (Chapuis)
Parker-Hale, Bisleyworks, Golden Hillock Rd., Sparbrook, Birmingham B11 2PZ, England
Ed Paul Sptg. Goods, 172 Flatbush Ave., Brooklyn, N.Y. 11217 (Premier)
Picard-Fayolle, 42-rue du Vernay, 42100 Saint Etienne, France
Precise, 3 Chestnut, Suffern, NY 10901
Premier Shotguns, 172 Flatbush Ave., Brooklyn N.Y. 11217
Leonard Puccinelli Co., P.O. Box 668, San Anselmo, CA 94960 (I.A.B., Rizzini of Italy)
RG Industries, Inc., 2485 N.W. 20th St., Miami, FL 33142 (Erma)
Richland Arms Co., 321 W. Adrian St., Blissfield, Mich. 49228
F.lli Rizzini, 25060 Magno di Gardone V.T., (Bs.) Italy
Rottweil, see: Eastern
Ruko Sporting Goods Inc., 195 Sugg Rd., Buffalo, NY 14225 (Tikka)
SKB Sports Inc., 190 Shepard, Wheeling, IL 60090
Sanderson's, 724 W. Edgewater, Portage, Wis. 53901
Victor Sarasqueta, S.A., P.O. Box 25, 3 Victor Sarasqueta St., Eibar, Spain
Sarco, Inc., 323 Union St., Stirling, NJ 07980/201-647-3800
Savage Arms Corp., Westfield, Mass. 01085 (Anschutz)
Security Arms Co., See: Heckler & Koch
Service Armament, 689 Bergen Blvd., Ridgefield, N.J. 07657 (Greener Harpoon Gun)
Sherwood Dist., Inc., 18714 Parthenia St., Northridge, CA 91324
Shore Galleries, Inc., 3318 W. Devon Ave., Chicago, IL 60645
Sile Distributors, 7 Centre Market Pl., New York, 10013
Simmons Spec., Inc., 700 Rogers Rd., Olathe, Kans. 66061
Sloan's Sprtg. Goods, Inc., 10 South St., Ridgefield, CT 06877
Franz Sodia Jagdgewehrfabrik, Schulhausgasse 14, 9170 Ferlach, (Kärnten) Austria
Solersport, 23629 7th Ave. West, Bothell, WA 98011 (Unique)
Steyr-Daimler-Puch of America, Inc., see: Mannlicher
Stoeger Industries, 55 Ruta Ct., S. Hackensack, NJ 07606/201-440-2700

Tradewinds, Inc., P.O. Box 1191, Tacoma, Wash. 98401
Uberti, Aldo & Co., Via G. Carducci 41 or 39, Ponte Zanano (Brescia), Italy
Ignacio Ugartechea, Apartado 21, Eibar, Spain
Ultra-Hi Products Co., 150 Florence Ave., Hawthorne, NJ 07506 (ML)
Valor Imp. Corp., 5555 N.W. 36th Ave., Miami, FL 33142
Ventura Imports, P.O. Box 2782, Seal Beach, CA 90740 (European shotguns)
Verney-Carron, B.P. 88, 17 Cours Fauriel, 42010 St. Etienne Cedex, France
Waffen-Frankonia, Box 6780, 87 Wurzburg 1, W. Germany
Weatherby's, 2781 Firestone Blvd., So. Gate, Calif. 90280 (Sauer)
Fabio Zanotti di Stefano, Via XXV Aprile 1, 25063 Gardone V.T. (Brescia) Italy
Zavodi Crvena Zastava, 29 Novembra St., No. 12, Belgrade, Yugosl.
Antonio Zoli & Co., 39 Via Zanardelli, 25063 Gardone V.T., Brescia, Italy

GUNS, U.S.-made

A.I.G. Corp., 7 Grasso Ave., North Haven, CT 06473
AMT (Arcadia Machine & Tool), 11666 McBean Dr., El Monte, CA 91732
A. R. Sales Co., 9624 Alpaca St., South El Monte, CA 91733 (Mark IV sporter)
Accuracy Systems, Inc., 2105 S. Hardy Dr., Tempe, AZ 85282
American Arms & Ammunition Co., 1015 N.W. 72nd St., Miami, FL 33150 (Budischowski)
American Heritage Arms, Inc., Rte. 44, P.O. Box 95, West Willington, CT 06279 (ML)
ArmaLite, 118 E. 16th St., Costa Mesa, Calif. 92627
Artistic Arms, Inc., Box 23, Hoagland, IN 46745 (Sharps-Borchardt)
Auto-Ordnance Corp., Box ZG, West Hurley, NY 12491
Bauer Firearms, 34750 Klein Ave., Fraser, MI 48026
Brown Precision Co., 5869 Indian Ave., San Jose, CA 95123 (High Country rifle)
Challanger Mfg. Corp., 118 Pearl St., Mt. Vernon, NY 10550 (Hopkins & Allen)
Champlin Firearms, Inc., Box 3191, Enid, Okla. 73701
Charter Arms Corp., 430 Sniffens Ln., Stratford, CT 06497
Classic Arms Ltd., 20 Wilbraham St., Palmer, MA 01069/413-596-9691 (BP guns)
Colt, 150 Huyshope Ave., Hartford, CT 06102
Commando Arms, Inc., Box 10214, Knoxville, Tenn. 37919
Crown City Arms, P.O. Box 1126, Cortland, NY 13045 (45 auto handgun)
Cumberland Arms, Rt. 1, Shafer Rd., Blanton Chapel, Manchester, TN 37355
Day Arms Corp., 2412 S.W. Loop 410, San Antonio, TX 78227
Leonard Day & Co., 316 Burts Pits Rd., Northampton, MA 01060 (ML)
Detonics 45 Associates, 2500 Seattle Tower, Seattle, WA 98101 (auto pistol)
DuBiel Arms Co., 1724 Baker Rd., Sherman, TX 75090/214-893-7313
EE-DA-How Long Rifles, Inc., 3318 Camrose Lane, Boise, ID 83705
EMF Co. Inc., Box 1248, Studio City, CA 91604 (T.D.A. rev.)
FTL Marketing Corp., 11100 Cumpston St., No. Hollywood, CA 91601
Falling Block Works, P.O. Box 22, Troy, MI 48084
Firearms Imp. & Exp. Corp., 4530 NW 135th St., Opa-Locka, FL 33054/305-685-5966 (FIE)
Freedom Arms Co., Freedom, WY 83120 (mini revolver, Casull rev.)
Freshour Mfg. Co., 1914 - 15th Ave. N., Texas City, TX 77590 (Ranger rifle)
Golden Age Arms Co., 14 W. Winter St., Delaware, OH 43015
Gwinn Firearms, #19 Freedom Industrial Park, Bangor, ME 04401/207-848-3333

Harrington & Richardson, Industrial Rowe, Gardner, MA 01440
Hatfield's, 2028 Frederick Ave., St. Joseph, MO 64501 (squirrel rifle)
A. D. Heller, Inc., Box 268, Grand Ave., Baldwin, NY 11510
High Standard Sporting Firearms, 31 Prestige Park Circle, East Hartford, CT 06108
Hopkins & Allen Arms, #1 Melnick Rd., Monsey, NY 10952
Hyper-Single Precision SS Rifles, 520 E. Beaver, Jenks, OK 74037
Ithaca Gun Co., Ithaca, N.Y. 14850
Iver Johnson Arms Inc., P.O. Box 251, Middlesex, NJ 08846
J & R carbine, (see: PJK Inc.)
Paul Jaeger, Inc., 211 Leedom St., Jenkintown, PA 19046
H. Koon, Inc., 1602 Stemmons, Suite D, Carrollton, TX 75006
L.E.S., 3640 Dempster, Skokie, IL 60076/312-674-6350
Ljutic Ind., Inc., P.O. Box 2117, Yakima, WA 98902 (Mono-Gun)
Marlin Firearms Co., 100 Kenna Dr., New Haven, Conn. 06473
Merrill Co. Inc., 704 E. Commonwealth, Fullerton, CA 92631/714-879-8922
O. F. Mossberg & Sons, Inc., 7 Grasso St., No. Haven, Conn. 06473
Mowrey Gun Works, Box 28, Iowa Park TX 76367
Navy Arms Co., 689 Bergen Blvd., Ridgefield, N.J. 07657
North Star Arms, R.2, Box 74A, Ortonville, MN 56278 (The Plainsman)
Numrich Arms Corp., W. Hurley, N.Y. 12491
PJK, Inc., 1527 Royal Oak Dr., Bradbury, Ca 91010 (J&R Carbine)
Plainfield Machine Co., Inc., Box 447, Dunellen, N.J. 08812
Plainfield Inc., 292 Vail Ave., Piscataway, NJ 08854
R G Industries, 2485 N.W. 20th SE., Miami, FL 33142
Raven Arms, 1300 Bixby Dr., Industry, CA 91745
Remington Arms Co., Bridgeport, Conn. 06602
Riedl Rifles, 15124 Weststate St., Westminster, CA 92683 (S.S.)
Ruger (see Sturm, Ruger & Co.)
Savage Arms Corp., Westfield, Mass. 01085
Sears, Roebuck & Co., 825 S. St. Louis, Chicago, Ill. 60607
Semmerling Corp., P.O. Box 400, Newton, MA 02160
Sharon Rifle Barrel Co., P.O. Box 1197, Kalispell, MT 59901
Sharps Rifle Co., 3428 Shakertown Rd., Dayton, OH 45430
Shiloh Products, 37 Potter St., Farmingdale, NY 11735 (Sharps)
Smith & Wesson, Inc., 2100 Roosevelt Ave., Springfield, MA 01101
Sporting Arms, Inc., 9643 Alpaca St., So. El Monte, CA 91733 (M-1 carbine)
Springfield Armory, 111 E. Exchange St., Geneseo, IL 61254
Sterling Arms Corp., 211 Grand St.,, Lockport, NY 14094/716-434-6631
Sturm, Ruger & Co., Southport, Conn. 06490
Thompson-Center Arms, Box 2405, Rochester, N.H. 03867
Trail Guns Armory, 1634 E. Main St., League City, TX 77573 (muzzleloaders)
Triple-S Development Co., Inc., 1450 E. 289th St., Wickliffe, OH 44092 (Wickliffe S.S. rifle)
United Sporting Arms, Inc., 35 Gilpin Ave., Hauppauge, L.I., NY 11787
United States Arms Corp., Doctors Path and Middle Road, Riverhead, NY 11901 (Abilene SA rev.)
Universal Firearms, 3740 E. 10th Ct., Hialeah, FL 33013
Ward's, 619 W. Chicago, Chicago, Ill. 60607 (Western Field brand)
Weatherby's, 2781 E. Firestone Blvd., South Gate, Calif. 90280
Dan Wesson Arms, 293 So. Main St., Monson, Mass. 01057
Wichita Eng. & Supply, Inc., P.O. Box 11371, Wichita, KS 67202
Wildey Firearms Co., Inc., P.O. Box 284, Cold Spring, NY 10516
Wilkinson Arms, 803 N. Glendora Ave, Covina, CA 91724 (Diane 25 ACP auto pistol)
Winchester Repeating Arms Co., New Haven, Conn. 06504
Winslow Arms Co., Inc., P.O. Box 783, Camden, SC 29020

HANDGUN ACCESSORIES

A. R. Sales Co., P.O. Box 3192, South El Monte, CA 91733
Baramie Corp., 6250 E. 7 Mile Rd., Detroit, MI 48234 (Hip-Grip)
Bar-Sto Precision Machine, 633 S. Victory Blvd., Burbank, CA 91502
Behlert Custom Guns, Inc., 725 Lehigh Ave., Union, NJ 07083
Belt Slide, Inc., 1114 N. Lamar, P.O. Box 15303, Austin, TX 78761/512-836-8772
Bingham Ltd., 1775-C Wilwat Dr., Norcross, GA 30093 (magazines)
C'Arco, P.O. Box 308, Highland, CA 92346 (Ransom Rest)
Case Master, 4675 E. 10 Ave., Miami, Fla. 33013
Central Specialties Co., 6030 Northwest Hwy., Chicago, Ill. 60631
D&E Magazines Mgf., P.O. Box 4579, Downey, CA 90242 (clips)
Bill Dyer, 503 Midwest Bldg., Oklahoma City, Okla. 73102 (grip caps)
Essex Arms, Box 345, Phaerring St., Island Pond, VT 05846 (45 Auto frames)
R. S. Frielich, 396 Broome St., New York, N.Y. 10013 (cases)
Jafin Prods., Jacob & Tiffin Inc., P.O. Box 547, Clanton,, AL 35045 (Light Load)
Laka Tool Co., 62 Kinkel St., Westbury, L.I., NY 11590 (stainless steel 45 Auto parts)
Lee Custom Engineering, Inc., 46 E. Jackson St., Hartford, WI 53027
Lee's Red Ramps, 7252 E. Ave. U-3, Littlerock, CA 93543 (illuminated sights)
Lee Precision Inc., 4275 Hwy. U, Hartford, WI 53027 (pistol rest holders)
Los Gatos Grip & Specialty Co., P.O. Box 1850, Los Gatos, CA 95030 (custom-made)
Mellmark Mfg. Co., P.O. Box 139, Turlock, CA 95380 (pistol safe)
W. A. Miller Co., Inc., Mingo Loop, Oguossoc, ME 04964 (cases)
No-Sho Mfg. Co., 10727 Glenfield Ct., Houston, TX 77096
Pachmayr, 1220 S. Grand, Los Angeles, Calif. 90015 (cases)
Pacific Intl. Mchdsg. Corp., 2215 "J" St., Sacramento, CA 95818 (Vega 45 Colt comb. mag.)
Pistolsafe, Dr. L., N. Chili, NY 14514 (handgun safe)
Platt Luggage, Inc., 2301 S. Prairie, Chicago, Ill. 60616 (cases)
Sile Distributors, 7 Centre Market Pl., New York, NY 10013
Sportsmen's Equipment Co., 415 W. Washington, San Diego, Calif. 92103

M. Tyler, 1326 W. Britton, Oklahoma City, Okla. 73114 (grip adaptor)
Whitney Sales, Inc., P.O. Box 875, Reseda, CA 91335
Dave Woodruff, Box 5, Bear, DE 19701 (relining and conversions)

HANDGUN GRIPS

Art Jewel Enterprises, Box 819, Berkeley, IL 60163
Bingham Ltd., 1775-C Wilwat Dr., Norcross, GA 30093
Crest Carving Co., 8091 Bolsa Ave., Midway City, CA 92655
Fitz, 653 N. Hagar St., San Fernando, CA 91340
Gateway Shooters' Supply, Inc., 10145-103rd St., Jacksonville, FL 32210
(Rogers grips)
The Gunshop, R. D. Wallace, 320 Overland Rd., Prescott, AZ 86301
Herrett's, Box 741, Twin Falls, Ida. 83301
Mershon Co., Inc., 1230 S. Grand Ave., Los Angeles, Calif. 90015
Mustang Custom Pistol Grips, 28715 Via Montezuma, Temecula, CA 92390
Robert H. Newell, 55 Coyote, Los Alamos, NM 87544 (custom)
Rogers Grips (see: Gateway Shooters' Supply)
Safety Grip Corp., Box 456, Riverside St., Miami, Fla. 33135
Jean St. Henri, 6525 Dume Dr., Malibu, CA 90265 (custom)
Sile Dist., 7 Centre Market Pl., New York, N.Y. 10013
Southern Gun Exchange, Inc., 4311 Northeast Expressway, Atlanta (Doraville), GA 30340 (Outrider brand)
Sports Inc., P.O. Box 683, Park Ridge, IL 60068 (Franzite)

HEARING PROTECTORS

AO Safety Prods., Div. of American Optical Corp., 14 Mechanic St., Southbridge, MA 01550 (ear valve)
Bausch & Lomb, 635 St. Paul St., Rochester, N.Y. 14602
Hodgdon, 7710 W. 50 Hiway, Shawnee Mission, Kans. 66202
Norton Co., Safety Prods. Div., 16624 Edwards Rd., Cerritos, CA 90701
(Lee-Sonic ear valve)
Safety Direct, 23 Snider Way, Sparks, NV 89431 (Silencio)
Smith & Wesson, 2100 Roosevelt Ave., Springfield, MA 01101
Willson Safety Prods Div., P.O. Box 622, Reading, PA 19603 (Ray-O-Vac)

HOLSTERS & LEATHER GOODS

American Sales & Mfg. Co., P.O. Box 677, Laredo, Tex. 78040
Andy Anderson, P.O. Box 225, North Hollywood, CA 91603 (Gunfighter Custom Holsters)
Bianchi Holster Co., 100 Calle Cortez, Temecula, CA 92390
Edward H. Bohlin, 931 N. Highland Ave., Hollywood, CA 90038/213-463-4888
Boyt Co., Div. of Welch Sptg., Box 1108, Iowa Falls, Ia. 51026
Brauer Bros. Mfg. Co., 817 N. 17th, St. Louis, Mo. 63106
Browning, Rt. 4, Box 624-B, Arnold, MO 63010
J. M. Bucheimer Co., P.O. Box 280, Airport Rd., Frederick, MD 21701/301-662-5101
Cathey Enterprises, Inc., 9516 Neils Thompson Dr., Austin, TX 78758
Chace Leather Prods., 507 Alden St., Fall River, MA 02722
Cobra Ltd., 1865 New Highway, Farmingdale, NY 11735/516-752-8544
Colt's, 150 Huyshope Ave., Hartford, Conn. 06102
Daisy Mfg. Co., Rogers, Ark. 72756
G. Wm. Davis, P.O. Box 446, Arcadia, CA 91006
Eugene DeMayo & Sons, Inc., 2795 Third Ave., Bronx, N.Y. 10455
El Dorado Leather Co., 1045 Vernon Way, El Cajon, CA 92020
Ellwood Epps (Orillia) Ltd., R.R. 3, Hwy. 11 North, Orillia, Ont. L3V 6H3, Canada/705-689-5333
The Eutaw Co., Box 608, U.S. Highway 176W, Holly Hill, SC 29059
Goerg Ent., P.O. Box 531, Renton, WA 98056/206-883-1529
Gunfighter (See Anderson)
Hoyt Holster Co., P.O. Box 69, Coupeville, WA 98239
Don Hume, Box 351, Miami, Okla. 74354
The Hunter Co., 3300 W. 71st Ave., Westminster, CO 80030
Jackass Leather Co., 7383 N. Rogers Ave., Chicago, IL 60626/312-338-2800
Jumbo Sports Prods., P.O. Box 280, Airport Rd., Frederick, MD 21701
George Lawrence Co., 306 S. W. First Ave., Portland, OR 97204
Leathercrafters, 710 S. Washington, Alexandria, VA 22314
S. D. Myres Saddle Co., P.O. Box 357, Millis, MA 02054/617-376-2315
Old West Inc. Leath. Prods., P.O. Box 2030, Chula Vista, CA 92012
Pancake Holsters, Roy Baker, Box 245, Magnolia, AR 71753
Pony Express Sport Shop Inc., 17460 Ventura Blvd., Encino, CA 91316
Ranger Leather Prods., Box 3198, East Camden, AR 71701
Red Head Brand Corp., 4949 Joseph Hardin Dr., Dallas, TX 75236/214-330-9134
Rickenbacker's, P.O. Box 532, State Ave., Holly Hill, SC 29059
Rogers Holsters, 10601 Theresa Dr., Jacksonville, FL 32216/904-641-9434
Roy's Custom Leather Goods, P.O. Box 852, Magnolia, AR 71753
Safariland Leather Products, 1941 Walker Ave., Monrovia, Calif. 91016
Safety Speed Holster, Inc., 910 So. Vail, Montebello, Calif. 90640
Buddy Schoellkopf Products Inc., 4949 Joseph Hardin Dr., Dallas, TX 75236
Sile Distr., 7 Centre Market Pl., New York, N.Y. 10013
Smith & Wesson, 2100 Roosevelt Ave., Springfield, MA 01101
Torel, Inc., 1053 N. South St., Yoakum, TX 77995 (gun slings)
Triple-K Mfg. Co., 568 Sixth Ave., San Diego, CA 92101
Whitco, Box 1712, Brownsville, Tex. 78520 (Hide-A-Way)

PISTOLSMITHS

Allen Assoc., 7502 Limekiln Pike, Philadelphia, PA 19150 (speed-cock lever for 45 ACP)
Bain and Davis Sptg. Gds., 559 W. Las Tunas Dr., San Gabriel, Cal. 91776

Bar-Sto Precision Machine, 633 So. Victory Blvd., Burbank, CA 91502
(S.S. bbls. f. 45 Acp)
Behlert Custom Guns, Inc., 725 Lehigh Ave., Union, NJ 07083 (short actions)
F. Bob Chow, Gun Shop, 3185 Mission, San Francisco, Calif. 94110
J.E. Clark, Rte. 2, Box 22A, Keithville, LA 71047
Custom Gun Shop, 725 Lehigh Ave., Union, NJ 07083
Cake Davis Co., 1200 Fifth St., Berkeley, CA 94710/415-526-9124
Day Arms Corp., 2412 S.W. Loop 410, San Antonio, TX 78227
Dominic DiStefano, 4303 Friar Lane, Colorado Springs, CO 80907 (accurizing)
Dan Dwyer, 915 W. Washington, San Diego, Calif. 92103
Ehresman Tool Co., Inc., 5425 Planeview Dr., Ft. Wayne, IN 46805 (custom)
Giles' 45 Shop, Rt. 2, Box 847, Odessa, FL 33556
The Gunshop, R. D. Wallace, 320 Overland Rd., Prescott, AZ 86301
Gil Hebard Guns, Box 1, Knoxville, Ill. 61448
Innovation Inc., P.O. Box 43, Angola, IN 46703
Lee E. Jurras & Assoc., Inc., P.O. Drawer F, Hagerman, NM 88232
Kart Sptg. Arms Corp., RD 2, Box 929-Broad Ave., Riverhead, NY 11901
(handgun conversions)
Lenz Firearms Co., 1480 Elkay Dr., Eugene, OR 97404
Rudolf Marent, 9711 Tiltree, Houston, TX 77075 (Hammerli)
Nu-Line Guns, 3727 Jennings Rd., St. Louis, MO 63121
Pachmayr Gun Works, 1220 S. Grand Ave., Los Angeles, Calif. 90015
Greg Roberts, 726 Water St., Santa Cruz, CA 95060
L. W. Seecamp Co., inc., Box 255, New Haven, CT 06502 (DA Colt auto conversions)
Silver Dollar Guns, P.O. Box 475, 10 Frances St., Franklin, NH 03235 (45 ACP)
Sportsmens Equipmt. Co., 915 W. Washington, San Diego, Calif. 92103
Irving O. Stone, Jr., 633 S. Victory Blvd., Burbank, CA 91502
Victor W. Strawbridge, 6 Pineview Dr., Dover Pt., Dover, NH 03820
A. D. Swenson's 45 Shop, P.O. Box 606, Fallbrook, CA 92028
Dennis A. "Doc" Ulrich, 2511 S. 57th Ave., Cicero, IL 60650
Vic's Gun Refinishing, 6 Pineview Dr., Dover, NH 03820
Walters Industries, 6226 Park Lane, Dallas, TX 75225
Dave Woodruff, Box 5, Bear, DE 19701

RELOADING TOOLS AND ACCESSORIES

Action LB, Box 100, Odessa, MO 64076 (spin wad)
Advance Car Mover Co., Inc., P.O. Box 1181, Appleton, WI 54911 (bottom pour lead casting ladles)
Advanced Mfg. Co., Inc., 18619 W. 7 Mile Rd., Detroit, MI 48219 (super fillerprimer tube)
American Wad Co., 125 W. Market St., Morrison, IL 61270 (12-ga. shot wad)
Anderson Mfg. Co., Royal, Ia. 51357 (Shotshell Trimmers)
Aurands, 229 E. 3rd St., Lewistown, Pa. 17044
B-Square Eng. Co., Box 11281, Ft. Worth, Tex. 76110
Bill Ballard, 830 Miles Ave., Billings, MT 59101 (ctlg. 50¢)
Ballistic Prods., Inc., 17610 19th Ave. No., Wayzata, MN 55391
Bear Reloaders, Inc., 807 Evans Ave., Akron, OH 44305
Belding & Mull, P.O. Box 428, Philipsburg, Pa. 16866
Berdon Co., P.O. Box 70131, Seattle, WA 98107 (metallic press)
Blackhawk SAA East, K2274 POB, Loves Park, Ill. 61131/812-633-7784
Blackhawk SAA Mtn., 2254 No. Dahlia St., Denver, CO 80207/303-757-8740
Blackhawk SAA West, Box 285, Hiawatha, KS 66434
Bonanza Sports, Inc., 412 Western Ave., Faribault, Minn. 55021
Gene Bowlin, 3602 Hill Ave., Snyder, Tex. 79549 (arbor press)
Brown Precision Co., 5869 Indian Ave., San Jose, Calif. 95123 (Little Wiggler)
A. V. Bryant, 72 Whiting Rd., E. Hartford, CT 06118 (Nutmeg Universal Press)
C-H Tool & Die Corp., 106 N. Harding St., Owen, WI 54461/715-229-2146
CPM Industries Corp., 330 Elm St., Clyde, OH 43410
Camdex, Inc., 23880 Hoover Rd., Warren, MI 48089
Carbide Die & Mfg. Co., Box 226, Covina, CA 91724
Carter Gun Works, 2211 Jefferson Pk. Ave., Charlottesville, Va. 22903
Cascade Cartridge, Inc., (See Omark)
Catco-Ambush, Inc., P.O. Box 300, Corte Madera, CA 94926 (paper bullet patches)
Chevron Case Master, R.R. 1, Ottawa, IL 61350
Clymer Mfg. Co., 14241 W. 11 Mile Rd., Oak Park, MI 48237 (#4-jack. swaging dies)
Lester Coats, 416 Simpson St., No. Bend, Ore. 97459 (core cutter)
Container Development Corp., 424 Montgomery St., Watertown, WI 53094
Continental Kite & Key Co., Box 40, Broomall, PA 19008 (primer pocket cleaner)
Cooper-Woodward, Box 972, Riverside, Calif. 92502 (Perfect Lube)
D. R. Corbin Mfg. & Supply Inc., P.O. Box 758, Phoenix, OR 97535
J. Dewey Mfg. Co., 125 Fenn Rd., Middlebury, CT 06762
Diverter Arms, Inc., P.O. Box 22084, Houston, TX 77027 (bullet puller)
Division Lead Co., 7742 W. 61st Pl., Summit, Ill. 60502
Edmisten Co. Inc., P.O. Box 1293, Hwy 105, Boone, NC 28607/704-264-1490
Efemtos Enterprises, P.O. Box 122M, Bay Shore, NY 11706 (Berdan decapper)
W. H. English, 4411 S. W. 100th, Seattle, Wash. 98146 (Paktool)
Farmer Bros., 1102 Washington St., Eldora, IA 50627 (Lage)
Fitz, 653 N. Hagar St., San Fernando, CA 91340 (Fitz Flipper)
Flambeau Plastics, 801 Lynn, Baraboo, Wis. 53913
Forster Products Inc., 82 E. Lanark Ave., Lanark, Ill. 61046
Geo. M. Fullmer, 2499 Mavis St., Oakland, CA 94601 (seating die)
Gene's Gun Shop, 3602 Hill Ave., Snyder, Tex. 79549 (arbor press)
Goerg Enterprises, P.O. Box 531, Renton, WA 98056/206-833-1529

Gopher Shooter's Supply, Box 278, Faribault, MN 55021
Griffin Mfg. Co., P.O. Box 935, Brownwood, TX 76801
The Gun Clinic, 81 Kale St., Mahtomedi, Minn. 55115
Hart Products, Rob. W. Hart & Son Inc., 401 Montgomery St., Nescopeck, PA 18635
Henriksen Tool Co., Inc., P.O. Box 668, Phoenix, OR 97535
Hensley & Gibbs, Box 10, Murphy, Ore. 97533
Herter's Inc., RR1, Waseca, Minn. 56093
Richard Hoch, The Gun Shop, 62778 Spring Creek Rd., Montrose, CO 81401/303-249-3625 (custom schuetzen bullet moulds)
B. E. Hodgdon, Inc., 7710 W. 50 Hiway, Shawnee Mission, Kans. 66202
Hoffman Prods., P.O. Box 853, Lake Forest, IL 60045 (spl. gallery load press)
Hollywood Reloading, (see: Whitney Sales, Inc.)
Hornady (see: Pacific)
Hulme Firearm Serv., Box 83, Millbrae, Calif. 94030 (Star case feeder)
Huntington Die Specialties, Box 991, Oroville, CA 95965
Independent Mach. & Gun Shop, 1416 N. Hayes, Pocatello, Ida. 83201
Ivy Armament, P.O. Box 10, Greendale, WI 53129
JASCO, Box 49751, Los Angeles, Calif. 90049
J & G Rifle Ranch, Box S80, Turner, MT 59542 (case tumblers)
Javelina Products, Box 337, San Bernardino, Cal. 92402 (Alox beeswax)
Neil Jones, 686 Baldwin St., Meadville, PA 16335 (decapping tool, dies)
Kexplore, 9450 Harwig #G, Houston, TX 77036
Kuharsky Bros. (see Modern Industries)
Lac-Cum Bullet Puller, Star Route, Box 240, Apollo, PA 15613/412-478-1794
Lage Uniwad Co., 1102 N. Washington St., Eldora, IA 50627 (Universal Shotshell Wad)
LanDav, 7213 Lee Highway, Falls Church, VA 22046 (X-15 bullet puller)
Lee Custom Engineering, Inc., 46 E. Jackson St. Hartford, WI 53027
Lee Precision, Inc., 4275 Hwy. U, Hartford, WI 53027
Leon's Reloading Service, 3945 No. 11 St., Lincoln, Neb. 68521
Lewisystems, Menasha Corp., 426 Montgomery St., Watertown, WI 53094
L. L. F. Die Shop, 1281 Highway 99 N., Eugene, Ore. 97402
Dean Lincoln, P.O. Box 1886, Farmington, NM 87401 (mould)
Ljutic Industries, 918 N. 5th Ave., Yakima, Wash. 98902
Lock's Phila. Gun Exch., 6700 Rowland, Philadelphia, Pa. 19149
Lyman Products Corp., Rte. 147, Middlefield, CT 06455
McKillen & Heyer, Box 627, Willoughby, O. 44094 (case gauge)
Paul McLean, 2670 Lakeshore Blvd., W., Toronto 14, Ont., Canada (Universal Cartridge Holder)
MEC, Inc. (see: Mayville Eng. Co.)
MTM Molded Prod., 5680 Webster St., Dayton, OH 45414
Magma Eng. Co., P.O. Box 881, Chandler, AZ 85224
Judson E. Mariotti, Beauty Hill Rd., Barrington, NH 03825 (brass bullet mould)
Marmel Prods., P.O. Box 97, Utica, MI 48087 (Marvelube, Marvelux)
Marquart Precision Co., Box 1740, Prescott, AZ 86301 (precision case-neck turning tool)
Mayville Eng. Co., 715 South St., Mayville, Wis. 53050 (shotshell loader)
Merit Gun Sight Co., P.O. Box 995, Sequim, Wash. 98382
Modern Industries, Inc., 613 W-11, Erie, PA 16501 (primer pocket cleaner)
Multi-Scale Charge Ltd., 3269 Niagara Falls Blvd., North Tonawanda, NY 14120
NL Industries Inc., Metal Div., P.O. Box 3618, Hightstown, NJ 08520/609-443-2209 (Lawrence Brand shot)
Normington Co., Box 6, Rathdrum, ID 83858 (powder baffles)
Ohaus Scale, (see: RCBS)
Omark-CCI, Inc., Box 856, Lewiston, Ida. 83501
Pacific Tool Co., P.O. Drawer 2048, Ordnance Plant Rd., Grand Island, NB 68801
Pak-Tool Co., 4411 S.W. 100th, Seattle, WA 98146
Personal Firearms Record Book, Box 201, Park Ridge, Ill. 60068
Ferris Pindell, R.R. 3, Box 205, Connersville, IN 47331 (bullet spinner)
Plum City Ballistics Range, Rte. 1, Box 29A, Plum City, WI 54761
Ponsness-Warren, Inc., P.O. Box 8, Rathdrum, ID 83858
Potter Eng. Co., 1410 Santa Ana Dr., Dunedin, FL 33528 (electric pots only)
Marian Powley, Petra Lane, R.R.I, Eldridge, IA 52748
Precise Alloys Inc., 69 Kinkel St., Westbury, NY 11590 (chilled lead shot; bullet wire)
Quinetics Corp., 5731 Kenwick, San Antonio, TX 78238/516-684-8561 (kinetic bullet puller)
RCBS, Inc., Box 1919, Oroville, Calif. 95965
Redding Inc., 114 Starr Rd., Cortland, NY 13045
Reloaders Equipment Co., 4680 High St., Ecorse, MI 48229 (bullet puller)
Remco, 1404 Whitesboro St., Utica, N.Y. 13502 (shot caps)
Republic Tool Mfg. Co., P.O. Box 112, Caldwell, NJ 07006 (port. rel. stand)
Rifle Ranch, Rte. 5, Prescott, Ariz. 86301
Rochester Lead Works, Rochester, N.Y. 14608 (leadwire)
Rorschach Precision Prods., P.O. Box 1613, Irving, Tex. 75060
Rotex Mfg. Co. (see Texan)
Ruhr-American Corp., So. East Hwy. 55, Glenwood, Minn. 56334
SAECO Rel. Inc., P.O. Box 778, Carpinteria, Calif. 93013
SSK Industries, Rt. 1, Della Drive, Bloomingdale, OH 43910 (primer tool)
Sandia Die & Cartridge Co., Rte. 5, Box 5400, Albuquerque, NM 87123
Shassere, Box 35865, Houston, TX 77096/713-780-7041 (cartridge case caddy/loading block)
Shiloh Products, 37 Potter St., Farmingdale, NY 11735 (4-cavity bullet mould)
Shooters Accessory Supply, see: D. R. Corbin
Sil's Gun Prod., 490 Sylvan Dr., Washington, Pa. 15301 (K-spinner)
Jerry Simmons, 715 Middlebury St., Goshen, Ind. 46526/219-533-8546 (Pope de- & recapper)
Fred Sinclair, Sinclair, Inc., 1200 Asbury Dr., Box 302, New Haven, IN 46774

Smith & Wesson Ammunition Co., Inc., 2399 Forman Rd., Rock Creek, OH 44084
J. A. Somers Co., P.O. Box 49751, Los Angeles, CA 90049 (Jasco)
D. E. Stanley, P.O. Box 833, Ringold, OK 74754 (Kake-Kutter)
Star Machine, Inc., 418 10th Ave., San Diego, CA 92101
T.E.S., Inc., 2807 N. Prospect St., Colorado Springs, CO 80907 (Vibra-Tek)
T&T Products, Inc., 6330 Hwy. 14 East, Rochester, MN 55901 (Meyer shotgun slugs)
Texan Reloaders, Inc., 807 Evans Ave., Akron, OH 44305
Trico Plastics, 590 S. Vincent Ave., Azusa, CA 91702
WAMADET, Silver Springs, Goodleigh, Barnstaple. Devon. England
Walker Mfg. Inc., 8296 So. Channel, Harsen's Island, MI 48028 (Berdan decapper)
Wammes Guns Inc., 236 N. Hayes St., Bellefontaine, OH 43311 (Jim's powder baffles)
Weatherby, Inc., 2781 Firestone Blvd., South Gate, Calif. 90280
Webster Scale Mfg. Co., Box 188, Sebring, Fla. 33870
Whits Shooting Stuff, P.O. Box 1340, Cody, WY 82414
Whitney Sales, Inc., P.O. 875, Reseda, CA 91335 (Hollywood)
L. E. Wilson, Inc., P.O. Box 324, 404 Pioneer Ave., Cashmere, WA 98815
Xelex, Ltd., P.O. Box 543, Renfrow K7V 4B1, Canada (powder)
Zenith Enterprises, 361 Flagler Rd., Nordland, WA 98358

SIGHTS, METALLIC

Accura-Site Co., Inc., Box 193, Neenah, WI 54956
B-Square Eng. Co., Box 11281, Ft. Worth, Tex. 76110
Behlert Custom Sights, Inc., 725 Lehigh Ave., Union, NJ 07083
Bo-Mar Tool & Mfg. Co., Box 168, Carthage, Tex. 75633
Maynard P. Buehler, Inc., 17 Orinda Highway, Orinda, Calif. 94563
Christy Gun Works, 875 57th St., Sacramento, Calif. 95819
Jim Day, 902 N. Bownen Lane, Florence, SD 29501 (Chaba)
E-Z Mount, Ruelle Bros., P.O. Box 114, Ferndale, MT 48220
Freeland's Scope Stands, Inc., 3734-14th Ave., Rock Island, Ill. 61201
Paul T. Haberly, 2364 N. Neva, Chicago, IL 60635
Paul Jaeger, Inc., 211 Leedom St., Jenkintown, PA 19046
Lee's Red Ramps, 7252 E. Ave. U-3, Littlerock, CA 93543/805-944-4487 (illuminated sights)
Jim Lofland, 2275 Larkin Rd., Boothwyn, PA 19061
Lyman Products Corp., Rte. 147, Middlefield, Conn. 06455
Marble Arms Corp., 420 Industrial Park, Gladstone, Mich. 49837
Merit Gunsight Co., P.O. Box 995, Sequim, Wash. 98382
Micro Sight Co., 242 Harbor Blvd., Belmont, Calif. 94002
Miniature Machine Co., 210 E. Poplar, Deming, NM 88030/505-546-2151
Modern Industries, Inc., 613 W-11, Erie, PA 16501
C. R. Pedersen & Son, Ludington, Mich. 49431
Poly Choke Co., Inc., P.O. Box 296, Hartford, CT 06101
Redfield Gun Sight Co., 5800 E. Jewell St., Denver, Colo. 80222
Schwarz's Gun Shop, 41 - 15th St., Wellsburg, W. Va. 26070
Simmons Gun Specialties, Inc., 700 Rodgers Rd., Olathe, Kans. 66061
Slug Site Co., Whitetail Wilds, Lake Hubert, MN 56469
Sport Service Center, 2364 N. Neva, Chicago, IL 60635
Tradewinds, Inc., Box 1191, Tacoma, WA 98401
Williams Gun Sight Co., 7389 Lapeer Rd., Davison, Mich. 48423

TARGETS, BULLET & CLAYBIRD TRAPS

Caswell Equipment Co., Inc., 1221 Marshall St. N.E., Minneapolis, MN 55413
Cole's Acku-Rite Prod., Box 25, Kennedy, N.Y. 14747 (Site Rite targets)
Detroit Bullet Trap Co., 2233 N. Palmer Dr., Schaumburg, Ill. 60195/312-397-4070
Electro Ballistic Lab., 1900 Embarcadero Rd., Suite 209, Palo Alto, CA 94303 (Electronic Trap Boy)
Ellwood Epps (Orillia) Ltd., R.R. 3, Hwy. 11 North, Orillia, Ont. L3V 6H3 Canada/705-689-5333, (hand traps)
Gopher Shooter's Supply, Box 278, Faribault, MN 55021 (Lok-A-Leg target holders)
Kory Shooting Equipment, 233 S. Wacker, Sears Tower/Suite 7130, Chicago, IL 60606 (electric ranges)
Laporte S.A., B.P. 212, 06603 Antibes, France (claybird traps)
Laporte Equipment Inc., 70 rue Martin St., Granby, Queb. J2G 8B3, Canada (claybird traps)
MCM (Mathalienne de Construction Mecanique), P.O. Box 18, 17160 Matha, France (claybird traps)
Millard F. Lerch, Box 163, 10842 Front St., Mokena, Ill. 60448 (bullet target)
National Target Co., 4960 Wyaconda Rd., Rockville, MD 20852
Outers Laboratories, Inc., Onalaska, Wis. 54650 (claybird traps)
Peterson Label Co., P.O. Box 186, Redding Ridge, CT 06876 (paste-ons)
Professional Tape Co., 355 E. Burlington Rd., Riverside, Ill. 60546 (Time Labels)
Recreation Prods. Res. Inc., 158 Franklin Ave., Ridgewood, NJ 07450 (Butts bullet trap)
Remington Arms Co., Bridgeport, Conn. 06602 (claybird traps)
Reproductions West, Box 6765, Burbank, CA 91510 (silhouette targets)
Rocky Mountain Target Co., P.O. Box 700, Black Hawk, SD 57718/605-787-5946 (Data-Targ)
Scientific Prod. Corp., 426 Swann Ave., Alexandria, VA 22301 (Targeteer)
Sheridan Products, Inc., 3205 Sheridan, Racine, Wis. 53403 (traps)
South West Metallic Silhouettes, P.O. Box 476, Uvalde, TX 78801
T-Magic Co., 33 Burnside Ave., East Hartford, CT 06108 (targets)
Time Products Co. (See Prof. Tape Co.)
Trius Prod., Box 25, Cleves, O. 45002 (claybird, can thrower)
Winchester-Western, New Haven, Conn. 06504 (claybird traps)